Physiology with Anatomy for Nurses

Physiology with Anatomy for Nurses

Sheila M. Jackson SRN SCM BTA RNT

*Education Officer (General Nursing), The English National
Board for Nursing, Midwifery and Health Visiting*

Penelope J. Bennett SRN OND RNT

*Acting Director of Nurse Education, North Hertfordshire School
of Nursing, Stevenage*

First Edition

Baillière Tindall
London Philadelphia Toronto Sydney Tokyo

| Baillière Tindall | 24–28 Oval Road |
| W.B. Saunders | London NW1 7DX |

West Washington Square
Philadelphia, PA 19105, USA

1 Goldthorne Avenue
Toronto, Ontario M8Z 5T9, Canada

ABP Australia Ltd
44–50 Waterloo Road
North Ryde, NSW 2113, Australia

Harcourt Brace Jovanovich Japan Inc.
Ichibancho Central Building, 22–1 Ichibancho
Chiyoda-ku, Tokyo 102, Japan

First published 1988

Typeset by Wyvern Typesetting Ltd, Bristol
Printed in Hong Kong

British Library Cataloguing in Publication Data

Jackson, Sheila M.
  Physiology with anatomy for nurses.
  1. Human physiology
  I. Title   II. Bennett, Penelope J.
  612'.0024613   RT69

ISBN 0-7020-1173-8

Contents

Colour Plates are located between pages 134 and 135

Preface

In April 1985 The English National Board for Nursing, Midwifery and Health Visiting circulated a document (1985 (19) ERDB) to schools of nursing to assist curriculum development groups; the stated purpose of the guidelines was 'to assist translation from the existing syllabus to a curriculum which will fulfil the needs of the students and institutions within a varied and changing social and economic structure'. The guidelines also 'encompass the competencies stated in the Nurses Rules' (Statutory Instrument 1983 No. 873 'The Nurses, Midwives and Health Visitors Rules Approval Order 1983').

Part A of the guidelines contains the theoretical foundation for nursing practice, and section 4.1 is headed 'Physiology with Anatomy'. The intention was to stress the importance of an understanding of normal function and to include just sufficient detail of the structure to enable that understanding. It is the changed emphasis which the authors have endeavoured to reflect in this new presentation of the topic, perviously covered by *Anatomy & Physiology for Nurses* in Baillière Tindall's Nurses' Aids Series.

The changes begin with the title and continue throughout the text, which has been divided into sections, each of which contains material pertaining to a specific function of the body. It will be seen for example that, instead of devoting several chapters to bone, one to joints, another to muscles and yet another to the circulation, the bones, joints and muscles of one part of the body follow closely one upon the other to facilitate an understanding of the whole. The same principle has been applied to the rest of the book.

It will also be seen that each chapter begins with learning objectives so that a student can see at the beginning what is to be achieved.

Most diagrams have been redrawn and labelling made clearer where necessary.

SHEILA M. JACKSON

It has been an honour and a pleasure to work with Miss Jackson on this edition of her well established book. However, it would not have been possible for me to do so, without the support of my husband and son, who had to fend, more than usual, for themselves on the domestic front over several months. Nor must I forget the guidance given me by Ms Richenda Milton-Thompson, without whose encouragement completion might never have been achieved. My thanks also go to the typist and art workers who took defaced manuscript and figure ideas, covered in illegible hieroglyphics, and transformed them into readable pages and good art work. To all these, I am indebted for their tolerance and help.

PENELOPE J. BENNETT

Acknowledgements

The following illustrations have been reproduced (with modifications) from other publications, with kind permission of the authors and publishers.

Fig. 18.15, from G. Barnes The nurse's contribution to the Medical Research Council's trial for mild hypertension *Nursing Times* vol. 77 (No. 29) p. 1243, July 15 1981.
Fig. 19.11, from N.A. Beischer & E.V. Mackay *Obstetrics and the Newborn* W.B. Saunders (Harcourt Brace Jovanovich, publishers), Sydney 1986.
Figs. 1.1, 2.10, 5.1 & 18.10, from A. Faulkner *Nursing: A Creative Approach* Baillière Tindall, London 1985.
Fig. 18.8, from J.H. Green *An Introduction to Human Physiology* Oxford University Press, Oxford 1976.
Figs. 10.14, 10.18, 18.9, 18.14, 21.11, 23.4 & 25.6, from A.B. McNaught & R. Callander *Illustrated Physiology* Churchill Livingstone, Edinburgh 1983.
Figs. 2.3, 2.5 & 2.6, from M.B.V. Roberts *Biology: A Functional Approach*, 2nd edn. Thomas Nelson, Walton-on-Thames 1976.
Figs. 3.2 & 21.6 and the colour plates, from J.R.W. Ross & K. Marks Baillière's Anatomy Illustrated Baillière Tindall, London 1986.
Figs. 4.6, 5.2, 5.3, 7.3, 7.11, 10.13, 10.16, 13.1, 16.3, 19.10, 23.2 & 23.12, from E.P. Solomon & P.W. Davis Human Anatomy and Physiology Holt, Rinehart & Winston, New York 1983.
Fig. 14.1, from A.E. Stalker Ear, Nose and Throat Nursing, 6th edn. Baillière Tindall, London 1984.
Figs. 10.12 & 10.15, from J.E. Watson & J.R. Royle Watson's Medical-Surgical Nursing and Related Physiology, 3rd edn. Baillière Tindall, London 1987.

SECTION 1

1

Introduction to Science

Objectives: After studying Chapter 1 you should be able to:

1 Distinguish between physiology and anatomy.
2 Differentiate between elements, compounds and mixtures.
3 Draw and label diagrams representing the structure of a molecule and an atom.
4 Define atomic number and atomic weight.
5 Describe an isotope.
6 Describe an ion and differentiate between an anion and a cation.
7 Describe an electrolyte.
8 Define matter and list its physical states.
9 Use the SI system.
10 Define a solution.
11 Compare the properties of acids and alkalis.
12 Define and describe diffusion, osmosis and ultrafiltration.

The nurse cares for human beings in illness and during vulnerable periods of their lives. In order to do this properly he or she needs to understand the function and structure of the body and to be able to relate this knowledge to the care of his or her patient. Each organ in the body plays its part in maintaining the health of the whole person and if one organ is at fault other parts of the body will be affected. Since the function of each part suggests its structure and the structure suggests its function, the study of the human body can be a logical process of thinking and reasoning, not merely of memorizing.

Terminology

Physiology is the study of the function of the body; *anatomy* is the study of its structure. Some knowledge of elementary physics and chemistry will help in the study of physiology and anatomy and will also be needed to enable the nurse to care for the patient and to carry out nursing procedures. *Physics* deals with the behaviour and characteristics of matter, e.g. whether it gives off heat and light or conducts electricity. *Chemistry* is the study of the composition

of matter and the reactions between different substances. It involves splitting matter into its various components to see what it is made of—this process is called *analysis*. It may also involve building up matter from its various components—this process is called *synthesis*.

Elements, compounds and mixtures

Some substances cannot be split into further separate components. These substances are called *elements*. There are over 90 elements known to exist, including oxygen, carbon, nitrogen, iron, silver and gold. Substances which can be split into different components are of two types: compounds and mixtures.

A *compound* is made of two or more elements which combine chemically to form a new substance with new properties. For example, hydrogen is a very light gas used to fill balloons. It is highly inflammable and can explode. Oxygen is a gas which supports combustion (i.e. other substances can burn in oxygen) but will not burn itself. These two gases combine to make a compound—water—which is a fluid, is not inflammable, will not explode, will not support combustion, and will not burn. In fact, it can be very useful for putting out a fire!

The elements which form a compound are always present in fixed proportions. For example, water consists of two parts of hydrogen combined with one part of oxygen. If the proportions of each gas were altered a compound might be formed, but it would not be water. Two parts of hydrogen combined with two parts of oxygen form a compound called hydrogen peroxide which looks like water but has very different properties.

Another characteristic of a compound is that it is not easy to separate the elements of which it is composed; to do this a chemical change must take place.

Compounds which contain the element carbon are known as *organic compounds*, e.g. proteins or sugars. All other compounds are known as *inorganic compounds*, e.g. water or hydrochloric acid. Most of the compounds in living matter, including the human body, are organic. However, many inorganic compounds have an important role in the body.

A *mixture* consists of two or more substances (compounds or elements) mixed together but not chemically combined. Air is a mixture of gases—mainly nitrogen and oxygen, with traces of carbon dioxide and other gases. A mixture has no new properties, just simply those of the substances which make up the mixture. The substances in a mixture can be separated fairly easily because they are not chemically combined.

The substances in a mixture do not necessarily have to be present in fixed proportions; e.g. three different samples of air may contain three different proportions of oxygen, yet each is still air. However, some mixtures are made up with fixed proportions of their constituents, e.g. three parts sugar to one part salt; many formulas for medicines are mixtures made up with fixed proportions.

Common elements

Over 90 elements are known to exist. Some are very rare, but there are a few which the student of nursing will frequently meet; these are given in Table 1.1.

Table 1.1 Common elements.

Element	Symbol	Description
barium	Ba	A solid (metal)
calcium	Ca	A solid (metal)
carbon	C	A solid (non-metallic)
chlorine	Cl	A gas
hydrogen	H	A gas
iodine	I	A solid (non-metallic)
iron	Fe	A solid (metal)
magnesium	Mg	A solid (metal)
mercury	Hg	A liquid (metal)
nitrogen	N	A gas
oxygen	O	A gas
potassium	K	A solid (metal)
sodium	Na	A solid (metal)
sulphur	S	A solid (non-metallic)

Elements found in the body

The body is made up of very complicated chemical compounds built out of a small number of elements.

Calcium makes teeth and bones hard. It is also essential for muscles to contract, for blood to clot and for nerve impulses to be transmitted.

Carbon is found in all living matter. It is important in that it can combine with several other atoms at one time. It is one of the elements formed as a waste product of cellular metabolism.

Chlorine is found in fluid surrounding the cells of the body (the interstitial fluid).

Hydrogen is present in all organic compounds and is necessary to form many of the important chemical compounds in the body.

Iodine is present in only very small amounts in the body, and is therefore called a *trace element*, but it is essential in the formation of the hormone thyroxine, which is produced by the thyroid.

Iron is another trace element essential for health; lack of iron is the most common cause of anaemia.

Magnesium is found in small quantities with calcium in the bones and teeth and is essential in the blood.

Nitrogen is found in all proteins and in nucleic acids (substances involved in protein synthesis and in storing the genetic information of a cell). Excretion of nitrogen from the body after protein breakdown is essential.

Oxygen is needed for cell metabolism and is essential to every living tissue in the body; without oxygen, cells cannot produce enough energy to live.

Potassium is present in all living matter. In the human body it is mainly found in the fluid within cells (intracellular fluid). It is also important for the correct functioning of nerves and muscle contraction.

Sodium is present in all living matter. In the human body it is mainly found in the interstitial fluid. It is of great importance in maintaining fluid balance in the body and in the conduction of nerve impulses.

Sulphur is found in most proteins.

Other important elements

Barium is used in X-ray examinations. It is opaque to X-rays and may be used to outline structures.

Mercury is used in clinical practice in the thermometer. The mercury in the thermometer expands (as do other substances) when heated. The degree of

Fig. 1.1 A glass thermometer.

expansion is proportional to the temperature rise. A thermometer is designed so that when the mercury in the bulb is heated and expands, it travels up a fine glass tube alongside a temperature scale (Fig. 1.1). The hotter the mercury, the more it expands and the further up the scale it travels. When the thermometer is removed from the source of heat, e.g. from the patient's mouth, the mercury would normally immediately contract down again, and it would be impossible to read what the temperature had been. However, contraction of the mercury is prevented by a small constriction in the fine glass tube near to the bulb and the temperature reading is therefore maintained. This also means that the mercury has to be shaken down past the constriction before the thermometer can be used again. Mercury is poisonous to the body so great care must be taken not to break the thermometer when using it.

Matter

Matter is anything that can occupy space.

The structure of matter

All matter is made up of particles called *molecules*. Molecules are held together only by the attraction of one molecule to another. This force of attraction between molecules of the same substance is called *cohesion*. Molecules of different substances, e.g. water and glass, also tend to attract one another; this force is known as *adhesion*.

A molecule is the smallest particle which can exist alone but which still has all the properties of the substance; e.g. one molecule of water has all the properties of water.

A molecule can be divided into smaller particles called *atoms*, but an atom cannot usually exist alone. A *molecule of an element* consists of atoms of that element; for example, a molecule of oxygen consists of two atoms of oxygen (written O_2). A *molecule of a compound* consists of atoms of the different elements present in the compound; for example, a molecule of water consists of two atoms of hydrogen and one atom of oxygen (written H_2O), a molecule of carbon dioxide consists of one atom of carbon and two atoms of oxygen (written CO_2), and a molecule of glucose (a simple type of sugar) consists of six atoms of carbon, twelve atoms of hydrogen and six atoms of oxygen (written $C_6H_{12}O_6$).

Water, carbon dioxide and glucose are examples of simple chemical compounds. In the more complicated compounds found in the human body there may be hundreds of atoms of any one element and many different elements may be present. Although all molecules are very small, they vary considerably in size and complexity.

Structure of an atom

The word atom means indivisible. This name was chosen when scientists thought that the atom could not be divided. Now, however, more is known about the structure of an atom and most people have heard about 'splitting the atom' and its connection with atomic energy. An atom consists of smaller particles of three different types (Fig. 1.2):

- *Protons*, which carry a positive electrical charge
- *Electrons*, which carry a negative electrical charge
- *Neutrons*, which do not carry a charge

The protons and neutrons are massed together to form the *nucleus* of the atom, while the electrons

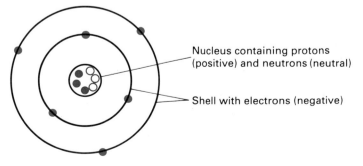

Nucleus containing protons
(positive) and neutrons (neutral)

Shell with electrons (negative)

Fig. 1.2 The structure of an atom.

whirl around the nucleus in one or more orbits known as *shells*.

Atomic number

Different elements have different numbers of protons and electrons in their atoms. In an atom the number of protons is always equal to the number of electrons and is called the *atomic number*. A hydrogen atom has one proton in its nucleus and one electron circling round it; therefore the atomic number of hydrogen is 1. It has no neutrons. A carbon atom has six protons (and six neutrons) in its nucleus and six electrons arranged in two shells circling round it, so the atomic number of carbon is 6. A sodium atom has 11 protons (and 12 neutrons) in the nucleus and 11 electrons in three shells circling round it, so the atomic number of sodium is 11.

These numbers do not have to be memorized because they can be obtained from tables. One table that is commonly used is the *periodic table*, in which the elements are arranged according to their atomic number (Fig. 1.3).

The presence of neutrons in the nucleus does not affect the atomic number.

Atomic weight

The weight of a neutron is roughly equal to the weight of a proton, and the number of neutrons in an atom added to the number of protons gives the *atomic weight*. The weight of an electron is so small that it is not significant. Hydrogen has an atomic weight of 1 as a hydrogen atom has one proton but no neutrons in its nucleus. Carbon has an atomic weight of 12 as a carbon atom has six protons and six

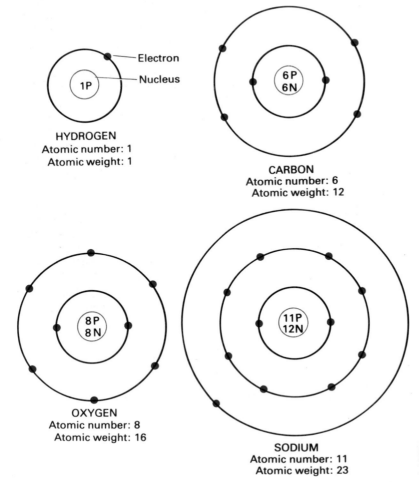

Fig. 1.3   The structure of atoms of hydrogen, carbon, oxygen and sodium. P = proton; N = neutron.

neutrons in its nucleus. Sodium has an atomic weight of 23 as a sodium atom has 11 protons and 12 neutrons in its nucleus.

Isotopes

Some atoms have more neutrons or fewer neutrons in the nucleus than a normal atom of the same element. Therefore two atoms of the same element can have a different atomic weight; the atom which has a different number of neutrons to normal is known as an *isotope* (Fig. 1.4).

Some isotopes are radioactive and are known as *radioisotopes*. The atoms of a radioisotope have a structure which is unstable. In order to form a more stable structure, the atoms emit either particles from the nucleus (alpha or beta decay) or energy in the form of gamma rays (gamma decay).

Radioisotopes can be useful in clinical medicine. For example, a radioisotope of iodine is used to investigate the function of the thyroid gland. Normal iodine has an atomic weight of 127 (53 protons and 74 neutrons). It is used by the thyroid to make the hormone thyroxine. One isotope of iodine that is radioactive has an atomic weight of 131 (53 protons and 78 neutrons). In order to investigate thyroid function, the radioisotope of iodine is given to the patient by mouth. It is absorbed from the gut and enters the bloodstream. The thyroid gland is unable to distinguish between the radioisotope and normal iodine and so removes it from the blood in order to use it to make thyroxine. The radioisotope is thus concentrated in the thyroid. The radiation from the radioisotope can be measured from outside the body and will indicate how well the thyroid is removing iodine from the blood and whether all parts of the gland are working evenly.

Ions and electrolytes

When certain elements are mixed together, transfer of electrons from one element to another occurs. This happens because these elements have a more stable structure if they lose or gain electrons, and substances will always tend to obtain as stable a structure as possible. Therefore if an element which has a more stable structure if it loses one electron, e.g. sodium (Na), is mixed with an element which has a more stable structure if it gains one electron, e.g. chlorine (Cl), one electron passes from each atom of sodium to an atom of chlorine. The number of protons and neutrons do not change. Atoms which have lost or gained electrons in this way are known as ions.

If an atom loses one or more electrons, one or more of the protons in the nucleus are left without a negative electron to balance their positive charge; the ion therefore has a positive charge and is known as a positive ion or a cation. If an atom gains one or more electrons, it will have more electrons than protons and will therefore have a negative charge; the ion is then known as a negative ion or an anion. Metal atoms tend to lose electrons and become positive ions, whereas non-metal atoms tend to gain electrons and become negative ions.

Ions are written as the symbol for the element or compound concerned followed by a raised plus or minus sign indicating the charge on the ion. For example, a sodium ion is represented by Na^+, and a chlorine ion (which is known as chloride) by Cl^-. Loss or gain of more than one electron is indicated by a raised number before the charge. For example, calcium (Ca) loses two electrons when it forms an ion and so is represented as Ca^{2+}.

When ions are formed there is an attraction between the particles carrying opposing charges. They combine to form ionic molecules, which have no overall charge. For example, Na^+ and Cl^- will combine to form the ionic molecule, NaCl. If such molecules are added to water, they will break up or dissociate to a lesser or greater extent into their constituent ions. For example, in water NaCl will

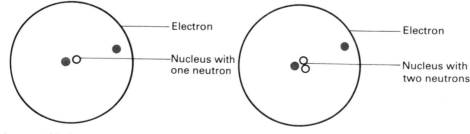

Fig. 1.4 The isotopes of hydrogen.

dissociate into Na^+ and Cl^-. When separated like this in solution, ions are known as electrolytes.

Physical states of matter

Matter has three physical states: solid, liquid and gas. Whether a substance is a solid, a liquid or a gas is determined by how much energy the molecules of matter have.

In a *solid* the attractive forces between the molecules are greater than the energy of the molecules. These forces hold the molecules together in a rigid arrangement. Therefore solids do not easily alter in shape.

In a *liquid* the molecules have enough energy to overcome some of the attractive forces, and so can move about more freely. However they do not have enough energy to completely overcome these forces and move independently of one another. Because the molecules can move freely but cannot escape from one another, a liquid will take up the shape of a container into which it is put, but does not alter in size. For example, if one litre of water is put into a two-litre jug, it will take the shape of the jug, but it will not fill it.

In a *gas* the molecules have enough energy to completely overcome the attractive forces between them and can move about freely and independently of one another. Therefore a gas does not have a definite shape or size, but will take the shape and size of any container into which it is put (Fig. 1.5).

The movement of the molecules in a gas exerts a pressure on any object they come into contact with. The pressure exerted by the air around us is known as *atmospheric pressure*. In a closed container, the pressure exerted on the walls of the container by the gas will depend on the number of molecules present.

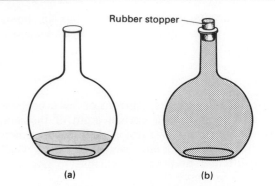

Fig. 1.5 Glass flasks each containing 100 ml of (a) fluid and (b) gas. Note how the gas expands to fill the flask.

If more gas is added to the container, the pressure will increase. If the pressure inside the container is greater than the pressure outside (i.e. atmospheric pressure), the gas is said to be under pressure, and opening or puncturing the container will result in escape of the gas. Many gases used in industry and medicine are stored under pressure in cylinders. As gas from the cylinder is used, the pressure in the cylinder will drop; the pressure can therefore be used to indicate how much gas remains in the cylinder.

Gases dissolved in liquids also exert a pressure. This is important in the transfer of the gases oxygen and carbon dioxide into and out of the blood.

Changes in physical state

The physical state of matter can be changed by altering the amount of energy the molecules have. As heat is a form of energy, changes in energy can be brought about by heating or cooling the molecules. For example, water is liquid at normal room

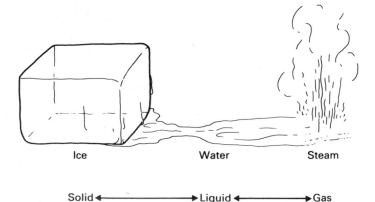

Ice   Water   Steam

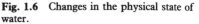

Solid ⟷ Liquid ⟷ Gas

Fig. 1.6 Changes in the physical state of water.

temperatures but becomes solid ice when heat is lost from it and water vapour or steam when heated (Fig. 1.6). Changes in the state of matter can be divided into:

- Melting
- Evaporation
- Condensation
- Consolidation

Melting

This is the changing of a solid into a liquid as a result of heating, e.g. the turning of ice into water.

As a solid is heated, the molecules in it gain energy and vibrate more. The forces holding the molecules in a rigid arrangement are still intact, but the solid is hotter than it was. As more heat energy is applied there will come a point at which the energy of the molecules is greater than that of the forces holding them rigidly together, and the molecules will break apart from one another to form a liquid.

Evaporation

This is the changing of a liquid into a gas as a result of heating, e.g. the turning of water into steam. Gases formed by evaporation are called *vapours*.

The molecules in the liquid gain energy as they are heated. Once they have sufficient energy, they break away from one another to form a gas. The temperature at which this occurs is called the *boiling point* of a substance. For example, the boiling point of water is 100°C (212°F). It is not possible to heat a liquid up to a temperature hotter than its boiling point. This is because at this temperature all extra heat is used in freeing the molecules to form a gas.

The fact that energy is required for evaporation explains why sweating cools the body. Heat from the body causes liquid sweat on the skin to warm up and then become a vapour. The energy needed for this to happen is therefore transferred from the body to the sweat, and the body is cooled.

Condensation

This is the turning of a gas into a liquid as a result of cooling, e.g. the turning of water vapour into water.

Cooling removes energy from the molecules of the gas. If sufficient energy is removed, the molecules will no longer be able to overcome completely the attractive forces between them, and they will form a liquid.

Consolidation

This is the turning of a liquid into a solid as a result of cooling, e.g. the turning of water into ice.

If sufficient energy is removed from the molecules in a liquid by cooling, they will not be able to counteract the forces drawing them together, and a rigid arrangement of molecules—a solid—will form.

Written Numbers

It is important to be clear about the correct way to write numbers, particularly large numbers and those which contain a decimal point. In English-speaking countries a dot is used to signify a decimal point. However, many other countries use a comma. For example:

English language	Many other languages
2.48	2,48

If a comma is used to break up large numbers, as has been the custom in the past, it may be confused with a decimal point. In order to avoid this confusion, large numbers should be written using spaces instead of commas. The spaces are used to divide them up into groups of three digits, starting from the right for a whole number and from the left for digits after a decimal point. A number which has only four digits before or after the decimal point should be written without spacing or a comma. The decimal point should be indicated by a dot on the line. Where there are no digits before a decimal point a nought must always be inserted. For example:

Old method	New method
1,000	1000
1,234,567	1 234 567
12·10362	12.103 62
6·3421	6.3421
1·23	1.23
·23	0.23

Index notation

Very small numbers and very large ones, particularly those which have a lot of noughts before or after the decimal point, are difficult to read and to understand and so an 'index notation' is used. The number is written as number between 1 and 10 and multiplied or divided by 10 a number of times. How many times the number is multiplied or divided by ten is indicated by a small raised number, called the *index*.

For *large numbers* the number between 1 and 10 is *multiplied* by ten a number of times; this is indicated by the index being a *positive* number.

For example:

$100 = 1 \times 10 \times 10 = 1 \times 10^2$ (can be written as just 10^2)
$5000 = 5 \times 10 \times 10 \times 10 = 5 \times 10^3$
$64\,000 = 6.4 \times 10 \times 10 \times 10 \times 10 = 6.4 \times 10^4$

It may be helpful to remember that for numbers greater than zero the index is the same as the number of places the decimal point has been moved to the *left* in order to produce a number between 1 and 10. For example, to produce a number between 1 and 10 from $5\,000\,000$ (5 million), the decimal point has to be moved six places to the left, and so the index will be 6:

$5\,000\,000 = 5 \times 10^6$

For *small numbers* the index is a negative number and indicates how many times the number is *divided* by 10.

For example:

$0.01 = 1 \div 10 \div 10 = 1 \times 10^{-2}$
$0.005 = 5 \div 10 \div 10 \div 10 = 5 \times 10^{-3}$
$0.00042 = 4.2 \div 10 \div 10 \div 10 \div 10 = 4.2 \times 10^{-4}$

It may be helpful to remember that for numbers less than zero the index is the same as the number of places the decimal point has to be moved to the *right* in order to produce a number between 1 and 10, but is negative. For example, to produce a number between 1 and 10 from 0.012, the decimal point has to be moved two places to the right, and so the index will be -2:

$0.012 = 1.2 \times 10^{-2}$

These large or small numbers are not generally used in measuring because the size of the unit can be adjusted by adding a prefix (see below).

Units of Measurement

In 1960 a series of international conferences recommended that a revised and extended system of metric units should be universally adopted. The scientific world now uses these *SI units* almost exclusively. The abbreviation SI stands for Système Internationale d'Unités (international system of units). It is illegal to prescribe or dispense drugs in any other units in the United Kingdom.

The SI system uses seven fundamental units. Many other units are formed from two or more of these fundamental units; these are known as derived units. Some of these units of measurement are more commonly used in medicine and nursing than others. The common ones are given in Table 1.2.

Table 1.2 Units of measurement commonly used in medicine and nursing.

Unit	Used for measuring:
Fundamental units	
metre	length
gram	mass (weight)
second	time
mole	amount of substance
kelvin	temperature
Derived units	
litre	volume (liquid or gases)
pascal	pressure
joule	energy

In many cases these units are too large or too small to be appropriate for the required measurement. In these cases one of a standard set of multiplying prefixes is used. There are sixteen prefixes altogether, but only five are commonly used in hospital practice:

kilo-	(k)	is 1000 times bigger
centi-	(c)	is 100 times smaller
milli-	(m)	is 1000 times smaller
micro-	(µ)	is 1 000 000 times smaller
nano-	(n)	is 1 000 000 000 times smaller

An example of the use of these prefixes is seen in

the measurement of mass or weight, the fundamental unit of which is the gram. A patient may weigh 70 000 g, but this is more conveniently expressed in kilograms (1000 times larger than a gram) as 70 kg. A dose of 0.001 g of a drug is better measured in milligrams (1000 times smaller than a gram) as 1 mg.

Wherever possible the use of a decimal point should be avoided by choosing a suitable prefix for the unit of measurement. For example, it is better to use 250 mg than 0.25 g.

Measuring length

The metre is the unit of length and is a fundamental SI unit. The international symbol for metre is a small letter m. A metre is a little longer than a yard; thus it is too small for measuring the difference from one town to another and too big for measuring the length of a bacterium. With the prefixes it becomes:

kilometre   (km)
centimetre   (cm)
millimetre   (mm)
micrometre   (μm)
nanometre   (nm)

It should be remembered that these are symbols, not abbreviations, so they do not need a plural form (an 's' on the end) or a full stop unless it is the end of a sentence. For example, ten kilometres should be written as 10 km, not 10 km. or 10 kms.

One kilometre	(1 km)	is 1000 metres
One centimetre	(1 cm)	is 1/100 (0.001) part of a metre
One millimetre	(1 mm)	is 1/1000 (0.0001) part of a metre
One micrometre	(1 μm)	is 1/1 000 000 part of a metre
One nanometre	(1 nm)	is 1/1 000 000 000 part of a metre

In older books a micrometre is sometimes called a micron, which was abbreviated to just the Greek letter μ, but this is obsolete and should not be used.

Measuring mass or weight

In everyday speech no differentiation is made between mass and weight. However, strictly speaking, the *mass* of an object is the amount of matter it contains, whereas the *weight* of an object is a measure of the force which gravity exerts on that object. When we speak of weight, what we really mean is mass. However, since the relationship between weight and mass is constant if gravity is constant, it is not necessary to always distinguish between them.

The gram is the basic unit of mass and is a fundamental SI unit. The international symbol for gram is a small letter g.

One kilogram	(1 kg)	is 1000 grams
One milligram	(1 mg)	is 1/1000 part of a gram
One microgram	(1 μg)	is 1/1 000 000 part of a gram

The kilogram is equivalent to approximately 2.2 lb.

Measuring time

The second is the basic unit of time and is a fundamental SI unit. The international symbol for second is a small letter s. However, in clinical medicine the minute (symbol: min), hour (symbol: h) and day (symbol: d) are also used. Sometimes, to avoid any chance of confusion, a measurement may be put in terms of '24 hours' (24 h) rather than 'day'.

Measuring the amount of a substance

Earlier it was stated that the number of neutrons added to the number of protons in an atom gives its *atomic weight*. Hydrogen has an atomic weight of 1 (as it has one proton and no neutrons) and oxygen an atomic weight of 16 (as it has eight protons and eight neutrons). A molecule of water, which consists of two hydrogen atoms and one oxygen atom (H_2O), will therefore have a weight of 18. This is known as its *molecular weight*. Understanding atomic and molecular weights is important in understanding how the amount of a substance is measured.

The amount of a substance can be expressed in terms of its mass, but in physiology and biochemistry it is more important to know *how many particles* (atomic, ionic or molecular) of the substance are present rather than their total mass. However, since even tiny amounts of a substance will contain many millions of particles, it would be very cumbersome to use such huge numbers. Therefore a unit defined as a standard large number of particles was devised. The number of particles chosen was the number of particles in that amount of a substance that has a mass equal to its molecular or atomic weight in grams; this number will always be 6.023×10^{23} and is referred to as Avogadro's number. For example, the atomic weight of carbon is 12, therefore 12 g of carbon will contain 6.023×10^{23} atoms of carbon. The molecular weight of water is 18, therefore 18 g of water will also contain 6.023×10^{23} molecules of water. The amount of substance containing this number of particles is called a *mole*, the symbol for which is mol.

The mole can be used to indicate the concentration of a substance in a solution. If one mole of a substance is added to one litre of water, the concentration of the substance in the resulting solution will be 1 mol/l. Because the mole is a measure of the number of particles, one mole of a molecule which breaks up into ions when added to water will produce one mole of each of the ions produced. For example, hydrochloric acid (HCl) breaks up into hydrogen ions (H^+) and chloride ions (Cl^-) when added to water. One molecule of HCl will produce one H^+ and one Cl^-. Therefore 6.023×10^{23} molecules of HCl (one mole of HCl) will produce 6.023×10^{23} H^+ (one mole of H^+) and 6.023×10^{23} Cl^- (one mole of Cl^-).

The mole is often too large a unit to describe the concentrations of substances encountered in clinical medicine. Therefore a prefix is used, as for other units. The prefix commonly used is milli-, one millimole (mmol) being 1000 times smaller than a mole. For example, the concentration of sodium chloride (NaCl) in the blood is 0.15 mol/l, but this is usually written as 150 mmol/l. A solution made up to have this same concentration of NaCl (i.e. 150 mmol/l) is known as *isotonic* or *physiological saline*.

Moles cannot be used for measuring the concentration of protein substances because the molecules are so complex that their molecular weight cannot be determined accurately. Such substances are therefore expressed in terms of their mass, i.e. in grams per litre or in milligrams (mg) per 100 ml. It is rarely necessary to convert from one to the other but if it should be the formula is:

$$\text{concentration in mmol/l} = \frac{\text{concentration in mg/100 ml} \times 10}{\text{molecular weight of substance}}$$

The concentrations of dissolved gases, e.g. in the blood, are often stated in terms of pressure rather than moles or grams because pressures are easier to measure (see page 13).

Measuring temperature

The SI unit for temperature is the kelvin (the symbol for which is K). This scale is used by physicists and is based on the fact that at a temperature of 0 K all particles in any type of matter will stop vibrating. It is equivalent to $-273°C$, and is therefore very cold. However, in clinical medicine the *Celsius scale* is used. A change of 1 K is identical to a change of one degree on the Celsius scale (written as 1°C), but the Celsius scale has a different zero point—on the Celsius scale 0°C is the freezing point of pure water. The boiling point of pure water is 100°C, and the normal body temperature is about 37°C. The term *centigrade* should not be used as in some countries this was a measurement of angle.

Measuring volume

The *litre* is the basic unit of volume and is used for measuring both liquids and gases. The litre is a derived unit because one litre is defined as the amount of water which weighs one kilogram. Therefore, one millilitre will weigh one gram. Other useful relationships are that:

- One thousand litres occupy one cubic metre
- One thousand litres weigh one thousand kilograms (or one metric tonne)
- One millilitre occupies one cubic centimetre

Some printers use the italic letter *l* as the symbol for a litre because there is a danger that the number 1 and the letter l may be confused. However, the correct abbreviation is a small letter l. Some values in medicine are still occasionally given in terms of 100 ml (one decilitre or 0.1 litre), e.g. the legal limit for blood alcohol in drivers is often written as 80 mg/100 ml, but this form is becoming increasingly rare.

Measuring pressure

Pressure is the force exerted divided by the area over which it acts; it is therefore another derived unit. In the SI system, pressure is equal to the force exerted measured in newtons divided by the area measured in square metres. This is written as N/m^2, but more commonly and conveniently expressed by the use of the word *pascal* (for which the symbol is Pa). This SI unit has not yet been adopted universally, although it is the standard unit for use in pathology departments.

The pascal is too small a measure for use in clinical

medicine; the unit used is usually the kilopascal (kPa), which is equal to 1000 pascals.

Blood pressure

Blood pressure is traditionally measured in terms of millimetres of mercury (mmHg) (the chemical symbol for mercury is Hg), but some new sphygmomanometers, particularly the dial type, have a scale marked in both mmHg and kPa. It is not usually necessary to convert pressures from one scale to the other, but if it is necessary the following formula may be used:

$$\text{pressure in kPa} = \frac{\text{pressure in mmHg}}{7.5}$$

A blood pressure of 120/80 mmHg will therefore be 16/10.7 kPa approximately.

Blood gas pressures

The pressures exerted by gases dissolved in the blood were also measured in millimetres of mercury, but are now being expressed in kPa.

Central venous pressures

Central venous pressures are usually measured in centimetres of water:

$$10 \, cmH_2O = 1 \, kPa$$

Pressure of gases in air

Atmospheric pressure at sea level is approximately 100 kPa. Because of this, the pressure measured in kilopascals of each gas in a mixture of gases will be almost the same as its percentage in the mixture. For example, an oxygen mask which delivers 28% oxygen will be supplying it at a pressure of 28 kPa at atmospheric pressure. A cylinder which contains a mixture of 5% carbon dioxide (CO_2) in oxygen (O_2) will supply CO_2 at a pressure of 5 kPa and O_2 at a pressure of 95 kPa.

Measuring energy

Energy is the amount of work done when a force acts through a distance. In the SI system, energy is equal to the force measured in newtons multiplied by the distance measured in metres. The SI unit, which is a derived unit, is the *joule*. This replaces the old unit of energy, the calorie. The symbol for a joule is J and it is the unit of both heat and energy in the SI system, since heat is a form of energy. Like the pascal, it is too small a unit for use in clinical measurement; the most common form is the kilojoule (kJ), which is 1000 joules.

1000 calories = 1 kilocalorie = 1 Calorie
1 kilocalorie = 4185.5 joules = 4.186 kilojoules

Rough conversion of dietetic Calorie values to kilojoules may be made by multiplying the number of Calories by four, e.g. 1000 Calories is approximately equal to 4000 kJ.

Energy values for foods are usually given per 100 g rather than per gram or per kilogram, as 100 g is nearest to the average portion size.

100 g of protein provides 1700 kJ of energy
100 g of fat provides 3800 kJ of energy
100 g of carbohydrate provides 1600 kJ of energy

Solutions

A *solution* is a liquid in which other substances are dissolved. For example, when a lump of sugar is put into a cup of hot water, the sugar dissolves and a solution of sugar is present in the cup. The molecules of sugar mix with the molecules of water until the sugar is evenly distributed throughout the liquid. The process can be speeded up by stirring but the even distribution of sugar will occur eventually without any stirring (Fig. 1.7). The liquid in which the substances are dissolved is known as the *solvent* and the dissolved substances are known as the *solutes*. Solutes may be solids, liquids or gases.

A certain amount of solvent will only dissolve a certain amount of solute; when the liquid has dissolved as much as possible it is called a saturated solution. If more solute is added it will not dissolve.

Water is the solvent found in living things. Approximately two-thirds of the human body is composed of water. Most of this water is inside the cells which make up the body, some of it surrounds the cells, and some is in the circulating blood and lymph.

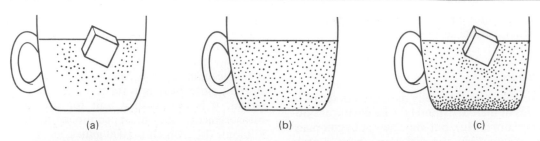

Fig. 1.7 (a) Sugar dissolves in water to form a solution. (b) As more sugar is added the solution becomes saturated with sugar molecules. (c) As the saturated solution cannot hold any more sugar molecules, the introduction of more sugar results in the formation of a deposit of sugar at the bottom of the cup.

Acids and alkalis

When in solution a substance may be acid, alkaline (basic) or neutral.

Acids

Molecules or ions which liberate hydrogen ions (H^+) when in water, thus increasing the concentration of hydrogen ions, are known as *acids*. For example, hydrochloric acid (HCl) breaks up or *dissociates* into hydrogen ions (H^+) and chloride ions (Cl^-) when added to water. This reaction can be represented as:

$$HCL \rightleftharpoons H^+ + Cl^-$$

The double arrow indicates that this reaction, like all chemical reactions, is potentially reversible. The end result of the reaction will depend on the balance between the reaction going to the right (i.e. HCl $\rightarrow$ $H^+ + Cl^-$) and the reaction going to the left (i.e. HCl $\leftarrow$ $H^+ + Cl^-$). In the case of HCl, there is a much greater tendency for HCl to dissociate into two ions than there is for the two ions to join together to form HCl. Therefore when HCl is added to water, all the molecules of HCl will dissociate into ions. This is an example of a *strong acid*.

In contrast, carbonic acid (H_2CO_3) is a *weak acid*. When added to water it dissociates into hydrogen ions (H^+) and bicarbonate ions (HCO_3^-). This can be represented as:

$$H_2CO_3 \rightleftharpoons H^+ + HCO_3^-$$

As before, the end result of the reaction will depend on the balance between the reaction going to the right (H_2CO_3) $\rightarrow$ $H^+ + HCO_3^-$) and the reaction going to the left ($H_2CO_3 \leftarrow H^+ + HCO_3^-$). In this case, there is a much greater tendency for the two ions to combine to form H_2CO_3 than there is for H_2CO_3 to dissociate into two ions. Thus when H_2CO_3 is added to water, only some of the molecules of H_2CO_3 will dissociate into ions.

Therefore the *strength* of an acid depends on the degree to which the substance *dissociates* in water.

Both hydrochloric and carbonic acid are found in the body; hydrochloric acid has an important role in helping the digestion of food in the stomach, and carbonic acid is found in the blood and elsewhere in the body.

Alkalis

Molecules or ions which liberate hydroxide ions (OH^-) or combine with hydrogen ions (H^+) when in water, thus decreasing the concentration of hydrogen ions, are known as *alkalis* or *bases*. Hydroxide ions reduce the concentration of hydrogen ions by combining with them to form water. This can be represented by:

$$OH^- + H^+ \rightleftharpoons H_2O$$

An example of an alkali is sodium hydroxide (NaOH). In water this dissociates to give sodium ions (Na^+) and hydroxide ions (OH^-), represented by:

$$NaOH \rightleftharpoons Na^+ + OH^-$$

An important alkali in the blood is the bicarbonate ion (HCO_3^-), which can accept hydrogen ions to form carbonic acid (H_2CO_3). This can be represented as:

$$HCO_3^- + H^+ \rightleftharpoons H_2CO_3$$

The strength of an alkali depends on the degree to which hydroxide ions are liberated or hydrogen ions can be accepted.

Measuring the acidity or alkalinity of a solution

The acidity or alkalinity of a solution depends on the number of hydrogen ions present.

Pure water is *neutral*, i.e. not acid or alkaline. Solutions with more hydrogen ions than water has are said to be *acid* in reaction, whereas solutions with less hydrogen ions than water has are said to be *alkaline* in reaction. Therefore, a solution of an acid substance in water will be acid, and a solution of an alkaline substance in water will be alkaline.

The acidity or alkalinity of a solution containing both an acid substance and an alkali substance will depend on the relative amounts of acid and alkali present. The hydrogen ions liberated by the acid can be accepted or 'mopped up' by the alkali. However, if more hydrogen ions are liberated by the acid than can be accepted by the alkali, some 'free' hydrogen ions will remain and the solution will be *acid*. Conversely, if more hydrogen ions can be accepted by the alkali than have been liberated by the acid, there is unused capacity to mop up hydrogen ions, and the solution will be *alkaline*.

Taste may be used to differentiate between acid and alkaline solutions. An acid solution (e.g. vinegar) has a sour taste, whereas an alkaline solution (e.g. a solution of sodium bicarbonate) tastes bitter. However, this method is not advocated as many substances are poisonous or at the very least have a nasty taste!

The reaction of a substance may also be tested with *litmus paper*. An acid solution will turn litmus paper red, whereas an alkaline solution will turn it blue. This is the method commonly used by nurses for testing body fluids. However, litmus paper does not give an indication of *how* acid or how alkaline a solution is.

A more accurate measure of the acidity or alkalinity of a solution is the concentration of hydrogen ions present. The concentration of hydrogen ions in water (which is neutral) is 100 nmol/l, which can also be written as 10^{-7} mol/l. The concentration of hydrogen ions is higher than this in acid solutions and lower than this in alkaline solutions. The *pH scale* is a more convenient way of representing the concentration of hydrogen ions. The pH of a solution is defined as the negative logarithm of the hydrogen ion concentration. Put more simply, this is the index (the raised number after the 10) of the hydrogen ion concentration in mol/l; the minus sign is ignored. Thus, the hydrogen ion concentration in water of 10^{-7} mol/l gives a pH of 7. Solutions with a higher concentration of hydrogen ions (i.e. an acid solution) will have a lower pH; e.g. a hydrogen ion concentration of 10^{-5} mol/l will have a pH of 5. Solutions with a lower concentration of hydrogen ions (i.e. an alkaline solution) will have a higher pH; e.g. a hydrogen ion concentration of 10^{-11} mol/l will have a pH of 11.

The pH scale runs from 0 to 14 (Fig. 1.8). Because the pH depends on the index in the hydrogen ion concentration, a change of one pH unit represents a *tenfold* change in the hydrogen ion concentration. Thus a small change in pH indicates a much larger change in hydrogen ion concentration. This is of great importance when interpreting pH results. For example, the pH of blood is normally 7.4, but a slightly lower reading of 7 could indicate some great disturbance, and if left untreated could lead to death.

The pH of a fluid can be measured roughly using specially designed sticks or more accurately in the laboratory using a pH meter.

Buffers

One way in which the normal pH range in a fluid is maintained is by the presence of *buffers*, which can prevent marked changes in the pH of a solution when an acid or alkali is added to it. Buffers consist of two substances and are therefore often called *buffer pairs*. An example of a buffer pair important in

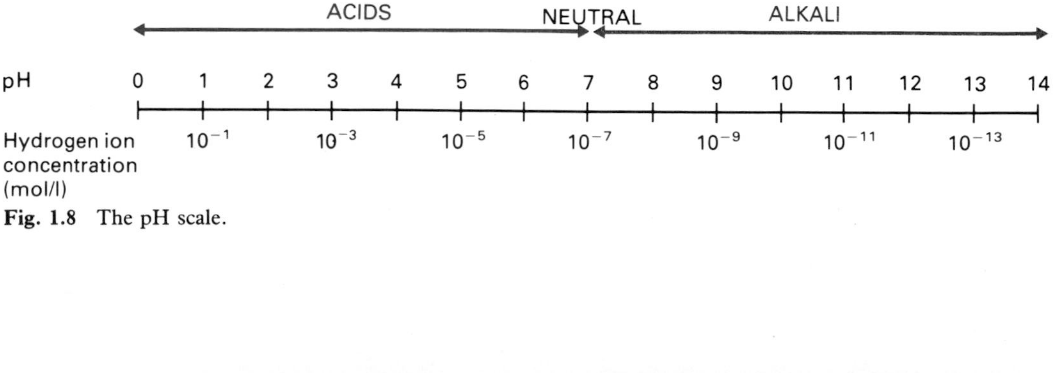

Fig. 1.8 The pH scale.

maintaining the pH of the blood is *bicarbonate* and *carbonic acid*.

In the presence of excess hydrogen ions (i.e. pH too low) bicarbonate ions (HCO_3^-) combine with the hydrogen ions (H^+) to form carbonic acid (H_2CO_3). This can be represented as:

$$HCO_3^- + H^+ \rightleftharpoons H_2CO_3$$

Although carbonic acid can dissociate and release hydrogen ions (i.e. $H_2CO_3 \rightarrow HCO_3^- + H^+$), it is a *weak* acid and so does not readily dissociate in this way. The end result is therefore that most of the excess hydrogen ions are mopped up.

In the presence of too few hydrogen ions (i.e. pH too high), carbonic acid will tend to dissociate into bicarbonate ions and hydrogen ions, i.e. the above reaction is reversed.

Acidosis and alkalosis

In some diseases the changes in the pH of the blood are so great that the buffers and other systems for maintaining the pH are not able to compensate fully.

Acidosis occurs when the blood becomes more acid than normal. Causes of acidosis include:
- *Respiratory failure*. If the ability of the body to get rid of carbon dioxide (CO_2) in expired air is reduced, the amount of carbon dioxide in the blood increases. Here it combines with water (H_2O) to form carbonic acid (H_2CO_3):

$$CO_2 + H_2O \rightleftharpoons H_2CO_3$$

- *Severe diarrhoea*. The intestinal juices in the lower intestine are alkaline. Excess loss of these juices will result in a relative increase in the acidity of the blood.
- *Uncontrolled diabetes mellitus*. The build-up of acidic ketone bodies leads to a decrease in the pH of the blood.

Alkalosis occurs when the blood becomes more alkaline than normal. Causes of alkalosis include:
- *Drugs*. The consumption of large quantities of alkaline drugs such as antacids (used to relieve indigestion) can lead to alkalosis.
- *Severe vomiting*. The juices in the stomach are acid. Loss of these juices will result in a decrease in the acidity of the blood.
- *Hyperventilation (over-breathing)*. If the amount of carbon dioxide expired is increased, less carbon

dioxide remains in the blood to form carbonic acid, and the blood is less acid than normal.

A blood pH of 7.8 or more is rarely compatible with life.

Each body fluid has a normal pH range which must be maintained to allow the normal functions of the body to be carried out. Some of these normal ranges are listed below:

Gastric juice	pH 1–2 (acid)
Urine	pH 5.5–5.7 (acid)
Pancreatic juice	pH 7.5–8.00 (alkaline)
Blood	pH 7.4 (alkaline)
Saliva	pH 6.8–7.2 (acid–neutral–alkaline)

Salts

When acids react with alkalis, a *salt* and water are formed. For example, when the alkali sodium hydroxide ($NaOH$) reacts with hydrochloric acid (HCl), the salt sodium chloride ($NaCl$) and water are produced. This can be represented as:

$$\underset{\text{(alkali)}}{NaOH} + \underset{\text{(acid)}}{HCl} \rightleftharpoons \underset{\text{(salt)}}{NaCl} + \underset{\text{(water)}}{H_2O}$$

Although the term 'salt' is used in everyday language to mean the sodium chloride we put on our food, it can be used to describe any compound formed in this way from an acid and an alkali.

If the alkali used is a mineral the salt produced is known as a *mineral salt*.

Diffusion

Diffusion is flow of substances from a higher concentration to a lower concentration due to the spontaneous movements of the individual molecules (Fig. 1.9). Diffusion will continue until both concentrations are equal. The difference between the two levels of concentration is known as a *gradient*. Diffusion is sometimes known as *passive transport* because it is a spontaneous process for which no outside energy is needed. The diffusion that occurs in the body is mostly of substances in solution, but diffusion of gases is very important in respiration. Diffusion is very important in the body for evening out local differences in concentrations.

Diffusion of a gas in a gas is rapid because the molecules are relatively far apart and there is plenty of room to move. Diffusion of molecules in a solu-

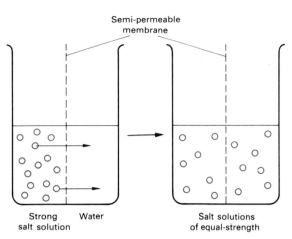

Fig. 1.9 The diffusion of liquids.

tion is slower than in a gas because the molecules of the solute and solvent are relatively closer to one another and so restrict each other's movement.

Membranes in the body may be *permeable*, when they allow fluid and all substances in solution to pass through, *impermeable*, when no fluid or substances in solution can pass through, or *semi-permeable*, when water and small molecules in solution can pass through, but not larger molecules. Diffusion obviously occurs through a permeable membrane, but it can also occur through a semi-permeable membrane. For example, if a strong solution of sodium chloride is separated from a weaker solution by a semi-permeable membrane, the sodium chloride molecules will pass through the membrane from the strong solution to the weaker one until both solutions are of equal strength.

The *rate of diffusion* refers either to the distance travelled or to the amount of the substance transported in a certain time. It depends on:

- The size of the molecules—the larger the molecules the slower the diffusion.
- The thickness or *viscosity* of the solution—the more viscous the solution, the slower the diffusion.
- The temperature of the solution—the higher the temperature the faster the diffusion. This is because the heat provides the energy for the molecules to move about faster and also reduces the viscosity of the solution.

Diffusion also occurs more quickly when the distance to be travelled is small, e.g. between adjacent

cells diffusion is practically instantaneous. However, the body relies on the blood to transport substances any distance greater than a fraction of a millimetre.

The rate of diffusion of certain substances in the body can be increased (*facilitated diffusion*), but this requires the use of energy.

Osmosis

Osmosis is the movement of water through a semi-permeable membrane from a weak solution to a stronger solution (Fig. 1.10). If a substance which has large molecules such as sugar is made into a solution and is separated from a weaker sugar solution by a semi-permeable membrane, diffusion of the sugar molecules does not occur as they are too large to pass. However, water will pass through the membrane from the weak solution to the strong solution.

The 'pull' exerted on the water by the more concentrated solution is known as the *osmotic pressure* (Fig. 1.11). This pressure will be present even if water is prevented from moving through the membrane, for example by the stronger solution already filling a closed compartment. This pressure is equal to the amount of pressure that would need to be applied to the stronger solution in order to prevent osmosis occurring (see Fig. 1.11).

Ultrafiltration

If a pressure greater than the osmotic pressure is applied to the stronger solution, water will leave the

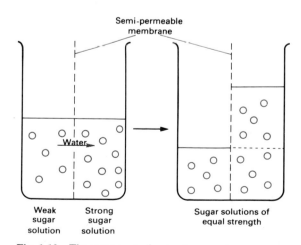

Fig. 1.10 The movement of water by osmosis.

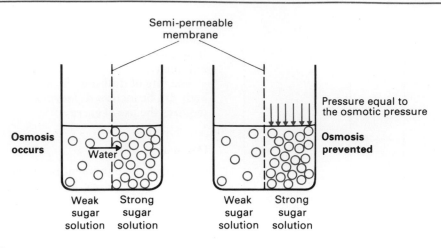

Fig. 1.11 Osmotic pressure.

stronger solution through the semi-permeable membrane (i.e. it moves in the opposite direction). This process is called *ultrafiltration* (Fig. 1.12).

Specific gravity

Specific gravity is the weight of a known volume of liquid divided by the weight of an equal volume of pure water:

$$\text{specific gravity} = \frac{\text{weight of substance}}{\text{weight of equal volume of water}}$$

The specific gravity of pure water is expressed as 1.000, whereas that of urine ranges from 1.010 to 1.020 and that of blood is about 1.055. The specific gravity gives an indication of the concentration of substances dissolved in the liquid.

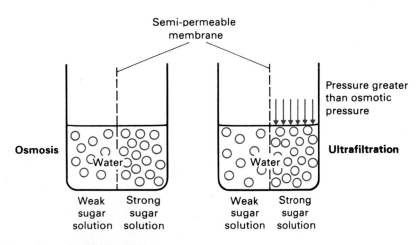

Fig. 1.12 A comparison of osmosis with ultrafiltration.

SECTION 2

2

Living Matter

Objectives: After studying Chapter 2 you should be able to:

1 List the characteristics of living matter.
2 Draw and label a diagram of a cell.
3 Describe mechanisms of transport across a cell membrane.
4 Explain the function of each organelle.
5 Summarize the functions of the nucleic acids and cell proteins.
6 Describe the methods by which cells in the human body may reproduce.
7 Define and describe homeostasis.

In recent years scientists have come very close to understanding the mechanisms of life. This new understanding has shown an underlying unity in all living matter. For example, the fundamental molecules and mechanisms in a cabbage are the same as those in a man and it is becoming possible to give some answers to the question, 'What is life?'

All living things are made of the same several dozen chemicals put together in similar ways and doing approximately the same job, no matter what organism they come from. In addition, in all living matter these substances are built up to form small units called *cells*. Some organisms, such as bacteria, consist of one single cell; others, like man, consist of many hundreds of millions of cells, all functioning together to make a complete whole.

Characteristics of Living Matter

Living matter, however simple or complex, has certain characteristics which are always present. These characteristics are (Fig. 2.1):
● Activity
● Assimilation
● Growth and repair
● Irritability
● Reproduction
● Storage and release of energy
● Excretion

Activity

All living organisms display activity of some kind. This may be very obvious, e.g. the ability of a human to walk and run, or may only occur within the cells which make up the organism.

Assimilation

Living organisms can take in material and then incorporate it into the substance of their cells. In humans this involves breaking down food (digestion) into simple molecules that can be used by the cells of the body.

Growth and repair

The ability to assimilate material enables living organisms to grow and to replace worn out or damaged cells.

Irritability

All living matter is able to respond to changes in its environment. For example, plants will grow towards a light, and humans respond to an increase in the surrounding temperature by sweating.

Reproduction

All living organisms can reproduce themselves. This may be a very simple process, such as the division of a one-celled animal (e.g. amoeba) into two, or very complex, such as the process of fertilization, pregnancy and childbirth which occurs in humans.

Storage and release of energy

All the above activities require the use of energy. Therefore living organisms are able to obtain energy

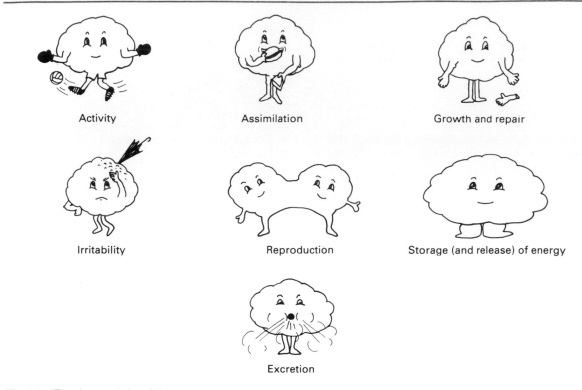

Activity

Assimilation

Growth and repair

Irritability

Reproduction

Storage (and release) of energy

Excretion

Fig. 2.1 The characteristics of living matter.

from their food, and then store it so that it can be used as needed by the cells.

Excretion

All living organisms are able to get rid of waste or toxic materials. These may be substances taken in as part of the organism's food which it cannot use, or may be produced during the processes that occur in the organism.

Cell metabolism

The chemical processes and reactions taking place within the cells which make up a living organism are known as *metabolism*. It involves the breaking down of materials into simple substances with the release of energy (*catabolism*), and the building up of simple substances into more complex ones for the growth and repair of the organism (*anabolism*). Oxygen is often necessary for these processes to take place.

The Structure of Human Cells

The electron microscope has shown that within each cell there is a structure as complex as the overall anatomy of the human body. Each cell contains about as many molecules as a human's body contains cells (Fig. 2.2).

There is no such thing as a typical cell—all cells in the human body are adapted and have specialized features related to their function. Each cell is surrounded by a membrane and contains a substance called *protoplasm*. Protoplasm consists of a body called the *nucleus*, which is usually well defined and bounded by a nuclear membrane, and a semi-fluid, colourless, opaque substance called *cytoplasm* (from the Greek 'cyto', meaning cell). Cytoplasm is a solution of protein and many other substances, such as organic and inorganic salts, glucose and nitrogen-containing substances. Within the cytoplasm are many complex structures called *organelles*.

Cells vary in size from $20\,\mu m$ to $2\,\mu m$. (A μm is a

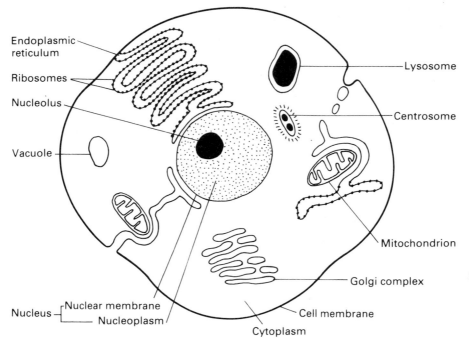

Fig. 2.2 The structure of a cell.

micrometre, i.e. one thousandth of a millimetre; (see page 11). For example, lymphocytes, a type of white blood cell, are about 8–10 μm in diameter.

All the cells in the body except those on the surface are surrounded by *extracellular fluid*.

The cell membrane

The cell membrane is a semi-permeable membrane that surrounds the cytoplasm. As only certain substances are able to pass through it, the internal environment of the cell can be maintained even though the external environment may change considerably. This steady internal environment can only continue because of the complex structure of the cell membrane.

The cell membrane is made up of a double layer of fatty molecules (*lipid*) with protein molecules interspersed amongst them. Research still continues into the structure of a cell membrane, but it is thought that there may be very tiny pores in the membrane to permit the passage of substances in and out of the cell. For a molecule to pass through the cell membrane it must either pass through the minute pores or diffuse through the fatty layers. Small molecules such as water and oxygen can pass through the

pores, but other substances have to dissolve in the lipid and diffuse through the membrane.

Transport mechanisms

For those molecules which are too large to pass through the pores and which are insoluble in lipid, special mechanisms exist to transport them across the cell membrane. Many of the proteins in the cell membrane are carrier molecules. They are able to bind to a substance on one side of the membrane, carry it across the membrane, and release it on the other side. Each is specific and can carry only one kind of molecule. If the energy required for the transport is provided by the transported molecule, this process is known as *facilitated diffusion*. This can only occur if a concentration gradient is present and the carrier molecules can only transport molecules from a higher to a lower concentration. Glucose is an example of a substance which is transported by facilitated diffusion.

When the energy needed by the carrier molecules is provided by the cell, this is known as *active transport*. In this form of transport, substances can be moved against a concentration gradient (i.e. from a lower to a higher concentration). Sodium ions

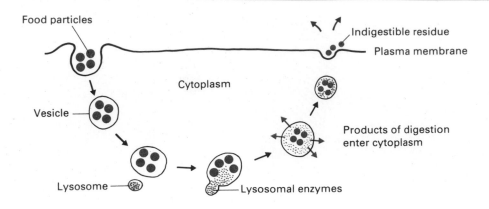

Fig. 2.3   The sequence of events in phagocytosis.

(Na$^+$) are an example of a substance which may be actively transported out of cells. The concentration of sodium ions might be 145 mmol/l outside the cell and 12 mmol/l inside. Under these circumstances sodium ions would normally diffuse slowly into the cell until the concentrations were equal, but the cell could not function with such a high concentration of sodium. To avoid this happening, energy is used to pump sodium ions out of the cell by active transport.

Pinocytosis is an active method of taking fluid into the cell which also requires expenditure of energy. A depression forms in the cell membrane and deepens until a small amount of the fluid just outside the membrane is enveloped. As the sac closes over it is pinched off from the membrane and moves into the cell. This fluid-filled sac (called a *vesicle*) then discharges its contents into the cell or unites with a digestive organelle known as a lysosome inside the cell so that enzymes can digest the contents of the vesicle before releasing them into the cytoplasm. *Phagocytosis* is a similar process by which solid material is taken into the cell (Fig. 2.3).

Secretion is a similar process to pinocytosis but occurs in the reverse direction. The membrane surrounding a secretory granule fuses with the cell membrane and the contents are ejected from the cell.

All substances taken into the cell and all waste products are disposed of in solution.

The nucleus

The *nucleus* is the largest structure in the cell. It is surrounded by a nuclear membrane which has two layers and, like the cell membrane, has distinct pores. The protoplasm within the nucleus is known as *nucleoplasm*. There is little variation in the appearance of the nucleoplasm unless the cell is dividing. However, sometimes spherical bodies called *nucleoli* can be seen; these are responsible for the production of ribosomes, which are found on the rough endoplasmic reticulum in the cytoplasm (see page 25).

The nucleus contains important structures known as chromosomes; these are not visible unless the cell is just about to divide. Different species may have different numbers of chromosomes in their cells. There are 23 pairs of chromosomes (i.e. a total of 46) in human cells, with the exception of ova and sperm which have only one of each pair (i.e. 23 in all). Chromosomes are made up of a substance called *deoxyribonucleic acid (DNA)*, which is a genetic material with two main functions:

- It provides the genetic blueprint which ensures that the next generation of cells is similar to the existing cell.
- It provides the plans for the synthesis of protein in the cell itself.

This information is stored in *genes* which are strung together to form the chromosomes.

Organelles

Mitochondria

Mitochondria are spherical or rod-shaped particles in the cytoplasm. They consist of two membranes, the inner one of which has many folds which increase the surface area available for chemical reactions to occur. Mitochondria can be thought of as the power stations of the cell as they are able to generate the energy which is needed by the cell to function. They convert the chemical energy contained in molecules of food into energy which may be used by the cell by producing a substance called *adenosine triphosphate (ATP)*. ATP contains three phosphate groups. When one phosphate group is split off from the molecule, a great deal of energy is released and can be used by the cell. The resulting molecule is known as adenosine diphosphate (ADP). ADP can then be converted back to ATP in the mitochondria. Production of ATP requires the breakdown of food molecules and occurs in several stages, each stage requiring the appropriate *enzyme*. An enzyme is a protein that can initiate and speed up a chemical reaction (i.e. act as a catalyst). The enzymes in the mitochondria are stored in the membranes in the required order so that the reactions occur in the correct sequence.

Lysosomes

Lysosomes do not have such a complex internal structure as mitochondria. They consist of a membrane surrounding enzymes which could digest the cell substance if they were not contained. These enzymes are used to digest foreign material which might invade the cell, such as bacteria, or worn-out parts of the cell. The substances to be digested become surrounded by a membrane bag. Several lysosomes discharge their contents into the bag, and digestion occurs. The products of digestion are absorbed into the surrounding cytoplasm.

Lysosomes are particularly active during body changes such as the reduction in the size of the uterus following pregnancy and the breasts following lactation, and also play a considerable part in the remodelling of bone following injury.

Following death of a cell the enzymes in the lysosome are released and digest the dead cell.

Endoplasmic reticulum

The endoplasmic reticulum consists of membranes which form a series of channels, dividing the cytoplasm into compartments. There are two types of endoplasmic reticulum: *rough* and *smooth*. Rough endoplasmic reticulum has ribosomes attached to it, whereas smooth endoplasmic reticulum does not. *Ribosomes* are tiny particles of *ribonucleic acid (RNA)* on which synthesis of proteins needed by the cell (including enzymes) takes place. They are formed in round bodies in the nucleus known as nucleoli.

The membranes of the endoplasmic reticulum also contain many enzymes which speed up chemical reactions within the cell.

The Golgi complex

The Golgi complex is a collection of membranous tubes and elongated sacs and plays a part in concentrating and packaging some of the substances made in the cell. For example, lysosomal enzymes are concentrated in the Golgi complex and then released into the cytoplasm surrounded by a membrane as active lysosomes. The complex also plays a part in the assembly of substances for secretion outside the cell.

The centrosome

The centrosome is found near the nucleus and consists of two rod-shaped *centrioles*; these are involved with chromosome movement during cell division. It is surrounded by a radiating thread-like structure.

Organic Molecules in Cells

The two most important types of organic molecules in a cell are the *nucleic acids*, which carry the hereditary instructions, and the *proteins*, which put the instructions into effect. An animal cell must be supplied with organic molecules such as glucose and amino acids (the end-product of protein breakdown or metabolism) from which to build nucleic acids and proteins, since it cannot synthesize organic substances from inorganic material.

Nucleic acids

Nucleic acids are very large molecules whose molecular weight may be in the millions. They consist of a long chain of *nucleotides*, which themselves are complex molecules. There are two main kinds of nucleic acids: *deoxyribonucleic acids (DNA)* and *ribonucleic acids (RNA)*.

DNA is the genetic material in the nucleus. The hereditary information is contained in the arrangement of the nucleotides from which it is synthesized. It provides the pattern or code for the synthesis of proteins (including enzymes) in the cell and in this way directs the chemical activity of the cell. However, since proteins are synthesized on the ribosomes in the cytoplasm and the DNA is in the nucleus, there must be a method of transmitting the information from the nucleus to the ribosomes. The DNA code is therefore transferred to a similar molecule of RNA, which acts as a messenger by carrying the code out of the nucleus to the ribosome. At the ribosome a protein is built up from amino acids, the order in which they are added being determined by the code on the RNA. In this way a particular arrangement of nucleotides in a molecule of DNA is translated into a specific sequence of amino acids in a molecule of protein.

Proteins

Among the most important of the proteins in the cell are the *enzymes*. These act as catalysts and without them the chemical reactions which take place in the body would be too slow for life to continue. Another function of some types of cell proteins is to act as *carriers* of molecules across the cell membrane, as has already been mentioned. A third function is to form part of the actual structure of the cell as components of the cell wall and the membranes of the organelles. Some proteins may have more than one function. In addition, certain cells have particular proteins which have special functions; for example, muscle cells contain the proteins actin and myosin, which have the ability to contract, and red blood cells contain haemoglobin, which is able to combine with oxygen.

Proteins are large molecules composed of varying numbers of *amino acids* linked together into a long chain by the formation of *peptide bonds*. If only a small number of amino acids are linked, the molecule is called a *polypeptide* rather than a protein. The sequence of amino acids is determined by the DNA in the chromosomes (see above).

Proteins which perform the same role in different species are not usually identical; for example, insulin from a horse is not composed of the same sequence of amino acids as insulin from a human.

Cell Reproduction

In order for the body to grow and to replace cells which have died, cells must be able to reproduce themselves. In some organisms this can occur by

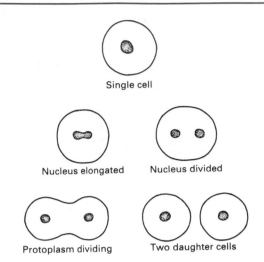

Single cell

Nucleus elongated   Nucleus divided

Protoplasm dividing   Two daughter cells

Fig. 2.4 Reproduction by simple fission.

simple fission (Fig. 2.4). The nucleus in a single cell becomes elongated and then divides to form two nuclei in one cell. The cytoplasm then divides between the nuclei to form two daughter cells, each one with its own nucleus.

In more complex organisms, including humans, cell reproduction is a complex process known as *mitosis*, in which the number of chromosomes in the cells produced (the *daughter cells*) is the same as in the parent cell.

Mitosis (Fig. 2.5)

Mitosis can be divided into four stages:
- Prophase
- Metaphase
- Anaphase
- Telophase

Before and after it has divided, the cell enters a stage known as *interphase*. Note that these stages are continuous—there is no sharp break between them.

Interphase

During interphase the cell does not look active. However, a number of important activities are occurring. Although the chromosomes are not visible because they are in the form of long threads, each one is duplicated so that there will be sufficient genetic information for the two daughter cells which are to be produced. In addition, extra cell organelles

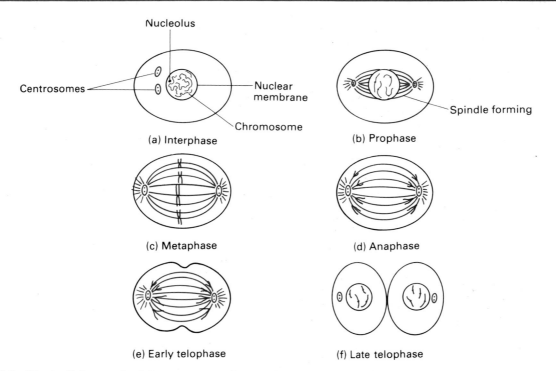

Fig. 2.5 Mitosis. Only two pair of chromosomes are shown.

are manufactured or produced by replication of existing organelles. This will ensure that the daughter cells will have sufficient organelles to function. The duplicated organelles include the centrioles; these are important in the next stage of mitosis. During interphase the cell builds up a store of energy which is required for the process of division.

Prophase

During prophase the long thread-like chromosomes become shorter and fatter and thus become visible. Because the genetic material in the chromosomes was duplicated during interphase, each chromosome now consists of two *chromatids*, each of which contains the same genetic information. They are joined together at an area known as the centromere, forming the shape of an X.

The other important event in prophase is the movement of one set of centrioles around the nucleus to the opposite side. Between the centrioles at each end of the cell a thread-like structure forms, which is known as the *nuclear spindle*. The two ends of the spindle, where the centrioles are, are known

as the *poles*. The middle of the spindle is known as the *equator*.

While this is occurring the nucleolus and nuclear membrane disappear.

Metaphase

During metaphase the 46 chromosomes, each consisting of two chromatids, move to the equator of the spindle, where they become attached to the spindle fibres.

Anaphase

During anaphase the chromatids in each chromosome are separated. One chromatid from each chromosome then moves towards each pole of the spindle.

Telophase

There are now 46 chromatids at each pole. These will form the chromosomes of the daughter cells. The cell membrane constricts in the centre of the cell, dividing it into two cells. The nuclear spindle disappears, and a nuclear membrane forms around the chromosomes in each of the daughter cells. The chromosomes become long and thread-like again, and therefore can no longer be seen. Cell division is now complete, and the daughter cells enter interphase to prepare for the next division.

Mitosis is the process by which one cell reproduces. However, reproduction of the whole organism, i.e. of the whole human being, depends on fusion of reproductive cells or *gametes* from each of the parents—a spermatozoon from the male and an ovum from the female. So that the cell formed when the gametes fuse has the normal number of chromosome (i.e. 46), each of the gametes must only have half this number (i.e. 23). Cells with the full complement of 46 chromosomes are known as *diploid cells*, whereas those with only 23 are known as *haploid cells*.

Gametes develop from ordinary cells with 46 chromosomes. As they mature to form reproductive cells they undergo a special type of cell division known as *meiosis*.

Meiosis

During meiosis (Fig. 2.6) the parent cell divides to form two cells, and these then divide again; therefore each parent cell produces four daughter cells.

For descriptive purposes, meiosis can be divided into eight stages:

- Prophase I ⎫
- Metaphase I ⎬ First meiotic division
- Anaphase I
- Telophase I ⎭
- Prophase II ⎫
- Metaphase II ⎬ Second meiotic division
- Anaphase II
- Telophase II ⎭

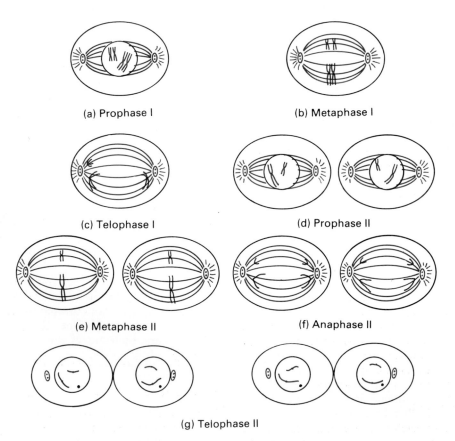

(a) Prophase I

(b) Metaphase I

(c) Telophase I

(d) Prophase II

(e) Metaphase II

(f) Anaphase II

(g) Telophase II

Fig. 2.6 Meiosis. Only two pairs of chromosomes are shown.

As in mitosis, these phases are continuous with one another.

Prophase I

This is similar to prophase in mitosis. However, instead of being scattered randomly, when they appear the chromosomes (each consisting of two chromatids) are arranged in pairs, 23 in all.

Each pair of chromosomes is known as a *bivalent*. Genetic material may be exchanged between the chromosomes in a pair; these exchanges are partly responsible for the differences between children of the same parents.

Metaphase I

As in mitosis the chromosomes become arranged at the equator of the spindle. However, they remain in pairs.

Anaphase I

One chromosome from each pair moves to each pole. There are now 23 chromosomes at each end of the spindle.

Telophase I

The cell membrane divides the cell into two, as in mitosis. Each cell now has half the number of chromosomes the parent cell had. The cells produced sometimes now enter an interphase, or they may undergo the second meiotic division immediately.

Second meiotic division

Both of the cells produced by the first meiotic division now divide again. Prophase II, metaphase II, anaphase II and telophase II are all similar to mitosis, and result in the separation of the chromatids. However, since there are now only 23 chromosomes in each cell, only 23 chromatids end up at each pole at the end of anaphase II. These chromatids form the chromosomes of the daughter cells. Thus four daughter cells are produced, each with only 23 chromosomes.

Fusion of the gametes

When the gametes, each with 23 chromosomes, fuse together, a cell known as a *zygote* with 23 paired chromosomes (i.e. 46 in all) is formed. One chromosome from each pair comes from the mother and one from the father.

The zygote cell divides by mitosis many times to form the *embryo*.

Sex determination (Fig. 2.7)

One particular pair of chromosomes in a cell are known as the *sex chromosomes*. In the female the two sex chromosomes are the same—they are both X chromosomes; this is often written as XX. In the male the two sex chromosomes are not the same—one is an X chromosome and one is a Y chromosome; this can be written as XY. As we have seen, during meiosis the pairs of chromosomes are separated. Therefore in the female the gametes (i.e. the ova) will all have one X chromosome, but in the male the gametes (i.e. the spermatozoa) will have either an X chromosome or a Y chromosome.

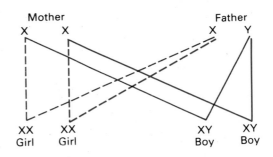

Fig. 2.7 Sex determination.

If a gamete from the mother (which will always have an X chromosome) fuses with a gamete with an X chromosome from the father, the resulting zygote will be XX and will therefore be female; if it fuses with a gamete with a Y chromosome from the father, the resulting zygote will be XY and will therefore be male.

Unicellular and Multicellular Organisms

Unicellular organisms

Unicellular organisms are organisms in which one cell forms a complete individual; examples are bacteria and amoebae. The single cell is able to carry out

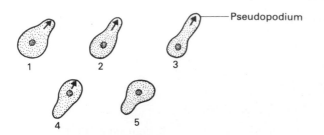

Fig. 2.8   Amoeboid movement.

all the characteristic activities of living matter (see page 21).

Movement is performed by the flow of protoplasm within the cell. A projection is pushed out in the direction in which the movement is to be made, and protoplasm streams slowly into the projection until the whole cell occupies a new position. The projection is called a *pseudopodium*, or false foot, and this type of movement is called amoeboid movement. In the human body, the white blood cells move in this way (Fig. 2.8).

Unicellular organisms are also able to ingest food. Two pseudopodia are put out, surrounding the food. Enzymes are then poured out of the cell into the sac in which the food is now enclosed. Gradually the food is digested and useful substances are absorbed by the cell, until only a small quantity of waste material remains. The cytoplasm then flows back, leaving the waste material behind (Fig. 2.9).

Multicellular organisms

Multicellular organisms consist of many cells. The multicellular organism in which we are particularly

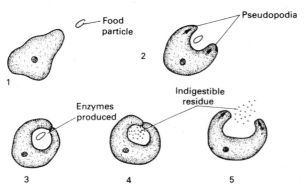

Fig. 2.9   Ingestion and digestion of food particles by unicellular organisms.

interested is the human body, which is a complex arrangement of millions of cells. Each living cell requires food, oxygen and water, a suitable temperature and the correct amount of acidity. However, different groups of cells are involved in performing different functions. For example, the cells of the lungs take in oxygen and the cells of the digestive tract absorb food. Each cell develops in a particular way so that it can carry out its special function. This specialized development is known as the *differentiation* of cells. Groups of specialized cells with a particular purpose are known as *tissues*, e.g. muscle tissue is involved in movement and bone tissue provides support.

Homeostasis

Each living cell in the body requires oxygen and raw materials, water, and an efficient method of waste disposal; without these it cannot survive. In addition, certain aspects of the immediate environment must be maintained within narrow limits in order for the cells to function properly (Fig. 2.10). These are:
• The temperature
• The osmotic pressure
• The pH
• The concentration of certain substances

Maintaining the stable environment required by cells is known as *homeostasis*; the mechanisms that bring this about are therefore called *homeostatic mechanisms*. These are triggered by a change in a physical property or the chemical composition of the extracellular fluid, which activates a compensating mechanism, opposing the change. For example, if a large amount of water is drunk, diluting the blood, the kidney excretes more water by producing a large volume of urine. The minimum requirements for such a mechanism to operate effectively are:
• *Detectors* (or *receptors*), which are sensitive to some aspect of the environment and can monitor values and detect differences
• *Effectors*, which effect or make the necessary changes
• *Co-ordinating mechanisms*, which link detectors to effectors and ensure that the response is appropriate

Many of the systems in the body are effector systems whose main function is to maintain homeostasis.

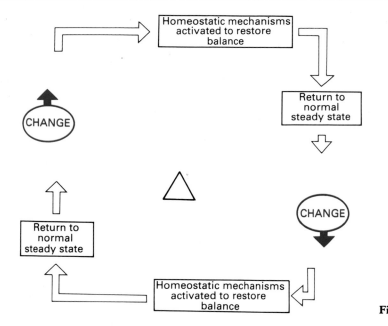

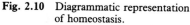

Fig. 2.10 Diagrammatic representation of homeostasis.

Examples are the respiratory system, which is concerned with the control of the concentrations of the gases oxygen and carbon dioxide, and the renal system, which helps control the volume and composition of the fluid in the body. Overall control of these effector systems depends on three co-ordinating and integrating systems:

- The nervous system
- The endocrine system
- The circulatory system

protein known as *keratin*. This provides a water-proof layer which prevents the whole of the epithelium from drying out. If the surface of the stratified epithelium is moist, as in the mouth, the cells survive until they are rubbed off, and keratin is not formed.

Transitional epithelium. Transitional epithelium is like stratified epithelium but the surface cells, instead of being flattened, are rounded and can spread out when the organ expands. It is found lining organs which must expand and must be waterproof, such as the bladder.

Glands

Glands develop from epithelial tissues and have the ability to manufacture substances from materials brought to them by the blood; they therefore have a good blood supply. These substances produced are called the *secretions* of the gland. Glands are of two types—exocrine and endocrine.

Exocrine glands. Exocrine glands pour their secretions out through a duct. The secretions of many of these glands contain enzymes. These enzymes act as catalysts for chemical reactions when they come into contact with specific substances but do not themselves enter into the reaction. Exocrine glands may be simple or compound (Fig. 3.6).

Simple glands have one duct leading from a single secretory unit. They can be divided according to their shape into:
- *Simple tubular glands*, e.g. the glands found in the walls of the small intestine and the stomach
- *Simple coiled glands*, e.g. sweat glands in the skin
- *Simple saccular glands*, e.g. sebaceous glands, which secrete a substance called sebum which lubricates hair and skin

Compound glands have several secretory units pouring their secretions into a number of small ducts which unite to form a larger duct. Again they can be divided according to their shape into:
- *Compound tubular glands*, e.g. the glands found in the duodenum
- *Compound saccular glands* (also called *racemose glands*), e.g. the salivary glands in the mouth

Endocrine glands. Endocrine glands pour their secretions directly into the bloodstream. These secretions are called *hormones*. Examples of endocrine glands

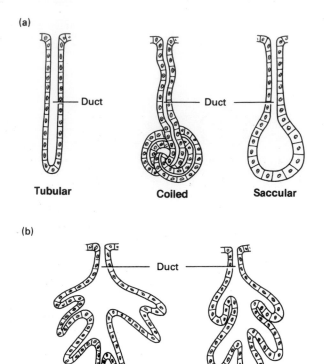

Fig. 3.6. Types of exocrine glands. (a) Simple glands. (b) Compound glands.

are the pituitary gland in the cranial cavity and the thyroid gland in the neck.

Membranes

The cavities and hollow organs of the body are lined with *membranes*. Membranes consist mainly of epithelium and they secrete lubricating fluids to moisten their smooth, glistening surfaces and to prevent friction. Three different types of membrane are found in the body:
- Synovial membrane
- Mucous membrane
- Serous membrane

Synovial membrane. Synovial membrane consists of a connective tissue layer (see below) covered with epithelium. It secretes a very thick fluid which is like the white of egg in consistency (hence the name—the prefix 'syn' meaning 'like' in the Greek, and 'ovum' being Latin for an egg). It is chiefly found

SECTION 3
The Tissues of the Body

3

Body Systems and Body Tissues

Objectives: After studying Chapter 3 you should be able to:

1 List the systems of the body.
2 Define the terms used in anatomy.
3 Define and classify the body tissues.

Before considering the systems of the body in greater detail, it is helpful to look at the overall organization of the body. The body consists of innumerable cells, each of which have specialized functions. The cells and their products which together perform a special function are known as *tissues*. A set of different tissues arranged together in order to carry out a specific task is known as an *organ* e.g. the stomach or the heart. Groups of organs carrying out the essential functions of the body are known as *systems*. An example is the digestive system, which is a group of organs concerned with the conversion of food into simpler substances that can be absorbed and utilized by the body.

Although the chapters of this book will deal with the structure and function of individual body systems, it is important to appreciate that no one system can function independently—each system depends on the others in order to function properly.

The control and transport systems of the body are central to its efficient functioning. The *nervous system* enables the body to be aware of the environment and makes it possible to respond to changes with the necessary precision. The *endocrine system* produces hormones which control a variety of functions in the body. The *circulatory system* is the transport system of the body and is responsible for carrying oxygen, foodstuffs, and chemicals such as hormones, as well as waste materials for excretion. The *locomotor system* is composed of the bones, joints and muscles. It allows movement and also gives support and protection to other tissues in the body.

Three systems are responsible for the taking in of substances essential to life and the elimination of unwanted material. These are the *digestive system*, the *respiratory system*, and the *urinary system*.

The *reproductive system* is involved in producing offspring and is thus responsible for the survival of the species.

Terms Used in Anatomy

In order to achieve uniformity of description an *anatomical position* has been chosen and defined. The body is erect, facing the observer, with the arms at the sides and the palms facing forwards (Fig. 3.1).

The following terms are commonly used when relating one part of the body to another:

- *Superior*: upper or above
- *Inferior*: lower or below
- *Anterior* or *ventral*: towards the front
- *Posterior* or *dorsal*: towards the back
- *Distal*: furthest from the body trunk
- *Proximal*: nearest to the body trunk
- *Medial*: nearest to the midline
- *Lateral*: furthest from the midline
- *Superficial*: towards the surface
- *Deep*: within the body

Anatomical planes and sections have also been defined (Fig. 3.2). The anatomical position is selected and the body is 'cut' into sections along certain angles or planes:

- *Median* or *mid-sagittal*: through the body vertically at the midline to form right and left halves
- *Transverse*, *horizontal* or *cross-section*: through the body at right angles to the midline to form upper and lower parts
- *Sagittal*: through the body parallel to the midline to form right and left parts
- *Coronal* or *frontal*: through the body to form anterior and posterior parts

Terms used to describe movement

The movements of the body are described using the anatomical position as a reference point:

- *Adduction*: movement of a part towards the body

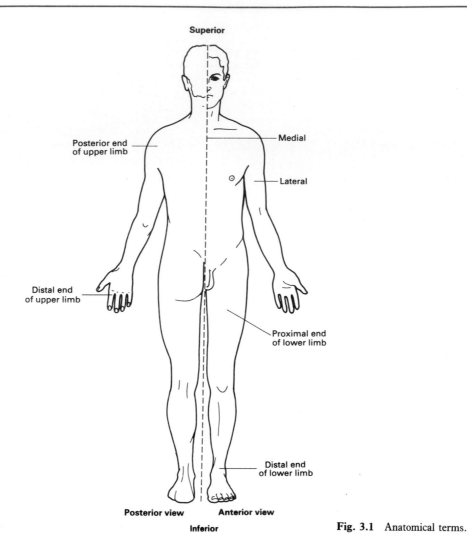

Fig. 3.1 Anatomical terms.

- *Abduction*: movement of a part away from the body
- *Flexion*: movement of a part so that the angle between the anterior surfaces is decreased (except in knee flexion); a bending movement
- *Extension*: movement of a part so that the part is returned to its anatomical position; a straightening movement
- *Hyperextension*: a continuation of extension so that the part is moved beyond its anatomical position
- *Rotation*: a turning movement on an axis
- *Circumduction*: a movement comprising flexion, abduction, extension and adduction in sequence; a circular movement

- *Pronation*: turning downward; usually restricted to the palm being turned downwards
- *Supination*: turning upwards; usually restricted to the palm being turned upwards
- *Inversion*: turning inwards
- *Eversion*: turning outwards
- *Protraction*: moving a part forwards
- *Retraction*: moving a part backwards

These movement terms, used in conjunction with positional terms, indicate the direction of movement, e.g. to rotate anteriorly means to turn towards the front. It must be remembered that when one part is moved in one direction, another part is often moved in the opposite, so two movements are made; for example, when the lateral aspect of the forearm is

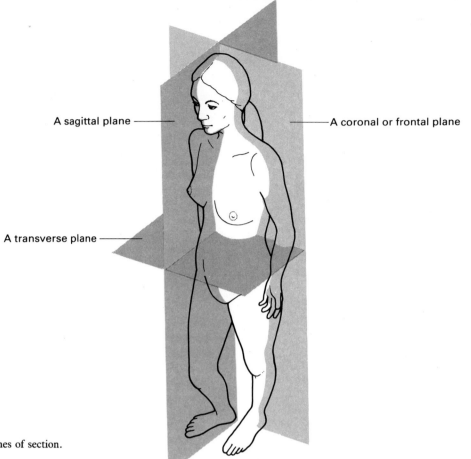

A sagittal plane ——————

A coronal or frontal plane

A transverse plane ——————

Fig. 3.2 Planes of section.

rotated anteriorly, the medial aspect is rotated posteriorly.

Cavities of the Body

The body has two main cavities, each subdivided into smaller cavities (Fig. 3.3). The *ventral cavity* lies within the trunk and contains:
- The *thoracic cavity* or *thorax*
- The *abdominal cavity* or *abdomen*, which is separated from the thoracic cavity by the muscular diaphragm
- The *pelvic cavity* or *pelvis*, which is continuous with the abdomen

The *dorsal cavity* contains the central nervous system and is divided into:
- The *cranial cavity*, which contains the brain
- The *spinal cavity*, which contains the spinal cord

Body tissues

There are four main types of tissues in the body:
- Epithelial tissue
- Nervous tissue
- Connective tissue
- Muscular tissue

Epithelial tissue

Epithelial tissue provides covering and lining membranes for the free surfaces inside and outside the body and is the tissue from which the glands of the body develop. Epithelial tissue protects underlying tissue from wear and tear. It is therefore often worn out quickly and must be continually renewed.

Some epithelial cells are specially developed to be able to absorb substances; linings made up of such cells are only one cell in thickness and often have a specialized surface called a '*brush border*'. Some epithelial tissue, particularly glandular tissue, has

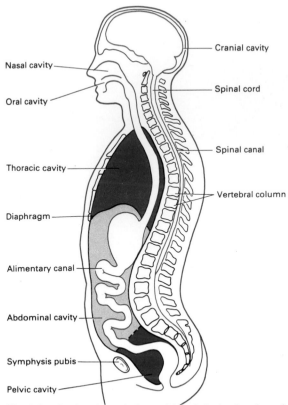

Fig. 3.3. Section through the cavities of the head and trunk.

the ability to secrete substances manufactured within the cells.

Epithelial cells are arranged on a *basement membrane*, which plays a part in holding them together. Epithelial tissue does not contain blood vessels—the nearest ones are in the underlying connective tissue, which may be one or many cells away. Nutrients reach the epithelial cells by diffusing through the intervening tissue.

Covering and lining epithelia

Covering epithelia may be classified according to the arrangement and shape of their cells (Fig. 3.4).

Simple epithelium. Simple epithelium is composed of a single layer of epithelial cells attached to a basement membrane; it is very delicate and is found where there is little wear and tear.

Simple pavement epithelium is composed of flat cells which form a smooth lining. It is found lining the blood vessels and forming the peritoneum.

Simple cuboidal epithelium is composed of cells shaped like cubes. It is found covering the ovary.

Simple columnar epithelium is composed of taller cells. It is found where wear and tear is great, e.g. lining the stomach and intestine. Different types of columnar epithelium are found where it has to perform different functions:

- *Ciliated columnar epithelium* has microscopic hair-like processes known as *cilia* projecting from the free surface of the cells. The cilia move together with a wave-like motion, and thus move mucus and other particles along. This type of epithelium is found in the respiratory tract.
- *Goblet cells* are special columnar cells which secrete mucus, the mucus collecting in the cells until the cytoplasm becomes distended.
- A *brush border* is often found on cells involved in

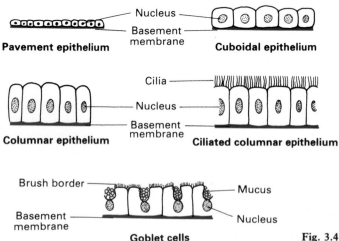

Fig. 3.4 Types of simple epithelium.

Table 3.1 Classification of tissues.

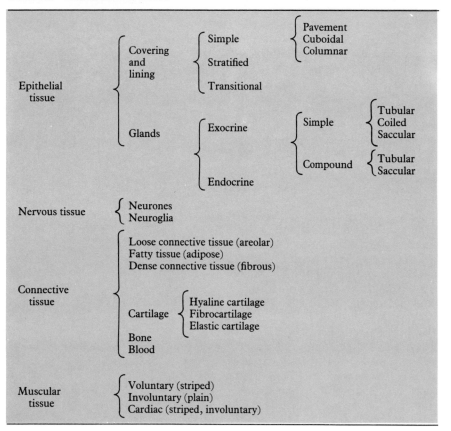

Epithelial tissue	Covering and lining	Simple	Pavement / Cuboidal / Columnar
		Stratified	
		Transitional	
	Glands	Exocrine	Simple → Tubular / Coiled / Saccular
			Compound → Tubular / Saccular
		Endocrine	
Nervous tissue	Neurones / Neuroglia		
Connective tissue	Loose connective tissue (areolar) / Fatty tissue (adipose) / Dense connective tissue (fibrous)		
	Cartilage	Hyaline cartilage / Fibrocartilage / Elastic cartilage	
	Bone / Blood		
Muscular tissue	Voluntary (striped) / Involuntary (plain) / Cardiac (striped, involuntary)		

absorption. It consists of finger-like projections from the surface of the cell; these increase the area through which absorption can occur. Epithelium with a brush border is found in the small intestine.

Stratified epithelium. Stratified epithelium is made up of many layers of cells. The deepest cells, called the *germinal layer*, lie on the basement membrane and are columnar in shape. As they divide, and this occurs frequently, the parent cells are pushed nearer the surface and become more and more flattened. The cells on the surface are rubbed off and are continually replaced from below (Fig. 3.5).

Because the blood supply is below the basement membrane, the surface cells die if the surface of the epithelium is dry, as on the skin. As the cells move towards the surface of the skin they manufacture a

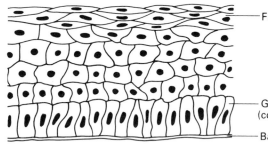

Flattened surface cells

Germinal layer (columnar cells)

Basement membrane

Fig. 3.5 Stratified epithelium.

protein known as *keratin*. This provides a water-proof layer which prevents the whole of the epithelium from drying out. If the surface of the stratified epithelium is moist, as in the mouth, the cells survive until they are rubbed off, and keratin is not formed.

Transitional epithelium. Transitional epithelium is like stratified epithelium but the surface cells, instead of being flattened, are rounded and can spread out when the organ expands. It is found lining organs which must expand and must be waterproof, such as the bladder.

Glands

Glands develop from epithelial tissues and have the ability to manufacture substances from materials brought to them by the blood; they therefore have a good blood supply. These substances produced are called the *secretions* of the gland. Glands are of two types—exocrine and endocrine.

Exocrine glands. Exocrine glands pour their secretions out through a duct. The secretions of many of these glands contain enzymes. These enzymes act as catalysts for chemical reactions when they come into contact with specific substances but do not themselves enter into the reaction. Exocrine glands may be simple or compound (Fig. 3.6).

Simple glands have one duct leading from a single secretory unit. They can be divided according to their shape into:
- *Simple tubular glands*, e.g. the glands found in the walls of the small intestine and the stomach
- *Simple coiled glands*, e.g. sweat glands in the skin
- *Simple saccular glands*, e.g. sebaceous glands, which secrete a substance called sebum which lubricates hair and skin

Compound glands have several secretory units pouring their secretions into a number of small ducts which unite to form a larger duct. Again they can be divided according to their shape into:
- *Compound tubular glands*, e.g. the glands found in the duodenum
- *Compound saccular glands* (also called *racemose glands*), e.g. the salivary glands in the mouth

Endocrine glands. Endocrine glands pour their secretions directly into the bloodstream. These secretions are called *hormones*. Examples of endocrine glands

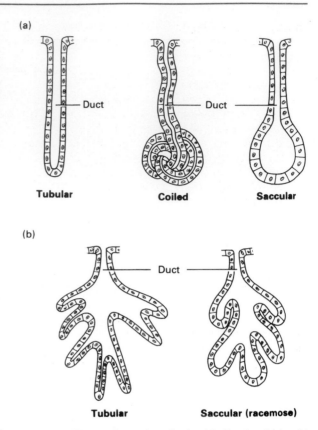

Fig. 3.6. Types of exocrine glands. (a) Simple glands. (b) Compound glands.

are the pituitary gland in the cranial cavity and the thyroid gland in the neck.

Membranes

The cavities and hollow organs of the body are lined with *membranes*. Membranes consist mainly of epithelium and they secrete lubricating fluids to moisten their smooth, glistening surfaces and to prevent friction. Three different types of membrane are found in the body:
- Synovial membrane
- Mucous membrane
- Serous membrane

Synovial membrane. Synovial membrane consists of a connective tissue layer (see below) covered with epithelium. It secretes a very thick fluid which is like the white of egg in consistency (hence the name—the prefix 'syn' meaning 'like' in the Greek, and 'ovum' being Latin for an egg). It is chiefly found lining joint cavities, where it lubricates the movement of the bones on one another. It is also found over bony prominences and between ligaments and bones or tendons and bones. At some sites it forms small sacs called *bursae* which act as water cushions, facilitating the movement of one part on another; for example, there are bursae around the shoulder, knee and elbow joints. Synovial membrane also forms sheaths for long tendons. For example, the tendons of the muscles in the forearm that straighten the fingers, and can be seen running across the back of the hand, are surrounded by sheaths of synovial membrane.

Mucous membrane. Mucous membrane secretes a rather thinner fluid called *mucus*. It is found lining the digestive tract from the mouth to the rectum, the air passages from the nose downwards, and the genito-urinary tract, all structures which are connected with the external skin. Mucus-secreting tubular glands are found in the membrane in areas where much secretion is produced. These glands are single or branching tubes lined with secreting cells.

Serous membrane. Serous membrane consists of flattened cells which secrete a small quantity of thin watery fluid called *serous fluid*. Serous membrane is found lining internal cavities such as the thorax and the abdomen (the *parietal layer*), and covering the organs they contain (the *visceral layer*), providing smooth, glistening, moist surfaces which slide easily over one another when one part moves on another.

Nervous tissue

Nervous tissue is specially developed to receive and transmit impulses. The basic cell is called a *neurone*. The neurones are surrounded by a special type of connective tissue cells known as *neuroglia*. Further details are given in Chapter 10.

Connective tissue

Connective tissue is tissue which supports and binds together all other tissues. There are many varieties of connective tissue which differ greatly in appearance, but all have a similar function. Connective tissue consists of:
- Cells
- Intercellular substance called matrix
- Fibres

Matrix and fibres are non-living products of the cells and form the supporting material of the body. The fibres are of two main types:
- Collagenous
- Elastic

Collagenous fibres are made up of *collagen*, which is manufactured from substances secreted by cells called *fibroblasts*. These coarse fibres occur in wavy bundles and can only stretch a little without tearing (Fig. 3.7).

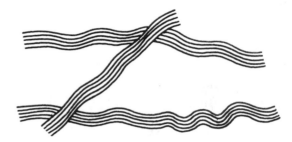

Fig. 3.7 Collagenous fibres.

Elastic fibres are fine, branching fibres which are highly elastic (Fig. 3.8).

In some areas of the body connective tissue needs to be firm and unyielding, whereas in others a degree of elasticity is required. For example, the fibrous layers surrounding arteries must be elastic to allow for swelling when they are full of blood, but the fibrous tendons that join muscle to bone must be inelastic, since if they were elastic the tendon would stretch when the muscle contracted and the bone would not move.

There are six main varieties of connective tissue:
- Loose connective tissue (areolar tissue)
- Fatty tissue (adipose tissue)
- Dense connective tissue (fibrous tissue)
- Cartilage
- Bone
- Blood

Fig. 3.8 Elastic fibres.

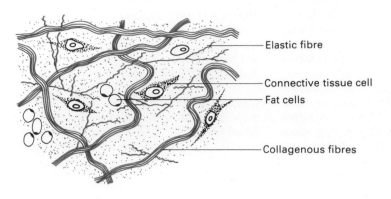

Fig. 3.9   Loose connective tissue.

Loose connective tissue

This type of tissue is also called *areolar tissue*. It consists of a loose network of collagenous and elastic fibres together with small scattered groups of fat cells and some fibroblasts. Some blood vessels and nerves are found, but these are not very numerous. Areolar tissue forms a transparent layer, which is as thin as tissue paper but very tough, and it is found between and around the organs of the body (Fig. 3.9).

Fatty tissue

This is also known as *adipose tissue*. It is similar to areolar tissue, but the spaces of the network are filled in with many fat cells. Each fat cell contains a large globule of fat which pushes the cytoplasm and nucleus to the edge of the cell. Adipose tissue is useful because the fat forms a food reserve on which

the body can draw if necessary. It helps retain body heat because it is a poor conductor of heat, and it also protects delicate organs such as the eye and the kidney (Fig. 3.10).

Dense connective tissue

This tissue is also called *fibrous tissue*. It consists chiefly of bundles of collagenous fibres between which the fibroblasts lie. It is very strong compared with loose connective tissue. The fibres may be arranged regularly in parallel bundles, e.g. in tendons or ligaments, or irregularly, with the fibres running in different directions, e.g. in the sheath enclosing muscles, which is called *fascia* (Fig. 3.11).

Cartilage

Cartilage consists of cells called *chondrocytes* separated by fibres. It has no blood vessels so the

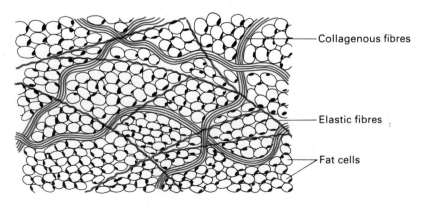

Fig. 3.10   Fatty or adipose tissue.

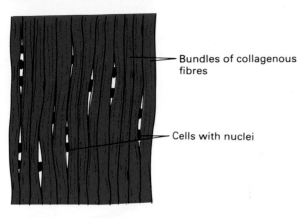

Bundles of collagenous fibres

Cells with nuclei

Fig. 3.11   Dense connective (fibrous) tissue.

cells obtain their nourishment from the fluid found between them. Cartilage is very tough but it is also pliant. There are three types of cartilage (Fig. 3.12):

- *Hyaline cartilage* consists of chondrocytes embedded in an apparently structureless matrix which is glassy in appearance and which has very fine collagen fibres running through it. It is found in the trachea and covering the ends of bones at a joint
- *Fibrocartilage* contains more collagen fibres than hyaline cartilage and is therefore stronger. It is found between bones forming slightly movable joints, e.g. between the vertebrae
- *Elastic cartilage* contains numerous elastic fibres embedded in the matrix. It can be found in the pinna or lobe of the ear and the epiglottis

Bone

Bone is a specialized type of cartilage in which the collagen is impregnated with mineral salts, chiefly calcium salts. The collagen fibres make the bone tough and the mineral salts make it rigid, giving support to the softer tissues. The cells between the collagen fibres are called *osteocytes*. Bone is richly supplied with blood vessels.

The structure of bone is dealt with more fully in Section Four.

Blood

Haemopoietic tissue is concerned with the formation of the blood. Blood may be regarded as a connective tissue, with the plasma forming the matrix which contains the cells. It is discussed more fully in Chapter 17.

Muscular tissue

This is dealt with in Chapter 4.

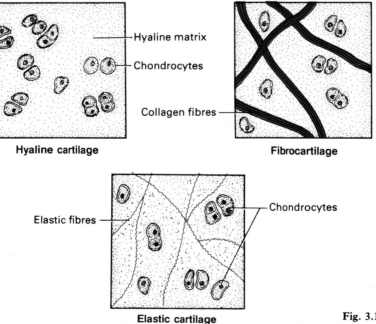

Hyaline matrix

Chondrocytes

Collagen fibres

Hyaline cartilage

Fibrocartilage

Elastic fibres

Chondrocytes

Elastic cartilage

Fig. 3.12   Types of cartilage.

4

Muscle Tissue and Muscle Function

Objectives: After studying Chapter 4 you should be able to:

1 Describe the different types of muscle tissue.
2 Describe the action and contraction of muscle.
3 Define muscle tone.

Muscle tissue is able to contract and is therefore able to produce movement. Wherever there is movement of the body there must be muscular tissue to produce it. Muscle cells are long and thin, and are often called *muscle fibres* because of their shape. The elastic fibres of connective tissue can recoil and return to their original length if they have been stretched, but muscle fibres can shorten without being stretched first.

There are three types of muscle tissue:
- Voluntary
- Involuntary
- Cardiac

Voluntary or striped muscle

Voluntary muscle (Fig. 4.1) forms the flesh of the limbs and trunk and is responsible for moving the skeleton. It consists of long fibres varying in length from a few millimetres in short muscles to 30 cm or more in long muscles. Arranged longitudinally in each cell are numerous parallel thread-like structures called *myofibrils* which are 0.01 to 0.1 mm in width. These myofibrils are regularly striped with alternate light and dark bands throughout their length and are arranged so that the dark and light parts of adjacent myofibrils line up, and the muscle fibre appears striped. Each fibre is enveloped in a membrane called the *sarcolemma*. The fibres are bound together into bundles by connective tissue called the *endomysium*. These bundles are in turn bound together by a sheath called the *perimysium* to form an individual muscle, the whole of which is

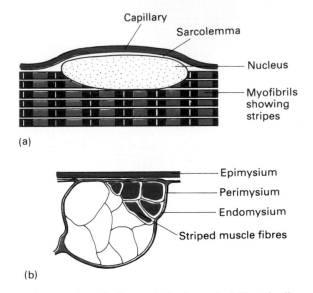

(a)

(b)

Fig. 4.1. Sections of voluntary (striped) muscle. (a) Longitudinal section of a muscle fibre. (b) Cross-section of part of a muscle.

surrounded by a sheath of fibrous tissue called the *epimysium*.

Each muscle fibre or cell has many nuclei, which are found just under the sarcolemma.

Striped muscle is under the control of the will and is therefore also known as voluntary muscle. It contracts strongly when stimulated by a nerve fibre but tires quickly. For strong contraction much energy is required, so voluntary muscle must have a good blood supply to bring oxygen and nutrients to the cells and to carry away waste products. Blood capillaries run between the individual muscle fibres to ensure they all have an adequate blood supply.

Involuntary or unstriped muscle

Involuntary muscle (Fig. 4.2) forms the wall of internal organs such as the stomach, bowel, bladder, uterus and blood vessels. It consists of spindle-

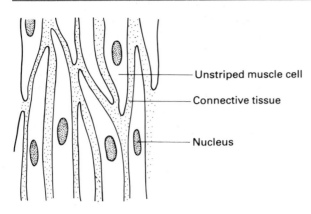

Fig. 4.2 Section of involuntary (unstriped) muscle.

shaped cells, each of which contains a nucleus. It is also called unstriped muscle as the cells do not show any stripes. The cells have no sheath but are bound together by connective tissue to form the walls of the various organs. They are not under the control of the will and act without any conscious effort or knowledge. They contract automatically but are supplied by autonomic nerves which affect their contractions. This type of muscle is capable of slow contraction over a long period and does not tire easily.

Cardiac muscle

Cardiac muscle (Fig. 4.3) is both involuntary and irregularly striped. It is found only in the heart wall and is different from any other muscle tissue. It consists of short, cylindrical, branched fibres with centrally placed nuclei. They have no sheath but are bound together by connective tissue. The cardiac

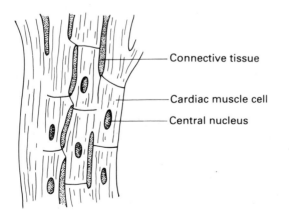

Fig. 4.3 Section of cardiac muscle.

muscle is not under the control of the will but contracts automatically in a rhythmic manner throughout life, though the rate of these rhythmic contractions is controlled by nerves which quicken or slow down its action. The fibres branch and join with one another so that impulses can spread from one fibre to another as well as along the length of the muscle.

The Structure of the Muscular System

Most voluntary muscles have *tendons* at one or both ends. Tendons are made of fibrous tissue and are usually cord-like in appearance. However, in some flat or sheet-like muscles the tendon is a thin, strong, fibrous sheet called an *aponeurosis*. Fibrous tissue also forms a protective covering or sheath around muscles, known as *fascia*; this also helps to hold the muscles in place.

Where one muscle is attached to another the fibres may interlace, the perimysium of one fusing with the perimysium of the other, or the two muscles may share a common tendon. A third type of connection occurs in the muscles of the abdominal wall; the aponeurosis of the muscles on the right side interlaces with that of the left side, forming the *linea alba*.

The blood supply to muscles comes from arterioles (small arteries) in the perimysium. These give off capillaries which run in the endomysium and across the muscle fibres.

Action of muscle (Figs. 4.4 and 4.5)

When a muscle contracts, one end normally remains stationary while the other end is drawn towards it. The end which remains stationary is called the *origin* and that which moves is called the *insertion*. It is not uncommon, however, for a muscle to be used, as it were, the wrong way round, so that the insertion remains fixed and the origin moves towards it. For example, the *gluteus maximus* has its origin in the sacrum at the base of the spine and it is inserted into the femur in the thigh. When the flexed thigh is straightened the insertion moves towards the origin (i.e. the femur moves while the sacrum stays fixed); when you stand up after bending forward the origin moves towards the insertion (i.e. the sacrum moves while the femur stays fixed). This arrangement economizes on the number of muscles required. Further economy is achieved by the placing of

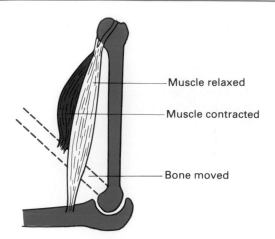

Muscle relaxed

Muscle contracted

Bone moved

Fig. 4.4 Bone movement caused by muscle contraction.

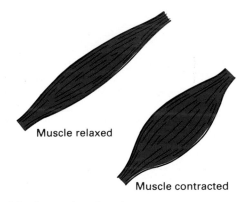

Muscle relaxed

Muscle contracted

Fig. 4.5 Contraction of a voluntary muscle.

muscles so that they can carry out more than one action.

Muscles must cross the joint they move. Some cross two joints, producing movement in both; for example, the biceps muscle crosses both the elbow and the shoulder joint, causing flexion of both.

Muscles only act by contracting and thus pulling; they cannot push. They can also contract without shortening and so hold a joint firm and fixed in a certain position. When the contraction passes off the muscles become soft but do not lengthen until stretched by the force of gravity or the contraction of muscles which have the opposite action known as *antagonists*.

Muscles never work alone; even the simplest movement requires the action of many muscles. Picking up a pencil requires movement of the fingers and thumb, the wrist and the elbow, and possibly of the shoulder and the trunk if the body

needs to lean forward. Each muscle must contract just enough and its antagonist must relax to allow the movement to take place smoothly and without jerking. The action of many muscles together in this way is termed *muscle co-ordination*. Any new skill involving co-ordination (such as riding a bicycle) requires time and practice until the new combination of muscle movement has been learned and only then can it be carried out without great mental effort and concentration.

Muscles contain specialized sensory nerves which carry information regarding the degree of contraction of the muscle to the central nervous system. Under normal circumstances the muscles are in a state of partial contraction known as *muscle tone*. It is because of muscle tone that a position can be maintained for long periods without exhaustion—different groups of fibres within the muscle contract and relax in turn, giving periods of rest and activity to each group. The muscles with the highest degree of tonicity in the human are those of the neck and back.

Muscle Contraction

Muscle is composed of:
- 75% water
- 20% protein
- 5% mineral salts, glycogen and fat

Muscle contraction occurs as a result of stimulation by a nerve impulse.

To understand how the muscle contracts it is necessary to look more closely at the structure of the *myofibril*. The myofibril contains *myofilaments*, of which there are two types (Fig. 4.6):
- *Thick filaments*, made of the protein *myosin*
- *Thin filaments*, made of the protein *actin*

In striped muscle (i.e. voluntary and cardiac) the thick and thin filaments are arranged lengthwise in the muscle cell so that they overlap. In areas where there are just thin, actin filaments the myofibril looks pale and in areas where there are just thick, myosin filaments or where the two types of filament overlap the myofibril looks dark. It is these alternating areas of pale and dark that give the myofibril and thus the muscle cells, a striped appearance (Fig. 4.7).

The filaments are held in place at the *Z line*. The length of myofibril between one Z line and the next is known as a *sarcomere*. The slighter pale zone in the

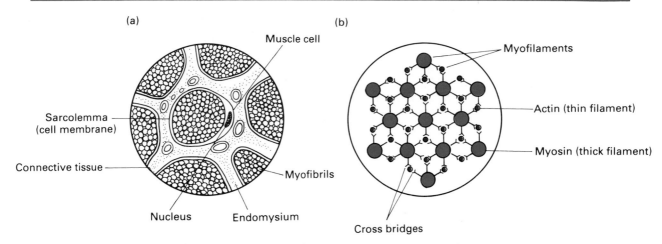

Fig. 4.6 (a) Microscopic view of muscle to show the myofibrils. (b) The arrangement of contractile filaments within a myofibril.

middle of the dark band, which is the area where there are only myosin filaments, is known as the *H zone*.

The actin and myosin filaments are joined to each other by many cross-bridges. When the muscle contracts these cross-bridges break and reform, sliding the filaments further in between one another and thus increasing the overlap. The length of the filaments themselves does not change, but the Z lines are drawn closer together. This process requires calcium, which is stored by the cell in part of the endoplasmic reticulum (which is known as *sarcoplasmic reticulum* in muscle cells) and released when the muscle is stimulated. When contraction has occurred the calcium is reabsorbed into the sarcoplasmic reticulum and the contraction ceases.

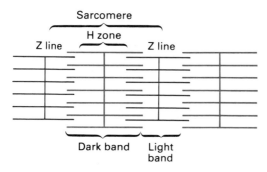

Fig. 4.7 Diagrammatic representation of the overlap between the thick and thin filaments in a myofibril to show how the striped appearance is produced.

In unstriped, involuntary muscles the mechanism of contraction is very similar. The actin and myosin filaments are not arranged into myofibrils, and so this type of muscle is not striped, but contraction again involves increasing the amount of overlap of the two types of filament.

In order for muscle fibres to contract, energy is required. This is obtained from food, particularly carbohydrates. During digestion in the gut carbohydrates are broken down to a simple sugar called glucose. The glucose which is not required immediately by the body is converted to *glycogen* and is stored in the liver and in the muscles. Muscle glycogen provides the source of energy for muscle contraction. Glycogen is broken down by a process known as *oxidation*, eventually forming carbon dioxide and water. During this process a compound called *adenosine triphosphate (ATP)*, which is rich in energy, is formed. When the muscle is stimulated to contract, the ATP is converted to *adenosine diphosphate (ADP)*, releasing energy which can be used in the contraction process.

During the oxidation of glycogen, *pyruvic acid* is formed. If plenty of oxygen is available, as is usually the case during ordinary movement, pyruvic acid is broken down into carbon dioxide and water. If insufficient oxygen is available, the pyruvic acid is converted to *lactic acid*. During violent exercise the muscles require more oxygen. The blood supply to the muscles is increased in order to produce more oxygen, but even so not enough oxygen may reach the muscle cells, particularly at the beginning of the exercise. Lactic acid accumulates in the muscle cells

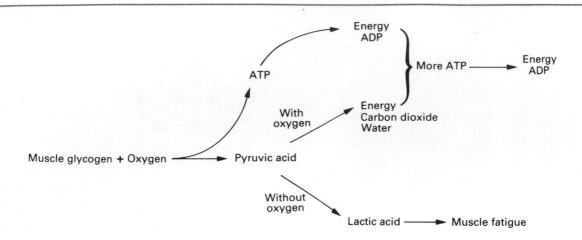

Fig. 4.8   The sequence of events during muscle contraction.

and diffuses into the fluid surrounding the cells and into the blood. The increasing amounts of lactic acid in the muscle produces a sensation of fatigue and cramp. The presence of lactic acid in the blood stimulates the respiratory centre in the brain, triggering an increase in the rate and depth of respiration. This leads to an increase in the amount of oxygen in the blood. These changes in respiration continue, even after the exercise is over, until sufficient oxygen has been taken in to allow the cells of the muscles and the liver to oxidize the lactic acid completely, or convert it to glucose or glycogen. This extra oxygen needed to remove the accumulated lactic acid is called the 'oxygen debt', which must be repaid after the exercise is completed (Fig. 4.8).

—5—

Bones and Joints

Objectives: After studying Chapter 5 you should be able to:

1 List the functions of the skeleton.
2 Describe the growth of bone.
3 Draw and label a diagram showing the structure of bone tissue.
4 List the three types of bones and give examples of each.
5 Describe the major types of joint and give examples of each.

Bones

The skeletal system is made up of just over 200 bones, joined together to provide a strong, movable, living framework for the body. The system has four main functions (Fig. 5.1):
- It supports and protects the surrounding soft tissues and vital organs.
- It assists in body movement by giving attachment to muscles and providing leverage at joints.

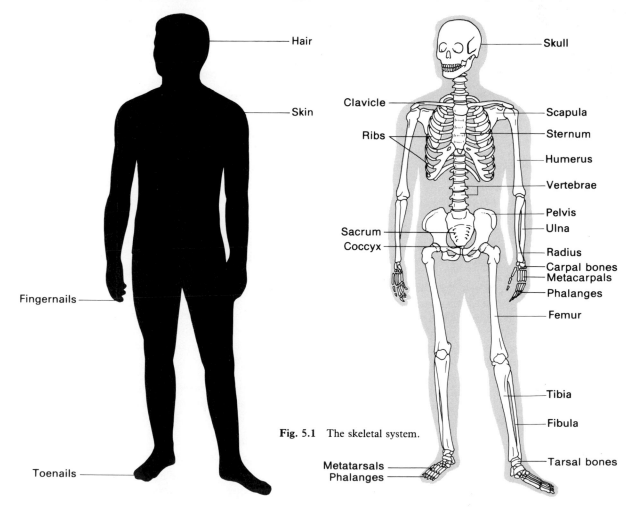

Fig. 5.1 The skeletal system.

- It manufactures blood cells in the red bone marrow.
- It provides storage for mineral salts, particularly phosphorus and calcium.

Cartilage provides the environment in which bone develops. Development is from spindle-shaped cells, called *osteoblasts*, which are found underneath the tough sheath of fibrous tissue that covers the bone, called the *periosteum*, and in cavities within the bone. Osteoblasts are able to convert the soluble salts of calcium in the blood, such as calcium chloride, into insoluble calcium salts, chiefly calcium phosphate. A second set of cells is also present which can change the insoluble calcium phosphate back into soluble calcium salts which are carried away by the blood. These cells are capable of causing the absorption of any unwanted bone and are known as *osteoclasts*. Both types of cell are active during the growth period, osteoblasts producing bone and osteoclasts removing it to maintain the form and proportion of the bone. For example, osteoblasts build up bone on the surface of a hollow bone, while osteoclasts absorb bone on the inner side to enlarge the cavity and prevent the bone from becoming too heavy.

Bone growth and repair

Plentiful supplies of calcium and phosphorus are essential in the diet of the pregnant and nursing mother, the growing child and when bone repair is taking place after injury or disease. Calcium is present in milk and eggs and in green vegetables, and phosphorus is present in meat, fish and the yolks of eggs.

Vitamin D is necessary for the absorption of calcium and phosphorus from the intestine and for their use within the body; lack of vitamin D causes rickets in children and osteomalacia in adults. Both these conditions cause soft bones which bend under the weight of the body; various deformities of the weight-bearing bones may result. Vitamin D is found in animal fat and fish oils and in margarine that has been artificially irradiated. The human body can also manufacture vitamin D. The action of the ultraviolet rays of the sun converts *ergosterol* in the skin into vitamin D.

Vitamin C is important in bone growth as it plays a part in laying down collagen, the main constituent of connective tissue. It is found in fresh fruit, particu-larly citrus fruit and blackcurrants, green vegetables, tomatoes and potatoes.

Growth and development of bone is also affected by both *exercise* and *rest*. Exercise causes an increased blood supply to the muscles and therefore to the underlying bones; because the blood carries the necessary building materials, exercise results in increased growth. Recognition of this fact is responsible for the emphasis on physical exercise in schools. The pull of developing muscles is an important factor in determining the shape of the bones and posture may also affect their shape by altering the stresses on bones. The importance of rest is interesting. The bones of a child are comparatively elastic, so that at the end of a day of standing and running about there is an appreciable loss of height. During rest the bones recover their full length, so a mid-day rest and a long night will help growth.

Growth is also controlled by the secretions of certain ductless glands (see Chapter 12).

Types of bone tissue

Bone tissue is of two types, compact and spongy.

Compact bone

Compact bone appears to be solid but when it is examined under a microscope it is found to consist of *Haversian systems* (Fig. 5.2). A Haversian system consists of:
- A *central canal*, called a Haversian canal, which contains blood vessels, nerves and lymphatics.
- Plates of bone, called *lamellae*, arranged round the central canal.
- Spaces between the lamellae called *lacunae*, which contain bone cells, called *osteocytes*, and lymph.
- Fine channels between the lacunae and the central canal called *canaliculi*, which carry lymph, bringing nutrients and oxygen to the osteocytes.

Between the Haversian systems there are tiny circular plates of bone called *interstitial lamellae*.

Spongy bone

Spongy bone is hard like all bone but has a spongy appearance to the naked eye. When examined under a microscope the Haversian canals are seen to be

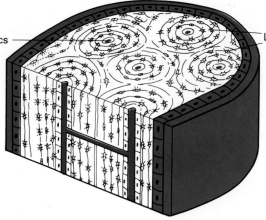

Haversian canal containing blood vessels, nerves and lymphatics

Lacunae containing bone cells

Fig. 5.2 The structure of compact bone.

much larger and there are fewer lamellae. The spaces in spongy bone are filled with *red bone marrow*, which consists of fat and blood cells and in which red blood cells are made.

Types of bones

There are three types of bones:
- Long bones
- Flat bones
- Irregular bones

Long bones

A long bone consists of a shaft and two extremities. The shaft has an outer layer of compact bone surrounding a central cavity called the *medullary canal* which contains yellow bone marrow. Yellow bone marrow, like red bone marrow, consists of fat and blood cells, but it does not have so rich a blood supply or contain so many red blood cells. The extremities consist of a mass of spongy bone containing red bone marrow covered by a thin layer of compact bone (Fig. 5.3).

The whole bone is covered by a tough sheath of fibrous tissue called the *periosteum*; this is richly supplied with blood vessels which pass into the bone to nourish it. Three distinct sets of blood vessels supply the long bones:
- Innumerable tiny arteries run into the compact bone to supply the Haversian systems.
- Many larger arteries pierce the compact bone to supply the spongy bone and red bone marrow. The openings through which these vessels enter

the bone can be seen quite easily by the naked eye.
- One or two large arteries supply the medullary canal. These are known as *nutrient arteries*. They pass through a large opening called the nutrient foramen, which runs obliquely through the shaft to the medullary canal.

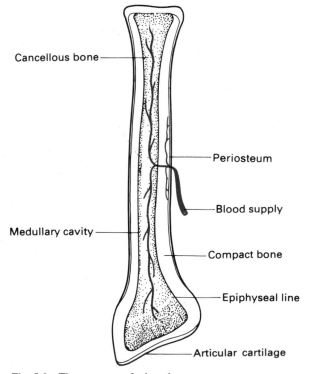

Cancellous bone

Periosteum

Blood supply

Medullary cavity

Compact bone

Epiphyseal line

Articular cartilage

Fig. 5.3 The structure of a long bone.

These three sets of vessels are linked by fine branch arteries within the bone.

If the periosteum is torn off, the underlying bone will die, but if the bone is destroyed by disease and the periosteum remains healthy it is able to build up new bone. The part of the periosteum nearest to the bone contains many osteoblasts, which are able to manufacture new bone tissue. In this way the bone can be repaired or can grow. The periosteum provides protection and also gives attachment to tendons of muscles. It is not present on the joint surfaces of a bone where it is replaced by hyaline cartilage, called *articular cartilage*, which provides a smooth surface so that joint movements can occur without friction.

Development of long bones. Long bones are first formed of cartilage, which is then replaced by bone, a process known as *ossification*. This begins from three or more groups of bone-forming cells (osteoblasts) known as *centres of ossification*, one in the shaft and one or more at either extremity. The centre of ossification in the shaft appears early in fetal life. The area of bone which develops from it is known as the *diaphysis*. The centres of ossification at the extremities begin to develop after birth, and the areas of bone formed are known as *epiphyses*.

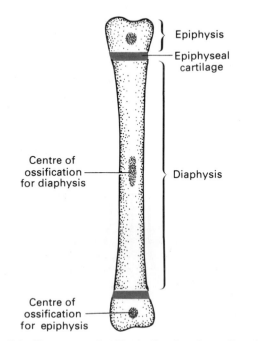

Fig. 5.4 The centres of ossification in a long bone. Growth in length occurs at the epiphyses.

From these centres ossification gradually spreads throughout the extremity and is well developed by 12 years of age, though there is still a line of cartilage

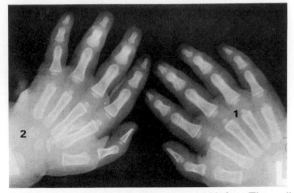

Fig. 5.5 X-ray of the hands of a one-year-old infant. The small long bones of the fingers and the thumb have their shafts well formed, but note the gaps between them and the knuckles (1), where the epiphyses are only beginning to form centres of ossification. Note also that only two of the eight bones in the wrist (2) have begun to ossify.

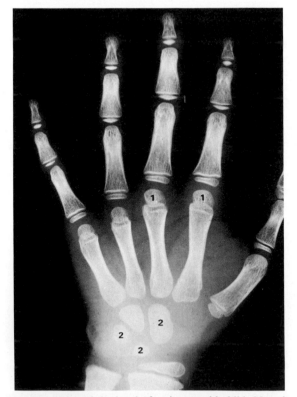

Fig. 5.6 X-ray of the hand of a six-year-old child. Note the development of the epiphyses of the long bones of the hand (1), and the ossification that has occurred in the bones of the wrist (2).

left between the epiphysis and the diaphysis, which is known as the *epiphyseal cartilage*. It is from this cartilage that growth in length occurs. The shaft grows longer by fresh bone being constantly produced at either end of it by the epiphyseal cartilage (Figs. 5.4–5.6). When full growth has been attained, between the ages of 18 and 25 years, the line of cartilage turns to bone and no further growth can occur. The timing of this event varies from one bone to another and from one end of a bone to the other. For example, the lower epiphysis of the humerus unites at about the 18th year, but the upper epiphysis does not join the shaft until about two years later.

Flat bones

Flat bones consist of two stout layers of compact bone joined by a layer of spongy bone. These bones are also covered by periosteum, from which two sets of blood vessels pass into the bone to supply the compact and spongy bone respectively. Flat bones are found in the head, trunk, shoulder girdle and pelvic girdle, where they give protection to the delicate organs underlying them and provide attachment for the powerful muscles required to control the freely movable shoulder and hip joints (Fig. 5.7).

The layers of compact bone in the flat bones of the skull are referred to as the *outer* and *inner tables* and the spongy bone is called the *diploë*. The outer table is thick and strong so that it is not readily broken. In some areas there are air-filled cavities in the spongy bone between the two tables, which are called *sinuses*.

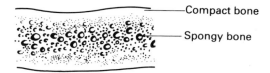

Fig. 5.7 Section through a flat bone.

Irregular bones

Irregular bones consist of a mass of spongy bone covered by a thin layer of compact bone. They are covered with periosteum, except on the articular surfaces, and, as with flat bones, this protective covering provides two sets of blood vessels to supply both the compact and the spongy bone. Irregular

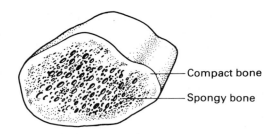

Fig. 5.8 Section through an irregular bone.

bones are found in the spinal column and the middle ear and also at the ankle and wrist; these latter are sometimes called *short bones* (Fig. 5.8).

Surface irregularities

The surfaces of all bones are very irregular and show numbers of *depressions* and *projections*. These may be divided according to function into:
- *Articular*, which are involved in the formation of joints and are smooth
- *Non-articular*, which give attachment to muscles or ligaments and are rough

Articular projections are named according to their shape:
- A *head* is round like a sphere or disc.
- A *condyle* is rounded but oval in outline.

Articular depressions are termed sockets or fossae.

Non-articular projections have many terms applied to them according to their nature:
- A *process* is a rough projection for muscle attachment.
- A *spine* is a pointed, rough projection.
- A *trochanter* is a broad, rough projection. It is also known as a *tuberosity*.
- A *tubercle* is a small tuberosity.
- A crest is a long, rough, narrow, projecting surface.

All these rough projections give attachment to muscles; the stronger the muscle and the more it is used, the larger and rougher the projection is, providing a larger surface for muscle attachment. In a paralysed limb the processes either fail to develop, or atrophy, according to age.

Non-articular depressions are termed:
- Fossa—a notch in the bone
- Groove—a long, narrow depression

Other terms applied to bone irregularities are:
● Foramen—an opening in the bone
● Sinus—a hollow cavity in the bone

Joints

A joint or articulation is formed wherever two bones meet, but not all joints of bones allow movement. There are three groups of joints:
● *Fibrous* or fixed joints
● *Cartilaginous* or slightly movable joints
● *Synovial* or freely movable joints

However, not all joints fit rigidly into this classification: there are some fibrous joints which are slightly movable (e.g. the joint between the lower ends of the tibia and fibula) and some cartilaginous joints which are barely movable (e.g. the symphysis pubis).

The bones of most joints are joined to each other by ligaments, which are strong cords of fibrous tissue attached to the periosteum and running from one bone to another. These ligaments are yielding but inelastic and vary in strength and shape according to the work that they have to do. Because they are pliable, they allow movement to take place, but they are also strong, inelastic and rich in sensory nerves and in this way they protect the joints from excessive movement and strain.

Fibrous joints

One type of fibrous joint occurs where the margins of two bones meet and dovetail accurately into one another, separated only by a thin band of fibrous tissue. Joints such as these, which do not normally permit movement, are found between the bones of the cranium and are called *sutures*. In the infant at birth the line of fibrous tissue between these bones allows the edges to glide over one another, enabling the head to be moulded to ease its passage through the birth canal. Other fibrous joints occur where the roots of the teeth articulate with the upper and lower jaws and between the tibia and fibula, where the

Fig. 5.9 Section through a fibrous joint.

fibrous tissue is in the form of the *interosseous ligament* which binds the two bones together (Fig. 5.9).

Cartilaginous joints

A cartilaginous joint occurs where the bony surfaces are covered with hyaline cartilage and held together by a pad of fibrocartilage and by ligaments, which do not form a complete capsule round the joint. A limited degree of movement is possible because the cartilaginous pad can be compressed. The joints between the bodies of the vertebrae and between the manubrium and the body of the sternum are cartilaginous joints (Fig. 5.10).

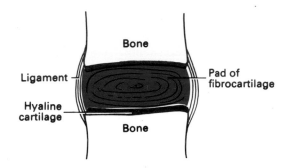

Fig. 5.10 Section through a cartilaginous (slightly movable) joint.

Synovial joints

A synovial joint occurs where the articulating surfaces are covered with hyaline cartilage and the joint is completely surrounded by a *fibrous capsule* lined with *synovial membrane*, which covers the whole of the interior of the joint with the exception of the bone ends, manisci and discs (see below). The joint cavity formed contains *synovial fluid*, which nourishes the articular cartilage (as it does not have a blood supply) and lubricates the joint. The bones are also connected by a number of ligaments. Some movement is always possible in a synovial joint even though it may be limited, as in the gliding movement between the adjoining metacarpal bones in the hand (Fig. 5.11).

In some synovial joints the cavity may be divided by an *articular disc* or *meniscus* consisting of fibrocartilage, which helps to spread synovial fluid around the joint, to reduce wear of the articular surfaces and to deepen the joint.

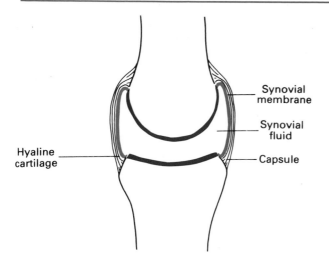

Hyaline cartilage

Synovial membrane

Synovial fluid

Capsule

Fig. 5.11   Section through a synovial (freely movable) joint.

Types of synovial joints

Synovial joints can be divided according to the type of movement which occurs into:

- *Hinge joints*, which allow movement in one direction only; the elbow is a good example.
- *Pivot joints*, which only allow rotation; for example, the radius and ulna at the elbow and the first and second cervical vertebrae allowing turning movements of wrist and head respectively.
- *Condylar joints*, which allow movement in two

directions but do not allow rotation. An example is the wrist joint.
- *Ball-and-socket joints*, which are formed by a hemispherical head fitting into a cup-shaped socket. They allow movement in two directions and rotation, and are therefore the most freely movable type of joint. Examples are the hip and shoulder joints.
- *Plane joints*, in which the bones glide over one another. The gliding movements are restricted by ligaments or bony prominences. Examples are the carpal and tarsal joints.

Joints are movable, but the movements are carried out by the various muscles around the joints. Like ligaments, the muscles run from one bone to another. Thus, in addition to producing movement, they help to hold the bones in position and give support to the joint capsule, as long as their normal tone is sustained. When the muscles are paralysed and limp, the looser joints can be dislocated comparatively easily, particularly the freely movable shoulder joint; however, when the muscles are paralysed, but rigid and shrunken, the joint may become completely immovable. This immobility can be prevented by moving the joint through as wide a range of movement as possible to maintain the elasticity of the muscles. Immobility may also result from the joint surfaces becoming adherent to one another or to the joint capsule as a result of disease or injury affecting the joint itself.

The Muscular Skeletal Framework

Colour Plates 1, 2, 4, 5 and 6 relate to this section. The plates are between pages 134 and 135.

SECTION 4

6

The Head

Objectives: After studying Chapter 6 you should be able to:

1 Given an individual bone from the head illustrated in this chapter, indicate its position on a skeleton.
2 Draw and label diagrams of the bones of the head and face.
3 Describe the joints in the head.
4 Demonstrate the action of the muscles in the head, face and neck.

It is not possible to study adequately the bones of the skeleton without access to an entire skeleton and to disarticulated bones which can be handled and examined closely.

The skeleton can be divided into:
● The bones of the head
● The bones of the trunk
● The bones of the upper limb and shoulder girdle
● The bones of the lower limb and pelvic girdle

The bones of the head and trunk are also known as the *axial skeleton*, the main support of the body, while the bones of the extremities are known as the *appendicular skeleton*.

The Bones of the Head

For the purposes of description the skull may be divided into (Fig. 6.1):
● The bones of the cranium
● The bones of the face

The bones of the cranium

The cranium is a box-like cavity which contains and protects the brain. It has a dome-shaped roof called the *calvaria* or skull cap and its floor is known as the *base of the skull*. The cranium consists of eight bones:
● One frontal bone
● Two parietal bones

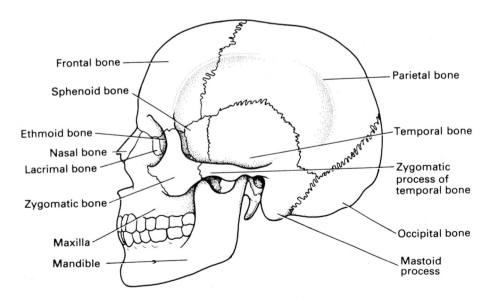

Fig. 6.1 The bones of the head.

- One occipital bone
- Two temporal bones
- One ethmoid bone
- One sphenoid bone

The frontal bone

The frontal bone is a large flat bone forming the forehead and most of the roof of the orbit of the eye. The rounded prominences, one on each side of the midline, which vary in size from one individual to another and which together form the forehead, are known as the *frontal tuberosities*. The frontal bone contains two irregular cavities called the *frontal sinuses*, which lie one over each orbit and which open into the nasal cavity. These sinuses contain air and are lined with mucous membrane which is continuous with the mucous membrane lining the respiratory tract. They add resonance to the voice and help to lighten the skull, but the mucous membrane may become infected, causing a condition known as sinusitis.

The parietal bones

The parietal bones form the sides and roof of the cranium; they articulate with the frontal bone, the occipital bone and with each other to form the *sutures* or joints of the cranium. On the internal surface of the parietal bones small grooves that carry the blood vessels supplying the brain and the impression of the folds or convolutions of the surface of the brain can be seen. At birth there are membranous gaps in the skull at the angles of the parietal bone called *fontanelles* (see page 63).

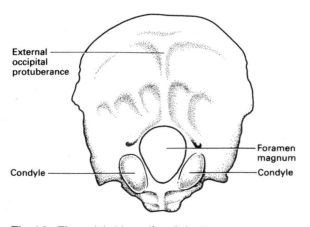

Fig. 6.2 The occipital bone (from below).

The occipital bone

The occipital bone forms the back of the skull. It has a roughened area called the *external occipital protuberance* to which muscles are attached. Below this there is a large oval opening, known as the *foramen magnum*, through which the spinal cord passes. On either side of the foramen are two smooth oval processes called the *occipital condyles*, which articulate with the first cervical vertebra. These joints allow the nodding movement of the head (Fig. 6.2).

The temporal bones

The temporal bones are situated at the sides and base of the skull. Each consists of four parts (Fig. 6.3):

- The *squamous part* forms the anterior and upper part of the bone and is thin and flat. A long arched process, called the *zygoma* or *zygomatic process* projects forward from the lower portion. This joins to the zygomatic bone of the face (see page 62).
- The *petromastoid part* forms the posterior portion of the bone and can be divided into two parts:
  (a) The *mastoid portion*, which has a conical projection called the *mastoid process* that can be felt just behind the ear. This process contains air cavities or sinuses that connect with the middle ear (see page 31).
  (b) The *petrous portion*, which lies between the occipital bone and the sphenoid. It contains the structures forming the inner ear (see page 132).
- The *tympanic part* is a curved plate lying below the squamous part and in front of the mastoid process. It contains the external auditory meatus.
- The *styloid process* projects downwards and forwards from the underneath of the bone.

The ethmoid bone

The ethmoid bone is very light and irregular in shape and consists of three parts:

- The *cribriform plate*, a small horizontal plate which forms the roof of the nasal cavity. It is perforated with many fine openings, or foramina, for the passage of the *olfactory nerves*, which transmit the sense of smell.
- The *perpendicular plate*, which descends from the cribriform plate. It forms the upper part of the nasal septum, which divides the nasal cavity into two.

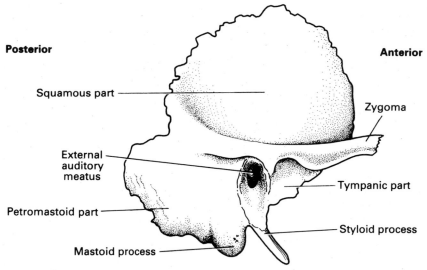

Fig. 6.3 The temporal bone.

- Two *labyrinths*, each consisting of a number of thin-walled air cavities or sinuses that communicate with the nasal cavity and thus may become infected from it. Two thin plates of bone called the *superior and middle nasal conchae* jut out into the nasal cavities from the labyrinths.

The sphenoid bone

The sphenoid bone is situated at the base of the skull, in front of the temporal bones. It is shaped rather like a bat with outstretched wings. The *body* contains two large air sinuses, which communicate with the nasal cavity, and a deep depression, known as the *hypophyseal fossa*, which contains the *hypophysis cerebri* or pituitary gland. The *greater and lesser wings* of the sphenoid bone are perforated by many openings or *foramina* through which nerves and blood vessels pass (Fig. 6.4).

The bones of the face

The bones of the face are:
- The maxillae
- The mandible
- Two zygomatic bones
- Two palatine bones
- The hyoid bone

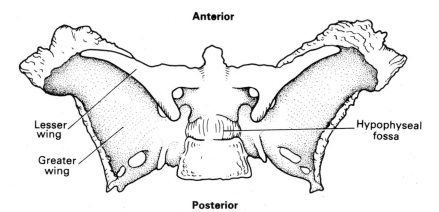

Fig. 6.4 The sphenoid bone (from above).

- Two inferior nasal conchae
- Two lacrimal bones
- Two nasal bones
- One vomer

The maxillae

The maxillae unite in the midline to form the whole of the upper jaw. They carry the upper teeth embedded in a ridge of bone called the *alveolar process*. The *palatine process* of the maxilla is a horizontal projection which forms a considerable part of the floor of the nasal cavity and the roof of the mouth. The *maxillary sinus* is an air-filled cavity within the body of the bone which communicates with the nasal cavity and which may become infected following nasal infection.

The mandible

The mandible is an irregular bone and is the only movable bone in the head. It is the largest bone of the face. It forms the lower jaw and carries the lower teeth embedded in the alveolar part. The *rami* are vertical projections that have a *condylar process*, which articulates with the temporal bone, and a *coronoid process*, which provides attachment for muscle. The upright and horizontal portions form the angle of the jaw. (Fig. 6.5)

The zygomatic bones

The zygomatic bones are irregular bones which form the prominence of the cheek and part of the walls of the orbit. The *temporal process* articulates with the zygomatic process of the temporal bone to form the *zygomatic arch*, which can be felt passing backwards from the side of the orbit to the ear.

The palatine bones

The palatine bones are irregular bones which form part of the hard palate, the lateral wall of the nasal cavity and the floor of the orbit.

The hyoid bone

The hyoid bone is U-shaped and lies at the base of the tongue, to which it gives attachment. It does not articulate with any other bone but is connected by ligaments to the styloid processes of the temporal bone (Fig. 6.6).

The inferior nasal conchae

The inferior nasal conchae are curved plates of bone which lie in the walls of the nasal cavity, below the superior and middle nasal conchae of the ethmoid bone.

The lacrimal bones

The lacrimal bones are the smallest and most fragile of the cranial bones and form part of the walls of the orbits. Each is grooved to contain the *lacrimal sac* and *nasolacrimal duct*, through which the *lacrimal*

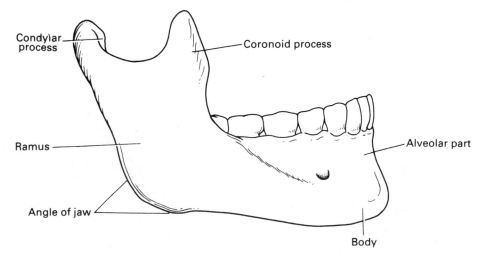

Fig. 6.5 The mandible.

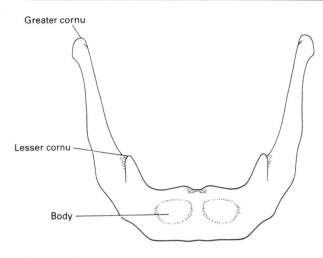

Greater cornu

Lesser cornu

Body

Fig. 6.6 The hyoid bone.

fluid, or tears, which washes constantly over the surface of the eye, is carried into the nasal cavity.

The nasal bones

The nasal bones are two small oblong bones which together form the bridge of the nose.

The vomer

The vomer is a flat bone which forms the lower part of the nasal septum. The upper part of the septum is formed by the perpendicular plate of the ethmoid bone.

The Joints of the Head

The temporomandibular joint

The temporomandibular joint, between the temporal bone and the head of the mandible, is the only movable joint of the head and it is peculiar in that movement can occur in all three planes: upwards and downwards, backwards and forwards and from side to side.

Sutures

The sutures between the skull bones have already been described (see page 54). However, in infants there are unossified membranous areas called *fontanelles* at the angles of the parietal bones (Fig. 6.7).

The *anterior fontanelle* is the largest and lies at the junction of the two parietal bones with the frontal bone. It is diamond-shaped and does not close completely till the age of 15 to 18 months. Severe dehydration in infancy causes the fontanelle to become depressed.

The *posterior fontanelle* lies at the junction of the parietal bones with the occipital bone. It is triangular in shape and closes shortly after birth.

Delay in the closure of the fontanelles may be caused by hydrocephalus, but also sometimes occurs in the normal child.

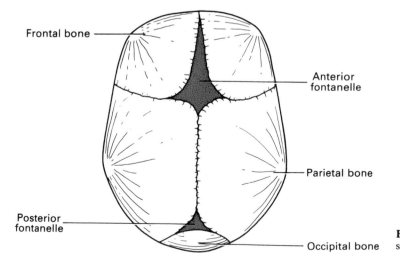

Frontal bone

Anterior fontanelle

Parietal bone

Posterior fontanelle

Occipital bone

Fig. 6.7 An infant's skull at birth, showing the fontanelles.

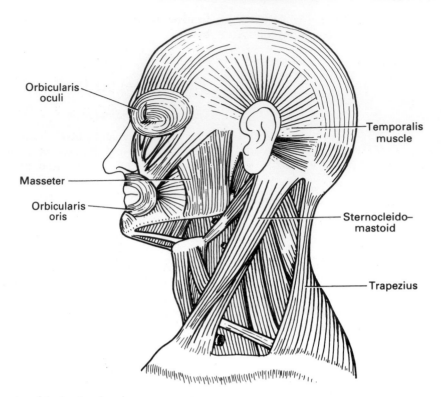

Fig. 6.8   The muscles of the head and neck.

The Muscles of the Head (Fig. 6.8)

The muscles of the head are divided into two groups according to their functions:
- The muscles of facial expression
- The muscles of mastication

The muscles of facial expression

The muscles of expression are attached to the skin rather than to the bone, so that they move the skin and change the facial appearance. Circular muscles, called *orbicularis oculi* and *orbicularis oris*, surround the eyes and mouth respectively, closing them. Small muscles raise and lower the eyebrows and upper lids, raise and lower the angles of the mouth and dilate the nostrils, causing a look of surprise, worry, happiness or sorrow. Small muscles also move the eyeballs in the orbits, both to direct the eyes for sight and also to change the expression.

The muscles of mastication

The muscles of mastication move the lower jaw up and down in biting, and also both from side to side and backwards and forwards in chewing. They are the *masseter* running to the angle of the jaw from the zygomatic arch, the *temporalis* muscle, lying over the temporal bone and inserted into the lower jaw, and the smaller muscles which also run from the skull to the lower jaw. These are the muscles which 'lock the jaw' in tetanus.

The Muscles of the Neck (Fig. 6.8)

The neck contains two large muscles:
- The sternocleidomastoid
- The trapezius

The sternocleidomastoid

The sternocleidomastoid lies at the side of the neck, running from the sternum and clavicle to the mastoid process and the surface of the occipital bone behind it. When the muscle on one side contracts it draws the head towards the shoulder on the same side and turns the head so that the face looks upwards. When both are used together they flex the neck.

The trapezius

The trapezius lies over the back of the neck and shoulder and is roughly triangular in shape. It is attached to the spine from the occiput down the back of the neck and the thorax. Some fibres are inserted into the scapula, whereas others come over the shoulder to be inserted into the clavicle. The trapezius draws the shoulders back when used as a whole, and also draws the scapula up and down, when the lower portion is used separately.

Table 6.1 Muscles of the neck.

Name	Position	Origin	Insertion	Action
Sternocleidomastoid	The side of the neck	Sternum and clavicle	Mastoid process and occipital bone	Used separately, turn the head to the side and tilt to same shoulder; used together, flex the neck
Trapezius	The back of the neck and shoulder	The occiput and the spines of the thoracic vertebrae	The clavicle and the spine of the scapula	Draws the scapula back, bracing the shoulders; raising and lowering the shoulder; extending the neck by exerting pull on the occiput

7

The Trunk

Objectives: After studying Chapter 7 you should be able to:

1 Draw and label diagrams of the bones of the trunk.
2 Describe the joints of the trunk.
3 List the muscles of the abdominal wall, the pelvic floor and those which move the spine.

The Bones of the Trunk

The bones of the trunk are:
● The sternum
● The ribs
● The vertebral column

The sternum

The sternum is a long flat bone which runs down the front of the thorax close under the skin. Its upper end supports the *clavicles* and it also articulates with the first seven pairs of ribs. The bone is in three parts (Figs. 7.1 and 7.2):
● The *manubrium* is triangular in shape and its lower border is covered with a thin layer of fibrocartilage for articulation with the upper end of the body.
● The *body* is longer and narrower than the manubrium. Along each side are notches for articulation with the cartilages of the second to the seventh ribs. The first notch is found at the point where the body joins the manubrium.
● The *xiphisternum* or *xiphoid process* is small and variable in shape and may not become completely ossified.

The ribs

The ribs are arched bones which are connected to the vertebral column. There are usually twelve pairs, the first seven of which are attached to the body of the sternum by the *costal cartilages* and are known as the *true ribs*. The next three are joined to the cartilage of the rib immediately above and are known as *false ribs*. The lower two are free at their anterior ends and are known as *floating ribs*.

The ribs form the curved walls of the thorax, sloping downwards towards the front. The cage they form increases in size from above downwards so that the thoracic cavity is roughly cone-shaped.

Each rib is curved and the under surface is grooved to accommodate the intercostal arteries, veins and nerves. The end which articulates with the vertebrae possesses a head, a neck and a tubercle. The head has two smooth facets which articulate with the bodies of two adjacent vertebrae. The tubercle has a small oval facet for articulation with the transverse process of the lower of these two vertebrae (Fig. 7.3).

The vertebral column

The vertebral column consists of a number of irregular bones called the *vertebrae*, which are firmly connected to one another but which allow a limited

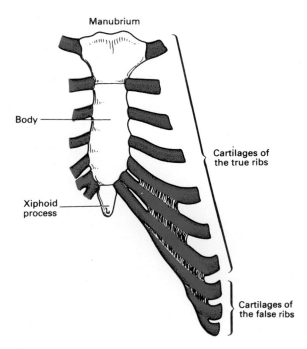

Fig. 7.1 The sternum and costal cartilages.

Manubrium

Body

Xiphoid process

Cartilages of the true ribs

Cartilages of the false ribs

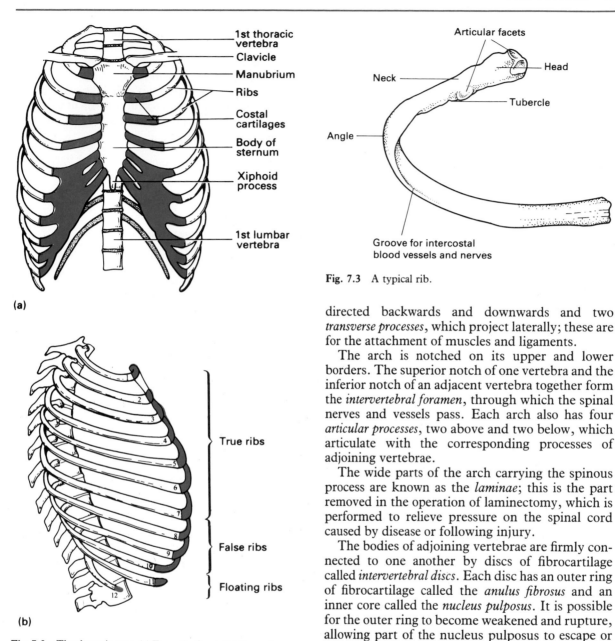

Fig. 7.2 The thoracic cage. (a) From the front. (b) From the side.

Fig. 7.3 A typical rib.

amount of movement. The column provides support for the trunk and also protects the spinal cord, which it surrounds. A typical vertebra consists of a cylindrical *body* lying to the front, and a *vertebral arch* projecting backwards and enclosing a space called the *vertebral foramen* through which the spinal cord passes. The arch has a *spinous process* or *spine* directed backwards and downwards and two *transverse processes*, which project laterally; these are for the attachment of muscles and ligaments.

The arch is notched on its upper and lower borders. The superior notch of one vertebra and the inferior notch of an adjacent vertebra together form the *intervertebral foramen*, through which the spinal nerves and vessels pass. Each arch also has four *articular processes*, two above and two below, which articulate with the corresponding processes of adjoining vertebrae.

The wide parts of the arch carrying the spinous process are known as the *laminae*; this is the part removed in the operation of laminectomy, which is performed to relieve pressure on the spinal cord caused by disease or following injury.

The bodies of adjoining vertebrae are firmly connected to one another by discs of fibrocartilage called *intervertebral discs*. Each disc has an outer ring of fibrocartilage called the *anulus fibrosus* and an inner core called the *nucleus pulposus*. It is possible for the outer ring to become weakened and rupture, allowing part of the nucleus pulposus to escape or herniate. This may then press on an adjoining nerve root, causing pain. The intervertebral discs act as shock absorbers, cushioning any jarring which occurs, for example, as a result of jumping from a height and landing on the feet. They also help the vertebrae column to be flexible.

The vertebrae are divided into five groups:
- Seven cervical vertebrae
- Twelve thoracic vertebrae
- Five lumbar vertebrae

- Five sacral vertebrae
- Four coccygeal vertebrae

The cervical vertebrae

The seven cervical vertebrae are the smallest vertebrae and can be easily identified because their transverse processes are perforated by foramina for the passage of the vertebral arteries. The spinous process is forked and gives attachment to muscles and ligaments (Figs. 7.4 and 7.5).

The first cervical vertebra is called the *atlas*. It has no body or spinous process, but consists of a ring of bone with two facets which articulate with the

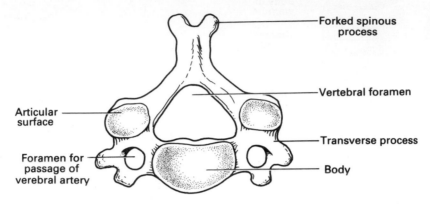

Fig. 7.4 A typical cervical vertebra.

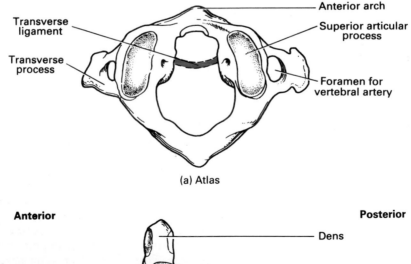

(a) Atlas

(b) Axis (side view)

Fig. 7.5 The first and second cervical vertebrae. (a) The atlas. (b) The axis (side view).

occipital bone. A ligament called the transverse ligament divides the ring of the atlas into two.

The *axis*, or second cervical vertebra, carries a strong tooth-like process called the *dens* (or odontoid process) which projects upwards from the body and provides a pivot on which the atlas, and therefore the skull, rotates, allowing a turning movement of the head. The dens is held in position by the transverse ligament of the atlas, behind which lies the spinal cord.

The seventh cervical vertebra is different in that it has a very long spinous process which is not forked. This can be seen and felt through the skin at the base of the neck.

The thoracic vertebrae

The twelve thoracic vertebrae are larger than the cervical vertebrae and they increase in size from above downwards. The body is roughly heart-shaped and has two distinguishing features:

- It has additional facets on each side to articulate with the head and tubercle of the corresponding rib.
- It has long pointed spinous processes which project downwards and backwards.

The heads of the ribs lie between the vertebrae and articulate with one facet on the vertebra above and one on the vertebra below (Figs. 7.6 and 7.7).

The lumbar vertebrae

The five lumbar vertebrae are the largest vertebrae and have no facets for articulation with the ribs. The

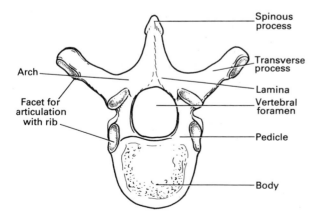

Fig. 7.6 A typical thoracic vertebra (from above).

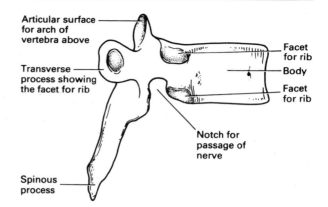

Fig. 7.7 A typical thoracic vertebra (side view).

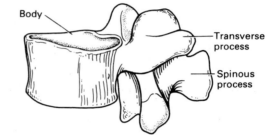

Fig. 7.8 A typical lumbar vertebra.

spinous processes are large and strong and give attachment to muscles (Fig. 7.8).

The sacral vertebrae

The five sacral vertebrae are fused together to form a large bone, the *sacrum*, which is triangular in shape and forms a wedge between the two hip bones with which it articulates. The inside surface of the bone is concave, and the anterior projection at the upper end is known as the *sacral promontory* (see Fig. 7.10). Because the vertebrae are fused together, the vertebral foramina are also fused to form the *sacral canal*. The intervertebral foramina, which elsewhere are formed by notches in adjacent vertebrae, appear as four openings in the sacrum (Fig. 7.9).

The coccygeal vertebrae

The four coccygeal vertebrae are fused together to form a small triangular bone known as the *coccyx*. This articulates with the sacrum. The joint allows

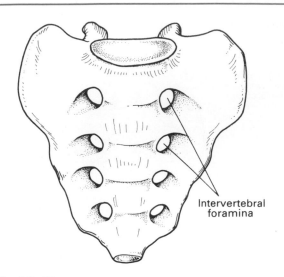

Intervertebral foramina

Fig. 7.9   The sacrum.

slight movement backwards and forwards, which increases the size of the pelvic outlet during childbirth.

Curves of the vertebral column

The vertebral column is the main support of the head and trunk as well as giving protection to the spinal cord. When viewed from the side it has four curves (Fig. 7.10):
- The cervical curve
- The thoracic curve
- The lumbar curve
- The sacral curve

The thoracic and sacral curves are known as *primary curves* as they are present during fetal life. The cervical and lumbar curves are *secondary curves*, as they appear or are accentuated when the child begins to hold up its head and sit up (cervical) and when it begins to stand and walk (lumbar).

Movement of the vertebral column

There is only limited movement between any two adjoining vertebrae, but there is considerable movement in the vertebral column as a whole. The curves of the spine enable it to bend without breaking. However, a blow on the column is likely to cause a fracture or a dislocation because the vertebrae are so firmly united to one another.

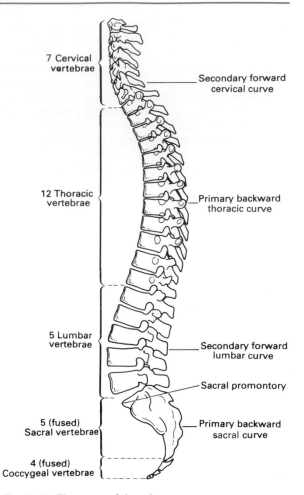

7 Cervical vertebrae

Secondary forward cervical curve

12 Thoracic vertebrae

Primary backward thoracic curve

5 Lumbar vertebrae

Secondary forward lumbar curve

Sacral promontory

5 (fused) Sacral vertebrae

Primary backward sacral curve

4 (fused) Coccygeal vertebrae

Fig. 7.10   The curves of the spine.

The Joints of the Trunk

There are joints between all the vertebrae from the second cervical to the sacrum. Cartilaginous joints lie between the vertebral bodies, and synovial joints between the articular processes of the vertebral arches. Although each of these joints only allows a small amount of movement, because the joints are so numerous the spinal column as a whole has considerable mobility. *Anterior* and *posterior longitudinal ligaments* run down the anterior and posterior surfaces of the spine from the skull to the sacrum, giving support. Other ligaments run between the vertebral arches.

Between the ribs and the vertebrae are the *costovertebral joints* (Fig. 7.11); these are synovial joints that allow gliding movements. The joints between the costal cartilages of the true ribs (i.e. the first seven ribs) and the sternum are known as the *sternocostal joints*. The first of these—the joint between the first costal cartilage and the manubrium—is cartilaginous and so does not allow movement. The other sternocostal joints are synovial and allow gliding movements.

The Muscles of the Trunk

The chief muscles of the trunk can be grouped according to their function into:
- Muscles forming the abdominal wall
- Muscles moving the spine
- Muscles forming the pelvic floor

The muscles which are used in respiration are described in Chapter 21.

Muscles forming the abdominal wall (Figs. 7.12 and 7.13)

The chief muscles of the abdominal wall are:
- The rectus abdominis, forming the front wall
- The external oblique ⎫ forming the side
- The internal oblique ⎬ wall and lying
- The transversus abdominis ⎭ one under the other
- The quadratus lumborum

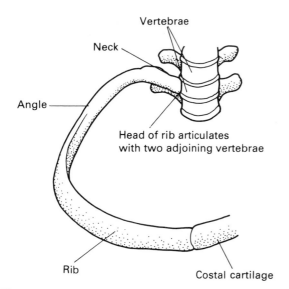

Fig. 7.11   A costovertebral joint.

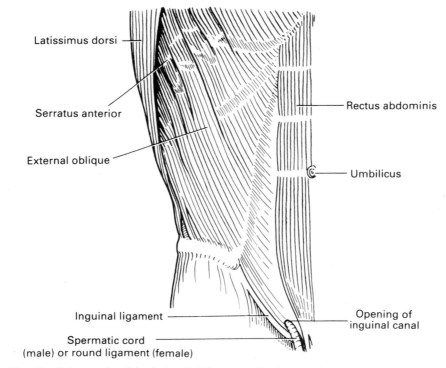

Fig. 7.12   The right side of the anterior abdominal wall. (The rectus sheath is not shown.)

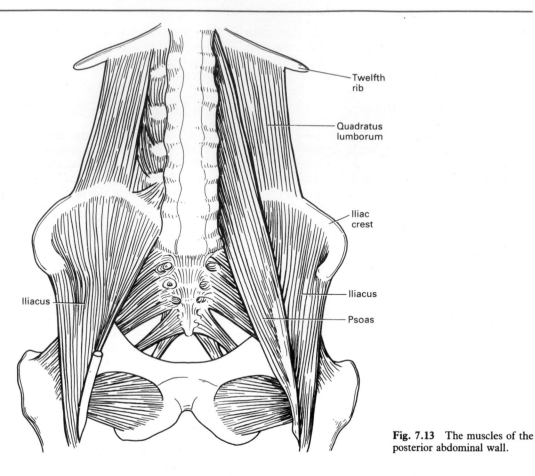

Fig. 7.13 The muscles of the posterior abdominal wall.

Beneath the muscles the abdominal wall is lined with a continuous layer of connective tissue known as *fascia*.

The rectus abdominis

The rectus abdominis forms the anterior abdominal wall, running up from the pubis (which forms the anterior part of the hip bone) to the sternum and costal cartilages. Its fibres run straight up and down, hence its name, the Latin word 'rectus' meaning 'straight'. It is enclosed in a fibrous sheath known as the *rectus sheath*, which is formed from the aponeuroses of the external oblique, the internal oblique and the transversus abdominis. The left and right rectus sheaths are joined together in the midline by a line of fibrous tissue known as the *linea alba*. The rectus abdominis is crossed by three lines of fibrous tissue. These strengthen the muscle and help to prevent it stretching.

The external oblique

The external oblique muscle forms the outer layer of the side wall of the abdomen. It arises from the lower ribs, from where the fibres run downwards and forwards. It is inserted by a large broad aponeurosis into the xiphoid process, the linea alba, the pubis and the iliac crest (see page 71). Between the anterior superior iliac spine and the pubic tubercle the lower border of the aponeurosis is folded back on itself to form the *inguinal ligament*. This forms the firm edge of the abdominal wall across the groin, where the muscles are not inserted into the bone, leaving a gap for muscles, blood vessels and nerves to pass under it into the limb from the trunk. It also gives attachment to other muscles.

The internal oblique

The internal oblique forms the second layer of the side wall of the abdomen. Its fibres run upwards and forwards. It arises from the iliac crest and the inguinal ligament and is inserted into the lower ribs and their cartilages. It also forms an aponeurosis, passing partly in front and partly behind the rectus and joining those of the external oblique and transversus abdominis to form the rectus sheath.

The transversus abdominis

The transversus abdominis forms the inner layer of the side wall of the abdomen, lying under the internal oblique. Its fibres run straight round the abdominal wall. It arises from the iliac crest and the fascia in the lumbar region, by which it is joined to the lumbar vertebrae. It is inserted via an aponeurosis, which runs across the front of the abdomen and behind the rectus, into the linea alba.

The quadratus lumborum

The quadratus lumborum forms the posterior wall of the abdomen, and runs from the iliac crest to the twelfth rib and upper lumbar vertebrae. It holds the twelfth rib steady during breathing.

The inguinal canal

The inguinal canal is a passage that runs obliquely through the abdominal wall in each groin. It begins as a hole in the fascia beneath the transversus abdominis and passes downwards and medially between this fascia and the aponeurosis of the external oblique, lying immediately above and parallel to the inguinal ligament. It ends at a hole in the external oblique aponeurosis, near to the pubic tubercle. The canal contains structures which run

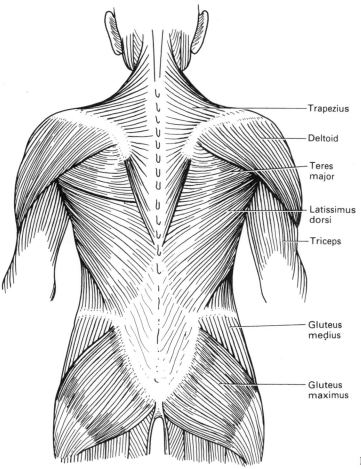

Trapezius

Deltoid

Teres major

Latissimus dorsi

Triceps

Gluteus medius

Gluteus maximus

Fig. 7.14 The muscles of the back.

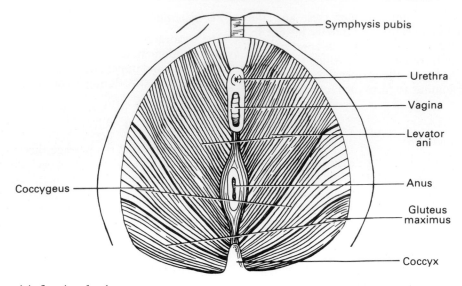

Fig. 7.15   The pelvic floor in a female.

from inside the abdominal or pelvic cavity to the outside of the abdominal wall. In the male it contains the spermatic cord, which consists of the deferent duct and the blood supply to the testis (see page 242). In the female it contains the round ligament of the uterus (see page 247).

Muscles moving the spine (Fig. 7.14)

The muscles of the abdominal wall flex and rotate the trunk—the rectus abdominis flexing, and the side muscles turning the thorax on the abdomen.

In addition, a number of muscles of different lengths run up the back of the trunk on either side of the spine. They arise from the back of the iliac crest and the sacrum, and are inserted into the ribs and upper vertebrae. They are responsible for extending the spine, and are therefore important in maintain-ing the body in an upright position. These muscles lie beneath the large muscles of the back, which are responsible for movement at the shoulder and hip joints (see Chapters 8 and 9).

Muscles forming the pelvic floor

The pelvic floor consists of muscles which support the pelvic organs. It runs from the pubis in front back to the sacrum and coccyx and out to the ischium on either side. It is like an open book in shape, sloping downwards from back to front and from either side towards the midline. It is composed of the *levator ani* and *coccygeus* muscles. It is pierced in the midline in the female by three openings for the passage of the urethra, the vagina and the rectum. In the male there are only two openings, for the urethra and the rectum respectively (Fig. 7.15).

—8—

The Upper Limb

Objectives: After studying Chapter 8 you should be able to:

1 Draw and label diagrams of the bones of the upper limb.
2 Describe the joints in the arm and shoulder.
3 Describe the muscles of the arm and those which move the shoulder.

Bones of the Upper Limb

The bones of the upper limb are:
- The scapula ⎫
- The clavicle ⎭ forming the shoulder girdle
- The humerus
- The radius ⎫
- The ulna ⎭ forming the forearm
- Eight carpal bones ⎫
- Five metacarpal bones ⎬ forming the wrist and hand
- Fourteen phalanges ⎭

The scapula

The scapula is a triangular flat bone (Fig. 8.1); it lies over the ribs at the back of the thorax, but does not articulate with them. It is held in place by muscles which attach it to the ribs and vertebral column. This arrangement gives great freedom of movement to the shoulder girdle, making it possible to reach widely both forwards and backwards and to either side of the body. The scapula is not often broken by falls as it is embedded in muscle. It has three borders and three angles; the inferior angle is the sharpest and is easily felt. The front surface is concave to fit over the ribs. The posterior surface is convex and carries a projecting ridge of bone known as the *spine of the scapula*, which gives attachment to muscles and forms two depressions or fossae, one above it (the *supraspinous fossa*) and one below it (the *infraspinous fossa*).

The outer angle carries a shallow socket known as the *glenoid cavity* or *fossa*, which receives the head of the humerus to form the shoulder joint. Above this two processes project:

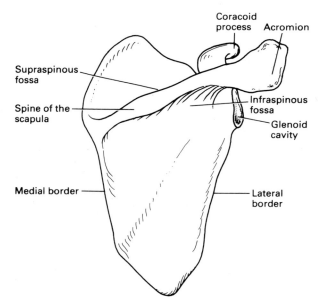

Fig. 8.1   The scapula.

- The *acromion*, the larger of the two, overlaps the socket and articulates with the clavicle to form the shoulder girdle.
- The *coracoid process* juts forward and is like a hook.

Both of these processes can easily be felt: the acromion can be located by following the spine of the scapula out towards the shoulder, and the coracoid process can be felt just below the clavicle next to the head of the humerus. They give attachment to muscles and also help to keep the head of the humerus in place, preventing upward dislocation.

The clavicle

The clavicle is a long bone and is roughly S-shaped (Fig. 8.2). It articulates with the sternum at its inner or sternal extremity and with the scapula at its outer or acromial extremity. The two extremities are easily distinguishable from one another. The inner extremity is roughly like a pyramid in shape, while

Fig. 8.2 The clavicle.

the outer is flatter and very similar in shape and form to the acromion process of the scapula, with which it articulates. The bone lies close under the skin and is easily felt along its whole course; starting from the sternal extremity it curves first forwards and then backwards. It keeps the scapula in position; when the clavicle is broken the shoulder drops forwards and downwards. It is the only bony link between the bones of the upper limb and the axial skeleton (the bones of the head and trunk), as the scapula does not articulate with either the ribs or vertebral column. The clavicle is easily broken by falls on the shoulder, as it is compressed between the sternum and the point of impact; it is, in fact, better that it should break than that there should be an injury to the root of the neck, where there are many important structures, or to the actual shoulder joint, where injury would be likely to limit subsequent movement.

The humerus

The humerus is the largest and longest bone of the upper limb (Fig. 8.3). The upper extremity has a hemispherical *head*, covered with hyaline cartilage, which articulates with the glenoid cavity of the scapula, forming the shoulder joint. The *anatomical neck* forms a slight constriction just below the head, and the *greater* and *lesser tuberosities* lie below the neck and give attachment to muscles. Between these the deep *bicipital groove* accommodates one of the tendons of the biceps muscle. The *shaft* of the humerus has many roughened areas for the attachment of muscles, the most obvious being the *deltoid tuberosity* on the outer side, to which the deltoid muscle is attached. A groove running obliquely round the shaft carries the radial nerve, one of the three main nerves of the upper limb.

The lower end of the humerus is divided into articular and non-articular portions. The articular portion, together with the radius and the ulna, forms the elbow joint. It is divided by a shallow groove into:

- The *capitulum*, a rounded projection that articulates with the radius

- The *trochlea*, which is shaped rather like a pulley and articulates with the ulna

Above the trochlea on the anterior and posterior surfaces of the humerus are two deep hollows. The posterior one is called the *olecranon fossa*; the olecranon process of the ulna moves into this fossa when the elbow is extended. The anterior one is called the *coronoid fossa*, and accommodates the coronoid process of the ulna when the elbow is flexed.

The non-articular portion of the lower end of the humerus has two projections known as the *media* and *lateral epicondyles*. These give attachment to muscles.

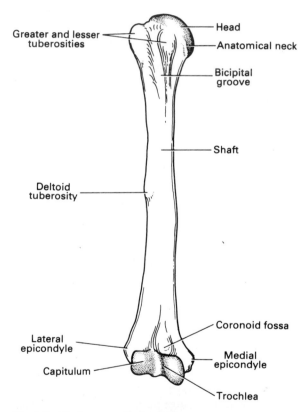

Fig. 8.3 The humerus (front view).

The radius (Fig. 8.4)

The *radius* is the lateral bone of the forearm when the arm is held by the side of the body with the palm facing forward. The upper end is smaller and has a disc-shaped *head* with a hollowed upper surface to articulate with the capitulum of the humerus. The head also articulates with the ulna. The *neck* of the radius is the constricted portion below the head; on the ulna side there is a projection called the *radial tuberosity*, which gives attachment to the biceps muscle. The *shaft* of the bone has a sharp ridge facing the ulna and from it a sheet of fibrous tissue called the *interosseous membrane* runs to the ulna, connecting the two bones. The lower end of the radius is the wider part and takes part in the formation of the wrist joint. It has a projection called the *styloid process*, which can be felt at the base of the thumb, and a depression known as the *ulnar notch*, which articulates with the head of the ulna.

The ulna (Fig. 8.4)

The ulna lies on the inner side of the forearm. The upper end is shaped like a hook and has two large projections:

- The *olecranon* fits into the olecranon fossa on the posterior surface of the humerus when the elbow

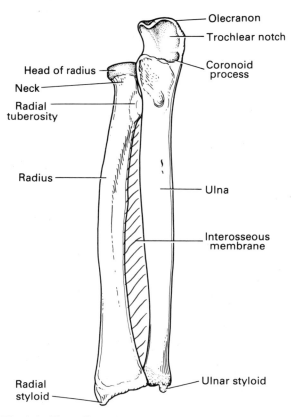

Fig. 8.4 The radius and ulna.

Labels on figure:
Olecranon
Trochlear notch
Head of radius
Coronoid process
Neck
Radial tuberosity
Radius
Ulna
Interosseous membrane
Radial styloid
Ulnar styloid

is extended. Its upper border forms the point of the elbow, and provides attachment for the triceps muscle.

- The *coronoid process* is smaller and projects forward. It fits into the coronoid fossa on the anterior surface of the humerus when the elbow is flexed.

These two processes help in the formation of the *trochlear notch*, which articulates with the trochlea of the humerus. The *radial notch* is a depression on the upper part of the coronoid process which articulates with the head of the radius and allows turning movements of the hand. When the hand is rotated so that the palm faces backwards, without moving the upper arm, the lower end of the radius is carried round the lower end of the ulna so that the shafts of the two bones cross each other in the middle of the forearm. This movement is known as *supination*; the opposite movement—returning the hand so that the palm faces forwards—is known as *pronation*.

The *shaft* of the ulna, like that of the radius, carries a sharp ridge for the attachment of the interosseous membrane which lies between the two bones.

The lower end of the ulna has a rounded part, known as the *head*, and a projection called the *styloid process*. The head articulates with the ulnar notch of the radius. The styloid process gives attachment to a ligament of the wrist joint; it may be felt just below the skin at the lateral side of the back of the wrist and is sometimes quite prominent.

The carpal bones

The carpal bones (or carpus) comprise eight bones which are arranged in two rows of four (Fig. 8.5). The bones of the first row are called the *scaphoid*, the *lunate*, the *triquetral* and the *pisiform*. The first three articulate with the radius. The bones of the second row are called the *trapezium*, the *trapezoid*, the *capitate* and the *hamate*.

The anterior surface of the carpal bones, which forms the base of the palm, is concave. A fibrous band, the *flexor retinaculum*, crosses this cavity, forming the *carpal tunnel*. Through this pass the median nerves and the tendons of the muscles that flex the fingers.

The metacarpal bones

The metacarpal bones (or metacarpus) are five miniature long bones running across the palm of the

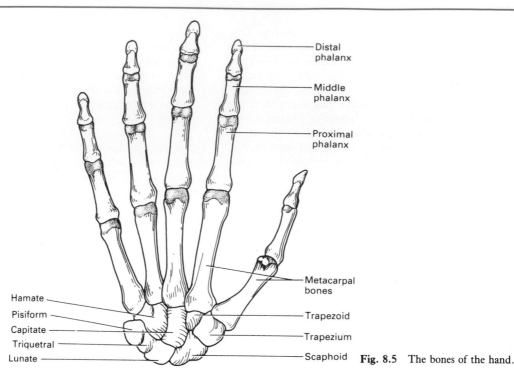

Distal phalanx

Middle phalanx

Proximal phalanx

Metacarpal bones

Trapezoid

Trapezium

Scaphoid

Hamate

Pisiform

Capitate

Triquetral

Lunate

Fig. 8.5   The bones of the hand.

hand. The *bases* of the bones articulate with the second row of carpal bones; the *heads* articulate with the phalanges. The first metacarpal, which articulates with the two phalanges that form the thumb, can be moved more freely than the other four.

The phalanges

The phalanges are also miniature long bones, three in each finger and two in the thumb.

The Joints of the Shoulder Girdle and Upper Limb

The sternoclavicular joint

The sternoclavicular joint is a synovial joint formed by the sternal end of the clavicle, the manubrium and the cartilage of the first rib. This is a ball-and-socket joint, but the degree of movement is limited.

The acromioclavicular joint

The acromioclavicular joint lies between the acromial extremity of the clavicle and the acromion of the scapula. It is a plane type of synovial joint and is usually involved in movements of the shoulder.

The shoulder joint (Fig. 8.6)

The shoulder joint is a ball-and-socket synovial joint, and is the most freely movable of the joints in the body. It is formed by the head of the humerus fitting into the small, shallow glenoid cavity. The articular surfaces are covered with articular cartilage and the glenoid cavity is enlarged and deepened by a rim of fibrocartilage which runs around it, called the *labrum glenoidale*. This lessens the risk of dislocation without limiting the movement as much as a larger and deeper bony socket would do. The bones are held together by a loose capsule of ligaments and by a number of small muscles that surround them. The long tendon of the biceps muscle also serves as an intracapsular ligament. It runs through the bicipital groove between the tuberosities of the humerus into the joint cavity and, since it arises from the scapula immediately above the glenoid cavity, it tends to hold the articular surfaces in position.

Movements of the arm beyond the limits imposed by the shoulder joint can be achieved by movement of the scapula over the back of the thorax.

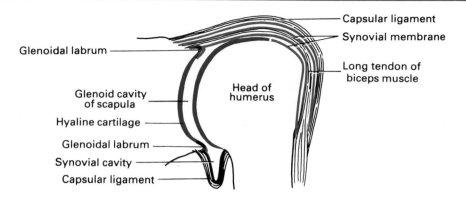

Fig. 8.6 Section through the shoulder joint.

The elbow joint

The elbow joint is a synovial hinge joint between the humerus and the radius and ulna—the capitulum articulates with the head of the radius, and the trochlea articulates with the trochlear notch of the ulnar. It allows flexion and extension of the forearm. The joint capsule is strengthened by ligaments running between the three bones.

The radio-ulnar joints

There are two joints between the radius and the ulnar.

The *superior radio-ulnar joint* is a synovial pivot joint between the head of the radius and the radial notch of the ulna. The two bones are held together by the *annular ligament*. This runs from one side of the radial notch, around the radius, to the other side of the radial notch, thus encircling the radius.

The *inferior radio-ulnar joint* is also a synovial pivot joint, and is formed by the head of the ulna articulating with the ulnar notch of the radius.

These joints allow supination and pronation of the forearm (see page 36).

The wrist joint

The wrist joint is a synovial condylar joint formed by the lower end of the radius and the scaphoid, lunate and triquetral bones. Together with the joints between the carpal bones, the movements of flexion, extension, adduction (ulna deviation), abduction (radial deviation) and circumduction can be carried out.

The metacarpophalangeal joints

These are also synovial condylar joints, and allow all the movements described for the wrist joint. In addition, the metacarpophalangeal joint of the thumb also allows some rotation. This enables the thumb to move across the palm to touch the tips of the other fingers.

The interphalangeal joints

These are all synovial hinge joints, and allow only flexion and extension of the fingers.

Muscles Moving the Shoulder

The chief muscles moving the shoulder are the powerful muscles covering the back and front of the chest. They include:

- The pectoralis major
- The trapezius (see page 65)
- The latissimus dorsi
- The serratus anterior

The *pectoralis major* covers the front of the chest, running from the sternum out to the humerus. The *latissimus dorsi* covers the back of the chest and abdomen, running from the thoracic and lumbar vertebrae and iliac crest up and out to the humerus. These muscles form the muscle in front of and behind the armpit. The *serratus anterior* runs round the side wall of the thorax from the ribs, under the scapula, and is attached to the medial border of the scapula.

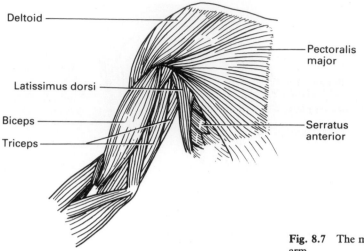

Deltoid

Pectoralis major

Latissimus dorsi

Biceps

Triceps

Serratus anterior

Fig. 8.7 The muscles of the shoulder and arm.

Table 8.1 The major muscles connecting the upper limb to the trunk.

Name	Position	Origin	Insertion	Action
Pectoralis major	Front of the chest	Sternum, clavicle and the cartilages of the true ribs	Humerus (bicipital groove)	Adducts the humerus, draws the arm across the front of the chest; internal rotation of humerus
Latissimus dorsi	Crosses the back from the lumbar region to the shoulder	Lower thoracic, lumbar and sacral vertebrae and the iliac crest	Humerus (bicipital groove)	Adducts the humerus; draws the arm backwards and downwards, as in bell-pulling and rowing; internal rotation of humerus
Serratus anterior	Over the sides of the thorax and under the scapula at the back	The front of the eight upper ribs	The medial border of the scapula	Draws the scapula forwards (antagonistic to the trapezius)

The Muscles of the Upper Limb

The muscles of the upper limb may be divided into the muscles of the upper arm, the forearm and the hand.

The muscles of the upper arm

The muscles of the arm are the largest and strongest of the limb and include (Figs. 8.7 and 8.8):
- The biceps brachii
- The triceps
- The deltoid
- The brachialis

The biceps brachii

The biceps brachii is so called because it has two heads (from 'bi' meaning 'two', and 'caput', the Latin for 'head'). It runs down the front of the arm, where it can easily be felt when it is contracted. The two heads arise one from the top of the glenoid cavity and one from the coracoid process of the scapula, and the muscle is inserted into the radial tuberosity in the forearm, crossing the front of the elbow joint. It is a powerful muscle which can flex and supinate the forearm. Hence the act of supination can be carried out with great force.

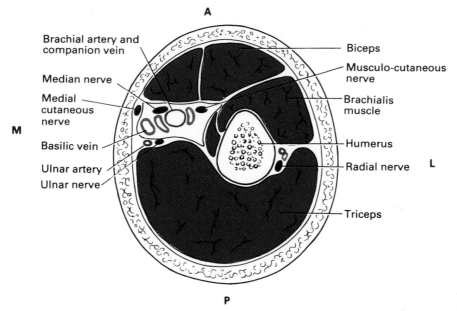

Fig. 8.8 Section of the arm, showing the relationship of the muscles to the bone and other structures. L = lateral; M = medial; A = anterior; P = posterior.

The triceps

The triceps is so called because it has three heads. It lies at the back of the arm. The three heads arise one from the scapula and two from the humerus, and the muscle is inserted into the olecranon of the ulna, at the back of the elbow joint. It extends the forearm and is therefore antagonistic to the biceps.

The deltoid

The deltoid is triangular in shape. It lies over the shoulder in the position of an epaulette, with the base of the triangle forming the origin and attached to the clavicle and scapula, just above the shoulder joint. It is inserted into the deltoid tuberosity on the outer side of the humerus. Its action is to abduct the

Table 8.2   The major muscles of the upper arm.

Name	Position	Origin	Insertion	Action
Biceps brachii (two heads)	The front of the arm	Coracoid process and above the glenoid cavity of the scapula	Radial tuberosity	Flexes and supinates the forearm
Triceps (three heads)	The back of the arm	One head from the axillary border of the scapula; two from the shaft of the humerus	Olecranon of ulna	Extends forearm
Deltoid	Over the shoulder	Acromion and spine of scapula; the clavicle	Deltoid tuberosity of humerus	Abducts the humerus to a right angle
Brachialis	Crosses the front of the elbow	Humerus	Anterior surface of coronoid process of ulna	Flexes the forearm

humerus to a right angle. (To raise the arm above a right angle, the shoulder girdle must also move, the trapezius drawing the scapula and clavicle up towards the occiput.) The front part of the deltoid muscle used alone helps to flex the arm, moving the humerus forwards and rotating it inwards, and the back portion used alone helps to extend the arm, moving the humerus backwards and rotating it outwards.

The brachialis

The brachialis lies lower in the front of the arm than the biceps, arising from the humerus and being inserted into the coronoid process of the ulna. It assists the biceps in the powerful action of flexion of the forearm.

The muscles of the forearm (Fig. 8.9)

The forearm contains numerous small, less powerful muscles which move the wrist and the digits.

In the front of the forearm lie:

- The flexors of the wrist (*flexor carpi ulnaris* and *flexor carpi radialis*)
- The superficial and deep flexors of the fingers (*flexor digitorum superficialis* and *flexor digitorum profundus*)—these muscles also flex the wrist
- The long flexor of the thumb (*flexor pollicis longus*)
- The pronators of the forearm (*pronator teres* and *pronator quadratus*)

The flexors of the fingers each divide into four tendons, which run under the flexor retinaculum and across the palm. The tendons of the superficial flexors are inserted into the middle phalanx, and the tendons of the deep flexors into the end phalanx.

At the back of the forearm lie:

- A flexor of the forearm (*brachioradialis*)
- The extensors of the wrist (*extensor carpi radialis longus*, *extensor carpi radialis brevis* and *extensor carpi ulnaris*)
- The extensors of the fingers (*extensor digitorum*, *extensor indicis* and *extensor digiti minimi*)
- The extensors of the thumb (*extensor pollicis brevis* and *extensor pollicis longus*)
- The abductor of the thumb (*abductor pollicis longus*)
- The supinator of the forearm (*supinator*)

The tendons of the extensors of the fingers pass under a fibrous band at the back of the wrist known as the *extensor reticulum*.

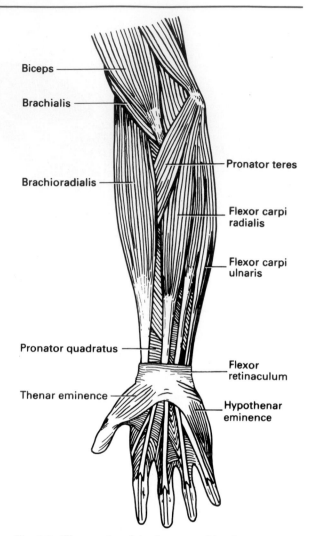

Fig. 8.9 The muscles of the forearm and hand.

The muscles of the hand

The hand contains very little muscle, as this would tend to make it clumsy and interfere with its usefulness in grasping and lifting. Many of the muscles which move it are therefore in the forearm.

However, the hand does contain a number of small muscles which move the digits. Those which move the thumb are well-developed and form the *thenar eminence* on the palm at the base of the thumb. Those which move the little finger are less well-developed and form the *hypothenar eminence* at the base of the little finger. In between the metacarpal bones there are a number of small muscles known as the *lumbricals* and the *interossei*. These enable the fingers to be spread apart or brought together again (abduction and adduction) and also help flex and extend the fingers.

—9—

The Lower Limb

Objectives: After studying Chapter 9 you should be able to:

1 Draw and label diagrams of the bones of the lower limb.
2 Describe the joints in the lower limb and hip.
3 Describe the muscles of the lower limb and those which move the hip.

Bones of the Lower Limb

The bones of the lower limb are:
- The hip bone, which forms part of the pelvis
- The femur
- The patella
- The tibia
- The fibula
- Seven tarsal bones
- Five metatarsal bones } forming the ankle and foot
- Fourteen phalanges

The hip bone

The hip bone is a large, irregularly shaped bone which articulates in front with the corresponding bone of the opposite side. Each bone consists of three parts, the *ilium*, the *ischium* and the *pubis*, which are united at the deep cavity on the outer aspect of the bone called the *acetabulum*. Full ossification is not completed until between the ages of fifteen and twenty-five; before that the bones are united by cartilage (Fig. 9.1).

The *ilium* includes the upper part of the acetabulum and the expanded flattened area of bone above it, the top of which is called the *iliac crest* and gives attachment to the lateral muscles of the abdominal wall. The crest ends in front at the *anterior superior iliac spine*, which is easily felt at the lateral end of the fold of the groin, and ends at the back at the *posterior superior iliac spine*, which is found under a small dimple in the lower part of the back. The ilium also has *anterior* and *posterior inferior*

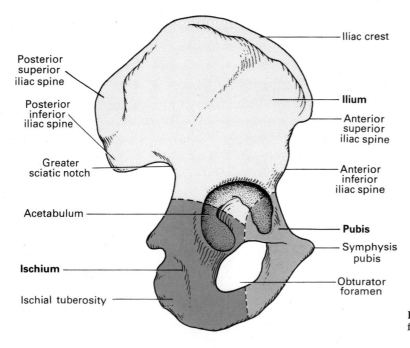

Fig. 9.1 The right hip bone, from the lateral side.

iliac spines, which provide attachment for powerful muscles. At the back there is an articular surface for articulation with the sacrum and below this there is a notch called the *greater sciatic notch*, through which part of the sciatic nerve passes.

The *ischium* is L-shaped and forms the lower posterior part of the hip bone. It has an *ischial tuberosity*, which gives attachment to muscles and supports the body in the sitting position.

The *pubis* is C-shaped and forms the anterior part of the hip bone. It meets the pubis of the opposite side in a cartilaginous joint called the *symphysis pubis*. The pubis consists of a *body* next to the symphysis, on which the *pubic tubercle* is found, and two branches, one running up to join the ilium and the other down to join the ischium. Between them these branches and the ischium form a large opening called the *obturator foramen*, which is filled with a sheet of fibrous tissue.

The *acetabulum* is the deep socket in the lower part of the side of the hip bone into which the head of the femur fits.

The *pelvis* is a bony ring composed of the two hip bones and the sacrum and coccyx behind. It is

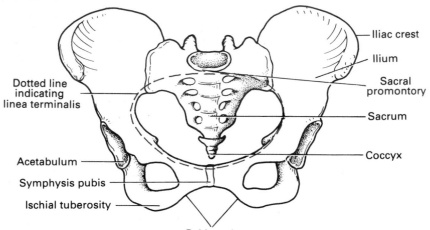

Fig. 9.2   The female pelvis.

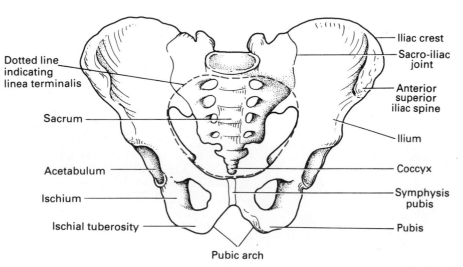

Fig. 9.3   The male pelvis.

divided into the *greater* (false) and the *lesser* (true) *pelvis* by the *linea terminalis* and the promontory of the sacrum; this line is also known as the *pelvic brim*. The greater pelvis is the upper expanded portion bounded on each side by the ilium and at the back by the base of the sacrum. The lesser pelvis consists of a short curved canal which is deeper at the back than the front.

The female pelvis is shorter than the male pelvis and is also wider. The brim of the female pelvis is larger and more nearly circular than that of the male, the brim of which is more typically heart-shaped (Figs. 9.2 and 9.3).

The femur (Fig. 9.4)

The femur is the longest and strongest bone in the body. The upper end of the bone has a hemispherical *head* which articulates with the acetabulum of the hip. Near its centre is a small depression called the *fovea* (see Fig. 9.7) which gives attachment to the ligament of the head of the femur; this ligament runs

to the base of the acetabulum. The *neck* of the femur projects at a marked angle from the shaft and enables free movement of the hip joint. Where the neck joins the shaft there are two processes, the *greater* and *lesser trochanters*, which give attachment to muscles. The greater trochanter is on the outer side and can be felt under the skin. The *shaft* of the femur is thinnest in the middle and widens considerably at the lower end. The posterior border is formed by a roughened vertical ridge called the *linera aspera* which gives attachment to muscles.

The lower end of the femur is widely expanded so that there is a good area for the transmission of the body weight to the tibia. It has two prominent condyles—the *medial* and *lateral condyles*—which articulate with the tibia; they are separated at the back by a deep gap called the *intercondylar fossa* and united in front by a smooth surface which articulates with the patella. Above the condyles at the back of the bone is the *popliteal surface*. This forms part of the *popliteal fossa*, which contains blood vessels and nerves.

The patella

The patella is situated in front of the knee joint in the tendon of the quadriceps muscle, which straightens the knee. Bones which develop in tendons in this way are called *sesamoid* bones. The patella is flattened and triangular in shape with the base of the triangle uppermost and the apex downwards. The posterior surface is smooth and articulates with the condyles of the femur; the anterior surface is roughened and is separated from the skin by a sac, similar to synovial membrane, called a *bursa*. The apex is attached to the tibia by the *patellar tendon*.

The tibia (Fig. 9.5)

The tibia is the stronger of the two bones of the leg and lies on the inner, or medial, side. The upper end is greatly expanded to provide a good surface for bearing the body weight. It has two prominent masses, called the *medial* and *lateral condyles*, which are smooth and articulate with the condyles of the femur. Between the condyles is a roughened area which gives attachment to the ligaments and cartilages of the knee joint. Below the condyles is a smaller projection called the *tuberosity of the tibia*, which gives attachment to the patella tendon. The lateral condyle has a small circular facet for articulation with the upper end of the fibula.

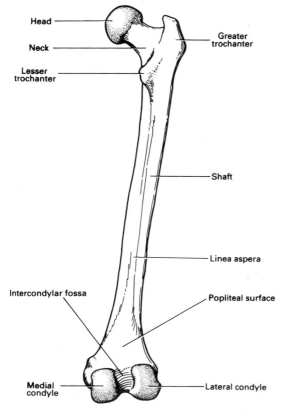

Head

Neck

Lesser trochanter

Greater trochanter

Shaft

Linea aspera

Intercondylar fossa

Popliteal surface

Medial condyle

Lateral condyle

Fig. 9.4 The femur (posterior)

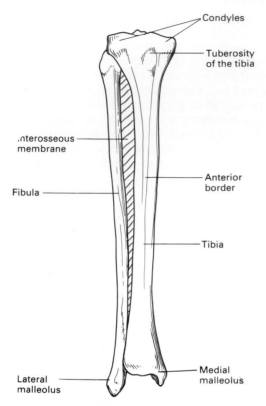

Condyles

Tuberosity
of the tibia

Interosseous
membrane

Fibula

Anterior
border

Tibia

Lateral
malleolus

Medial
malleolus

Fig. 9.5 The tibia and fibula (anterior)

The *shaft* of the tibia is roughly triangular in cross-section. The *anterior border* lies immediately under the skin and can be felt as the shin. A second border faces the fibula and gives attachment to the *interosseous membrane* which connects tibia and fibula. (This is similar to the way in which the ulna and radius are connected in the forearm.)

The lower end of the bone is slightly expanded and projects downwards on the inner side of the ankle to form the *medial malleolus*, which articulates with the talus. The lateral part of the lower end of the tibia also articulates with the fibula.

The fibula (Fig. 9.5)

The fibula is very slender compared with the tibia and lies on the outer side of the leg. The *head* of the fibula has a circular facet which articulates with the lateral condyle of the tibia but is not involved in forming the knee joint. The *shaft* is slender and ridged; one of the ridges gives attachment to the interosseous membrane connecting the tibia and fibula. The lower end of the fibula projects down-

wards to a lower level than the tibia and forms the bony prominence on the outside of the ankle known as the *lateral malleolus*. This articulates with the talus.

The tarsal bones

The *tarsal bones* (or tarsus) comprise seven bones which make up the posterior half of the foot:
- The *talus*. This is the principal connecting link between the foot and the leg and forms an important part of the ankle joint.
- The *calcaneus*. This is the largest and strongest of the tarsal bones; it projects backwards to form the prominence of the heel and to provide a lever for the muscles of the calf which are attached to its posterior surface.
- The *navicular bone*. This lies between the talus and the cuneiform bones.
- The three *cuneiform bones*. These are wedge-shaped and articulate with the navicular and the first three metatarsal bones.
- The *cuboid bone*. This is situated between the calcaneus and the fourth and fifth metatarsal bones.

The metatarsal bones

The metatarsal bones (or metatarsus) are five miniature long bones, resembling the metacarpal bones. The *bases* articulate with the cuneiform and the cuboid bones and the *heads* articulate with the phalanges.

The phalanges

The *phalanges* of the foot correspond in number and arrangement to those in the hand, there being only two in the big toe and three in each of the other toes.

The arches of the foot

The foot has two main functions:
- To support the weight of the body
- To propel the body forward when walking

To help fulfil these functions the foot has a number of arches (Fig. 9.6). Just as a bridge built from stones needs to be arched in order to bear weight, the arches of the foot enable the separate bones in the foot to bear the weight of the body. Two arches run along the length of the foot and are known as the *medial* and *lateral longitudinal arches*. Another arch

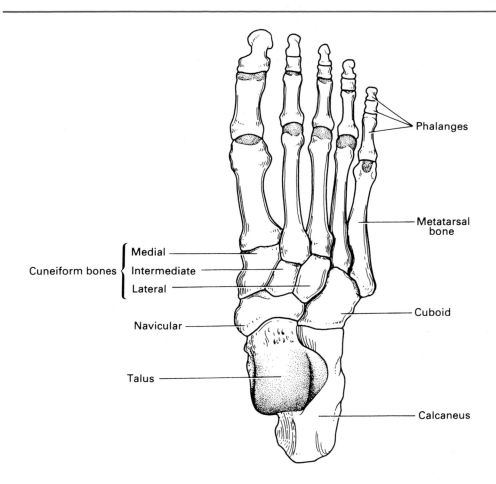

Phalanges

Metatarsal bone

Cuneiform bones { Medial

Intermediate

Lateral

Cuboid

Navicular

Talus

Calcaneus

Fig. 9.6 The foot.

runs across the sole of the foot and is known as the *transverse arch*. The arches are held in place by the shape of the bones and the arrangement of ligaments and muscles.

As well as helping to distribute the weight of the body, the arches also give spring to the walk.

The Joints of the Pelvis and Lower Limb

The sacroiliac joint

The sacroiliac joints are synovial joints between the sacrum and the two hip bones. They allow a small amount of rotatory movement during flexion and extension of the trunk.

The symphysis pubis

The symphysis pubis is a cartilaginous joint between the two pubic bones which moves very little.

However, during pregnancy the symphysis pubis, together with the other joints of the pelvis, undergoes changes which allow slightly greater movement.

The hip joint (Fig. 9.7)

The hip joint is a synovial ball-and-socket joint formed by the head of the femur fitting into the cup-shaped acetabulum. The joint surfaces are covered with articular cartilage and the acetabulum, like the glenoid cavity, is deepened by a rim of fibrocartilage called the *acetabular labrum*. The *ligament of the head of the femur* is attached to a small, roughened pit called the *fovea* near the centre of the head of the femur, and runs to the acetabulum. The joint has a strong *fibrous capsule* and many ligaments, one of which, the *ilio-femoral ligament*, lies across the front of the joint and prevents extension of the hip beyond a straight line with the trunk. A wide range of

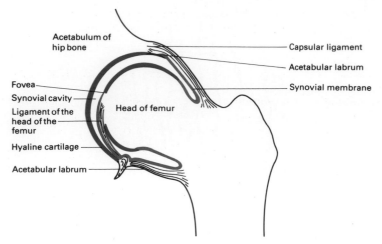

Acetabulum of hip bone

Capsular ligament

Acetabular labrum

Synovial membrane

Fovea

Synovial cavity

Ligament of the head of the femur

Head of femur

Hyaline cartilage

Acetabular labrum

Fig. 9.7   Section through the hip joint.

movement is possible at the hip joint, though when the knee is flexed, flexion of the hip is limited by the contact of the thigh with the anterior abdominal wall; also when the knee is extended, flexion of the hip is limited by tension in the hamstring muscles.

The knee joint (Fig. 9.8)

The knee joint is the largest joint of the body. It is a compound joint, consisting of:
- A synovial condylar joint, which gives articulation between the condyles of the femur and the tibia

- A synovial plane joint, which gives articulation between the patella and the femur

The joint has a *fibrous capsule*, which is replaced by the patella at the front and which is lined with synovial membrane. The *cruciate ligaments* are very strong and cross each other within the joint. They run from the intercondylar area of the tibia to the femur and are partially covered with synovial membrane. The extracapsular ligaments are strong and thick and help in controlling movement of the joint. The *menisci* (or *semilunar cartilages*) within the joint deepen the articular surfaces of the upper end of the

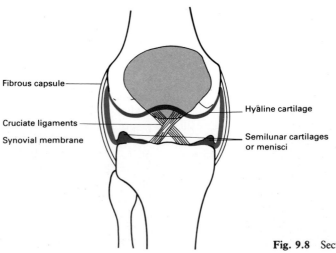

Fibrous capsule

Cruciate ligaments

Synovial membrane

Hyaline cartilage

Semilunar cartilages or menisci

Fig. 9.8   Section through the knee joint.

tibia. They are wedge-shaped, the outer border being thick and convex and the inner thin and concave, and they can be injured as a result of a twisting strain when the knee is flexed. However, if the knee is properly exercised they will reform.

The movements of the knee joint are mainly flexion and extension, although some rotation can also occur.

The tibiofibular joints

There are two joints between the tibia and the fibula. The *superior tibiofibular joint* is a synovial plane joint allowing a little gliding movement, while the *inferior tibiofibular joint* is a fibrous joint which allows a small amount of movement during some ankle movements.

The ankle joint (Fig. 9.9)

The ankle joint is a synovial hinge joint formed between the tibia, fibula and talus. The possible movements are flexion and extension, but these are usually spoken of as *dorsiflexion* (raising the foot) and *plantar flexion* (lowering the foot).

Joints of the foot

The joints between the different tarsal bones and between the tarsal bones and the metatarsal bones are synovial gliding joints and movement is limited. The *metatarsophalangeal joints* and the *inter-phalangeal joints* allow movements similar to the corresponding joints in the hand (see page 79).

Muscles Moving the Hip

The muscles in the trunk moving the hip are:
- The psoas ⎫ together known as the iliopsoas
- The iliacus ⎭
- The gluteus maximus ⎫
- The gluteus medius ⎬ together known as the gluteal muscles
- The gluteus minimus ⎭

The iliopsoas

The iliopsoas muscles form part of the posterior abdominal wall. The *psoas* arises from the transverse processes of the lumbar vertebrae, and the *iliacus* from the front surface of the inside surface of the ilium. They run downwards and forwards to enter the thigh under the inguinal ligament. They are both inserted into the lesser trochanter of the femur. They flex the thigh or, if the femur is fixed, they bend the trunk forwards (as in sitting up from a lying position).

The gluteal muscles

The gluteal muscles form the buttocks, running from the back of the sacrum and ilium to their insertion in the greater trochanter of the femur and the area just below it known as the gluteal ridge.

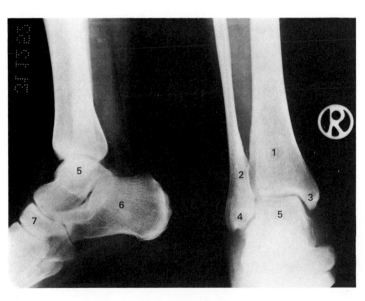

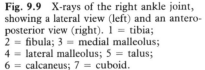

Fig. 9.9 X-rays of the right ankle joint, showing a lateral view (left) and an antero-posterior view (right). 1 = tibia; 2 = fibula; 3 = medial malleolus; 4 = lateral malleolus; 5 = talus; 6 = calcaneus; 7 = cuboid.

Table 9.1 The trunk muscles which move the hip.

Name	Position	Origin	Insertion	Action
Psoas	Crosses the groin behind the inguinal ligament	Transverse processes of the lumbar vertebrae	Lesser trochanter of the femur	Flexes the hip
Iliacus	Crosses the groin behind the inguinal ligament with the psoas	Anterior surface of iliac bone	Lesser trochanter of the femur	Flexes the hip
Gluteal muscles	Cross the back of the hip, forming the buttocks	Posterior surface of the ilium and sacrum	Greater trochanter and gluteal ridge of the femur	Extend, abduct and laterally rotate the hip

They extend the hip joint and also abduct and laterally rotate the hip, but when the femur is fixed, they extend the trunk on the lower limb (as in raising the trunk from a stooping position).

These muscles are commonly used as the site for intramuscular injections as they are thick and fleshy. Care must be taken to use the upper outer part of the buttocks, as the sciatic nerve passes through the other parts.

The Muscles of the Lower Limb

The muscles of the lower limb are much larger and more powerful than those of the upper limb, as the lower limb carries the whole weight of the body. They may be divided into the muscles of the thigh, the leg and the foot.

The muscles of the thigh

The muscles of the thigh are particularly strong and include (Figs. 9.10 and 9.11):
- The quadriceps femoris
- The hamstrings
- The sartorius
- The adductors of the hip joint

The quadriceps femoris

The quadriceps femoris is so called because it has four heads; in fact they are four muscles found in the front of the thigh that have a common insertion into the patella. Through the patellar ligament they join the tibia and are therefore extensors of the knee joint, used in standing and in the powerful action of kicking.

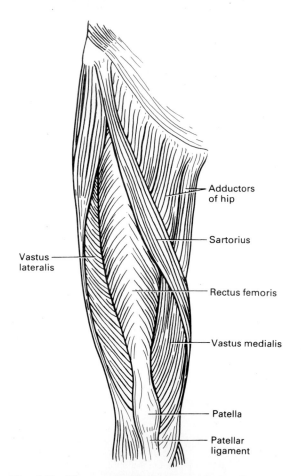

Fig. 9.10 The muscles of the front of the thigh (vastus intermedius is found beneath rectus femoris).

The four muscles which make up the quadriceps femoris are:
- The rectus femoris

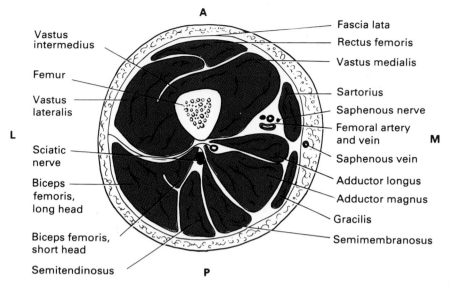

Fig. 9.11   Section through the thigh, showing the relationship of the muscles to the bone and other structures. L = lateral; M = medial; A = anterior; P = posterior.

- The vastus lateralis
- The vastus medialis
- The vastus intermedius

Of these the vastus lateralis is the longest muscle and lies on the outside of the thigh. It is occasionally used for the giving of intramuscular injections, as it is well away from the blood vessels, nerves and lymphatics of the limb.

The hamstrings

The hamstrings are the flexor muscles of the knee and are found in the back of the thigh. They are called the hamstrings because of their string-like tendons which are found on either side at the back of the knee. These tendons can be easily seen and felt when the knee is bent. The hamstring muscles are:
- The *biceps femoris*, so called because it arises by two heads, one from the ischial tuberosity, the other from the back of the femur. It is inserted into the fibula. It lies on the outside of the back of the thigh.
- The *semitendinosus*, so called because of the length of the tendon by which it is inserted into the tibia. It arises from the ischial tuberosity, with the biceps muscle, and lies in the middle of the back of the thigh.

Table 9.2   The main muscles of the thigh.

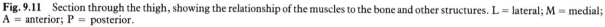

Name	Position	Origin	Insertion	Action
Quadriceps femoris	Front of thigh	Ilium and femur	Patella, through which it is joined to the tibia by the patellar ligament	Extends the knee and flexes the hip
Hamstrings	Back of thigh	Ischial tuberosity and femur	Tibia and fibula by tendons at either side of the back of the knee	Flexes the knee and extends the hip
Sartorius	Crosses front of thigh	Anterior superior iliac spine	Tibia, at inner side of the knee	Assists in flexion of hip and knee and external rotates the thigh
Adductors of the hip	Inner side of thigh	Pubis and ischium	Linea aspera and medial condyle of femur	Adduct the hip

- The *semimembranosus*, so called because of the membranous tendon by which it arises from the ischial tuberosity. It is inserted into the tibia and lies on the inner side of the back of the thigh.

The biceps thus forms the 'hamstring' tendon on the outer side of the back of the knee and the semitendinosus and the semimembranosus form the 'hamstring' tendon on the inner side of the back of the knee. The hamstring muscles are again a very powerful group of muscles which bend the knee in walking, jumping and climbing, and also, when the tibia is fixed, pull on the ischial tuberosity and help the gluteal muscles to extend the hip joint (as in standing up from a stooping position).

The sartorius

The sartorius runs from the anterior superior iliac spine across the front of the thigh to the inner side of the knee, and is inserted into the tibia. It flexes the hip and knee joints and also rotates the thigh outwards.

The adductor muscles

The adductor muscles form the flesh on the inside of the thigh and, as their name suggests, are involved in adduction of the thigh, in which they are assisted by the smaller, more superficial muscle, the *gracilis*. These muscles are particularly well developed in persons who ride horses, since the rider holds on by the knees, keeping the hips adducted. The adductor muscles are:
- The adductor longus
- The adductor brevis
- The adductor magnus

They run from the pubis and ischium and are inserted into the linea aspera and medial condyle of the femur. The adductor magnus is the largest of these muscles. There is a gap in the muscle where it is attached to the femur through which the femoral artery passes from the front of the thigh to the back of the knee.

The muscles of the leg

In the leg there are a few large muscles which move the ankle joint and many smaller ones which move

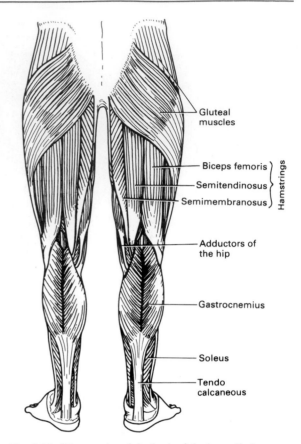

Fig. 9.12   The muscles of the back of the lower limbs.

the foot. The chief muscles are (Figs. 9.12 and 9.13):
- The gastrocnemius
- The soleus } the calf muscles
- The tibialis anterior
- The flexors and extensors of the digits

The calf muscles

The gastrocnemius and soleus together form the flesh of the calf, the soleus lying beneath the gastrocnemius. The *gastrocnemius* arises by two heads from the femur. The *soleus* arises from the tibia and fibula, and therefore does not cross the knee joint or affect its movements. Both muscles unite below to form a strong common tendon, the *tendo calcaneus* (or *Achilles tendon*), by which they are inserted into the calcaneus. The calf muscles raise the heel, causing extension or plantar flexion of the foot, as occurs in walking or running.

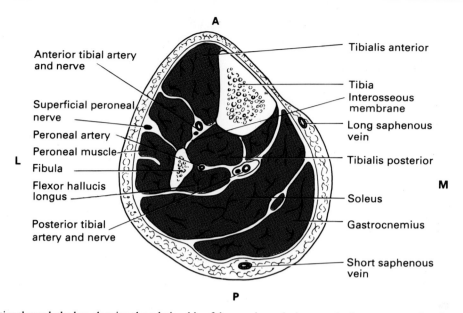

Fig. 9.13 Section through the leg, showing the relationship of the muscles to the bones and other structures. L = lateral; M = medial; A = anterior; P = posterior.

Table 9.3 The major muscles of the leg.

Name	Position	Origin	Insertion	Action
Gastrocnemius	The calf	Condyles of the femur	Calcaneus	Causes plantar flexion of the foot
Soleus	The calf	Tibia and fibula	Calcaneus	Causes plantar flexion of the foot
Tibialis anterior	Side of the leg	Tibia and interosseus membrane	Tarsals and metatarsals on the medial side of the foot	Causes dorsiflexion of the ankle; inverts the foot

The tibialis anterior

The tibialis anterior lies in front of the leg just lateral to the shin, where it can be seen to contract when the toes and ball of the foot are raised from the ground. It is this muscle which gets stiff when persons unused to walking up steep slopes begin to climb mountains. It arises from the tibia and the interosseous membrane below the knee joint, and is inserted into the tarsal and metatarsal bones on the medial side of the foot. Its tendon can be seen and felt readily at the ankle when the ball of the foot is raised from the ground and the sole turned to face in towards the midline. It produces flexion or dorsi-flexion of the foot. It also turns the sole of the foot inwards—a movement known as *inversion*.

The flexors and extensors of the digits

As in the hand, the foot itself contains little muscle, the chief muscles that move the foot lying largely in the leg. The extensors of the toes lie in the front of the leg, whereas the flexors lie at the back, beneath the calf muscles. The tendons of the extensors of the digits cross the top of the foot, the big toe having its own individual muscle and tendon. The tendons are held in place by two fibrous bands, the *extensor retinacula*. These are similar to the extensor retinaculum at the wrist. The tendons of the flexors of the digits cross the sole of the foot. They are strong and are very important in helping to support the arch of the foot. There is one flexor for all the small toes and one flexor for the big toe.

The muscles of the foot (Fig. 9.14)

A short flexor of the toes crosses the sole from the calcaneum to the phalanges, and helps give support to the arch. Small interosseous muscles between the metatarsal bones abduct and adduct the digits, but are little used and are therefore not well developed.

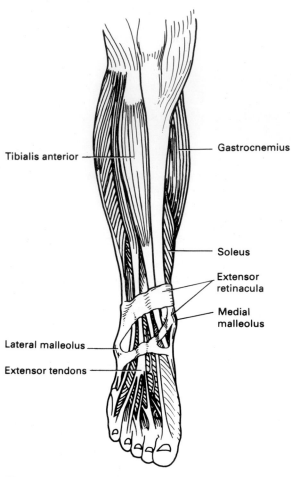

Tibialis anterior

Gastrocnemius

Soleus

Extensor retinacula

Medial malleolus

Lateral malleolus

Extensor tendons

Fig. 9.14   The muscles of the front of the leg and foot.

SECTION 5
The Co-ordinating Systems

In order for homeostasis (see page 30) to be maintained in the body, central controlling and integrating systems are required. The activity of the organs in the body is controlled in two ways. The *nervous system* receives and transmits stimuli through impulses passing along nerves, and the *endocrine system* secretes chemical substances called hormones which are carried through the circulatory system to organs in all parts of the body. Some organs are influenced by both systems.

Colour Plates 3, 8, 13, 17, 18 and 19 relate to this section. The plates are between pages 134 and 135.

10

The Central Nervous System

Objectives: After studying Chapter 10 you should be able to:

1   List the functions of the nervous system.
2   Draw and label a diagram of a neurone.
3   Differentiate between white matter and grey matter.
4   Describe the transmission of impulses along a nerve.
5   Describe how a nerve impulse is passed from a nerve fibre to a muscle or to another nerve.
6   Describe the main parts of the central nervous system.
7   Describe the motor and sensory systems.
8   Identify the functions of the meninges and cerebrospinal fluid.

The nervous system is the system of communication between the various parts of the body. It is the mechanism by which sensations of all kinds are received from the environment and from the tissues and organs of the body itself; it is also responsible for the interpretation of these sensations and for initiating action by the sending of impulses to other parts of the nervous system and other organs of the body. The nervous system can be divided into:
- The central nervous system, consisting of the brain and spinal cord
- The peripheral nervous system, including the autonomic nervous system

Nervous Tissue

Nervous tissue is designed to receive stimuli from inside or outside the body and to carry impulses rapidly to other tissues. It consists of nerve cells, called *neurones*, and a special supporting network of cells called *neuroglia*.

The *neurone* is the basic unit of the nervous system. The part of the cell containing the nucleus is known as the *cell body* and is comparatively large, though its shape and size both vary according to the position of the cell and its function. Each has a clearly defined nucleus and granular cytoplasm. Nerve cell bodies form the *grey matter* of the brain and spinal cord. The cell has several processes:
- *Dendrites* are short, branched processes through which nervous impulses enter the cell.
- The *axon* is a single fibre through which impulses pass out from the cell. They vary in length from a few millimetres to many centimetres.

Neurones can be divided according to the arrangement of the axon and the dendrites:
- A *multipolar neurone* has one axon and many dendrites arising from the cell body (Fig. 10.1).
- A *bipolar neurone* has one axon and just one dendrite, i.e. one process at each end of the cell.
- A *unipolar neurone* has one process arising from the cell body which then divides into two branches—the axon and a dendrite (Fig. 10.2).

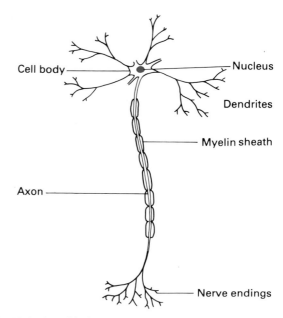

Fig. 10.1 A multipolar neurone.

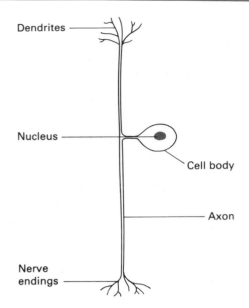

Dendrites

Nucleus

Cell body

Axon

Nerve
endings

Fig. 10.2   A unipolar neurone.

Some nerve fibres are surrounded by a thin layer of a fatty substance known as *myelin* (Fig. 10.3). This myelin sheath is produced by *Schwann cells*, which surround the nerve fibres and the sheath, providing a covering. This layer of cells is called the *neurilemma*.

There are gaps in the myelin sheath at intervals which are known as the *nodes of Ranvier*. At these points the nerve fibre is in contact with the surrounding tissues and can take in nutrients and excrete waste materials.

Myelinated nerve fibres form the *white matter* of the brain and spinal cord. The myelin sheath has an insulating effect on the nerve fibre so that impulses are not transmitted to adjacent nerves or tissues

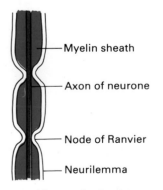

Myelin sheath

Axon of neurone

Node of Ranvier

Neurilemma

Fig. 10.3   An axon with a myelin sheath.

except through the end of the fibre. It also protects the fibre from pressure and injury. Myelinated fibres transmit nerve impulses much more quickly than non-myelinated fibres. Impulses pass along myelinated nerves at a speed of about 120 m per second but non-myelinated fibres only conduct impulses at a few metres per second.

Nerve cells are easily damaged by toxins and poisonous substances and by lack of oxygen. If they die they cannot be replaced, although it may be possible for their particular function to be taken over by other nerve cells to a limited extent.

Conduction of nerve impulses

In order for the nervous system to function, impulses must be transmitted along nerve fibres and passed on from neurone to neurone.

A nerve impulse can be thought of as a wave of electrical changes which passes along a nerve fibre. These electrical changes depend on the concentrations of various ions. The concentration of ions inside a nerve fibre is different to that outside:

- Inside, the concentration of potassium ions (K^+) is high and that of sodium ions (Na^+) is low.
- Outside, the concentration of potassium ions is low and that of sodium ions is high.

This imbalance is maintained by pumps in the cell membrane which pump potassium ions in and sodium ions out. Because the membrane is not very permeable to sodium ions, they cannot diffuse in again. However, potassium ions can slowly diffuse out of the nerve fibre.

The unequal concentrations of ions result in the inside of the fibre being negatively charged compared with the surrounding fluid. The difference in charge can be measured and is 70 millivolts (mV). Because this difference is expressed as the charge inside compared with the outside, it is therefore *minus* 70 mV. This negative difference is called the *resting potential* (Fig. 10.4).

When the end of a nerve is stimulated, the difference in charge between the inside and outside of the fibre is reduced in the adjacent part of the cell. When this difference reaches a certain threshold (usually about −40 mV), the sodium pump stops working, the membrane becomes more permeable to sodium ions and therefore sodium ions rush into the cell; this is known as *depolarization*. It results in the inside of the cell becoming positively charged compared with the outside (the opposite situation to

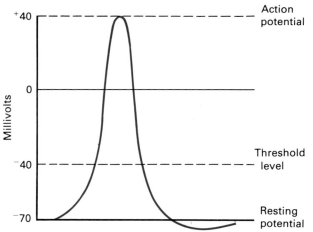

Fig. 10.4 The changes in difference in charge between the inside and outside of a nerve fibre that occur during depolarization and repolarization.

that in the resting cell); this difference in charge is known as the *action potential* and is about +40 mV.

The next part of the fibre will still have a resting potential of −70 mV. Small electric currents flow between the parts of the membrane which are at different potentials, and cause the next part of the fibre to become depolarized, and so on along the fibre. In this way, the impulse is transmitted along the nerve.

Immediately after a section of the nerve has depolarized, potassium ions leak out of the cell, restoring the voltage across the membrane to −70 mV (the resting potential); this is known as *repolarization*. The sodium pump then begins to work, pumping sodium ions out of the cell again; until this has occurred, this section of the nerve cannot transmit another impulse.

The processes of depolarization and repolarization take about one millisecond. Usually about 200 impulses pass down the fibre each second when a nerve is stimulated.

Nerve impulses do not pass continuously along myelinated nerves but jump from one node of Ranvier to the next, or to one further along the nerve. This type of conduction is known as *saltatory conduction* (from the Latin word 'saltare' meaning 'to leap').

When a nerve impulse arrives at the end of a nerve fibre it must be passed either to another nerve fibre at a *synapse*, or to a muscle fibre at a *neuro-muscular junction*.

The synapse (Fig. 10.5)

At a synapse the nerve fibre ends in a process which resembles a knob and is called a *terminal button* or a *synaptic knob*. Each button lies very near to the dendrites or cell body of another nerve cell. When a nerve impulse arrives at the button, a chemical substance which has been stored in vesicles is released into the minute gap between the button and the dendrite of the adjoining cell. The chemical may cause an increase or a decrease in the permeability of the membrane of the second nerve cell. If it causes an increase in permeability, sodium ions will enter the cell and the membrane will become depolarized; this initiates an impulse, which is then transmitted along the second nerve fibre. If it causes a decrease in permeability, the impulse will not be passed on to the second nerve; in fact, it will become more difficult to stimulate. Thus some synapses result in transmission of an impulse, and some inhibit the impulse.

There are a number of chemical transmitter substances; *acetylcholine* is the substance released at many synapses. The acetylcholine is destroyed very quickly by the enzyme *cholinesterase*, so that the next nerve impulse can be transmitted effectively. At some special areas of the nervous system other substances act as chemical transmitters. For example, in the basal ganglia of the brain *dopamine* is the transmitter substance at some synapses and *acetylcholine* at others.

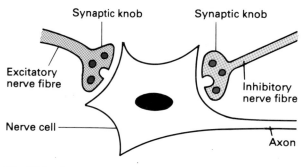

Fig. 10.5 A synapse.

The neuro-muscular junction

Near the junction between nerves and muscles a single nerve fibre branches so that more than one muscle fibre can be supplied. Where the ends of these branches meet the muscle fibres is known as

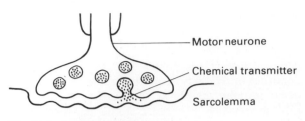

Fig. 10.6   A motor end-plate.

the *motor end-plate* (Fig. 10.6). As with a synapse, there is a small gap between the nerve fibre and the muscle fibre which is bridged by a chemical transmitter substance when a nerve impulse arrives. This substance is acetylcholine in some neuro-muscular junctions, but in parts of the autonomic nervous system it is *noradrenaline*.

Some drugs, called muscle relaxants, can block the action of the chemical transmitter so that nerve impulses cannot be passed across the neuro-muscular junction. Before the discovery of these drugs a much greater depth of anaesthesia had to be induced before surgery could be performed, so that the strong abdominal muscles were relaxed. Now much lighter anaesthesia may be given because the muscle relaxation is achieved by blocking the neuro-muscular junctions.

Properties of nerve fibres

The transmission of an impulse along a nerve fibre is described as working on an 'all or none' principle; it will convey the impulse completely or not at all. Variations in the intensity of the stimulation change the number of impulses sent or the number of nerves stimulated, but not the strength of the impulses.

Stimulation of a nerve fibre in the middle of its course causes a nerve impulse to travel in both directions along the fibre. However, since only the axon nerve endings, and not the dendrites, can liberate the chemical transmitter substance, the synapse acts as a directional conductor, only allow-ing impulses to travel in one direction. Nerve impul-ses may be temporarily held up at a synapse because of the time taken for the release of the transmitter substance and its diffusion across the gap. It is also important to remember that some synapses are inhibitory; if they were not, every impulse would spread across the entire nervous system.

The Brain (Fig. 10.7)

In order to study this section meaningfully it would be helpful to have models of the brain and spinal cord available.

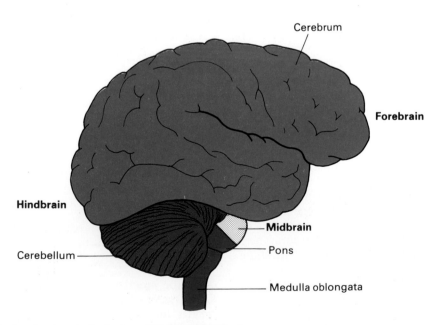

Fig. 10.7   The brain, showing the forebrain, midbrain and hindbrain.

The brain, when fully developed, is a large organ which fills the cranial cavity. Early in its development in the fetus the brain becomes divided into three parts known as the *forebrain*, the *midbrain* and the *hindbrain*.

The forebrain

The forebrain is the largest part of the brain. During its development in the fetus it produces two main structures:
- The cerebrum
- The diencephalon

The cerebrum (Fig. 10.8)

The cerebrum is divided into right and left *cerebral hemispheres* by the deep *longitudinal fissure*. The separation is complete at the front and the back but in the centre the hemispheres are joined by a broad band of nerve fibres called the *corpus callosum*. Each hemisphere is a 'mirror twin' of the other and each has a complete set of centres for receiving information (sensory areas) and sending out impulses (motor areas). Each half of the brain is associated for the most part with the opposite side of the body and if one area is damaged the corresponding area in the

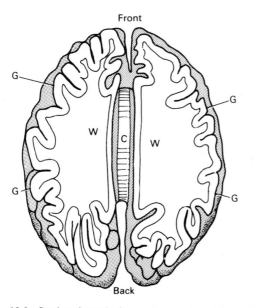

Fig. 10.8 Section through the cerebrum, viewed from above. G = grey matter; W = white matter; C = the corpus callosum, the bridge of white matter joining the two hemispheres.

other hemisphere may develop some influence over the functions of the damaged part.

The outer layer of the cerebrum is called the *cerebral cortex* and is composed of grey matter (cell bodies) arranged in numerous folds or convolutions called *gyri*, which are separated by fissures called *sulci*. This enables the surface area of the brain, and therefore the number of cell bodies it contains, to be increased greatly. The general pattern of the gyri and sulci is the same in all humans; three main sulci divide each hemisphere into four lobes, each named after the skull bone under which it lies, i.e. the *frontal lobe*, the *parietal lobe*, the *occipital lobe*, which forms the back of the hemisphere, and the *temporal lobe*, which extends back to the occipital lobe (Fig. 10.9).

The large fissure separating the frontal lobe and the parietal lobe is known as the *central sulcus*. The area lying at the back of the frontal lobe just in front of the central sulcus is known as the *pre-central gyrus* and is the *motor area*, from which arise many of the motor fibres of the central nervous system. Immediately behind it, at the front of the parietal lobe is the *post-central gyrus*, the *sensory area*, in the cells of which several kinds of sensation are interpreted.

Longitudinal section through a hemisphere shows grey matter (cell bodies) on the outside and white matter (nerve fibres) forming the interior. The nerve fibres connect one part of the brain with other parts and with the spinal cord. Within the white matter, groups of nerve cells can be seen forming areas of grey matter. These areas of grey matter are called *basal ganglia* or *cerebral nuclei*. The main function of these areas is co-ordination of movement and posture of the body; disorders of the basal ganglia, e.g. Parkinson's disease, cause jerky movements and unsteadiness.

The diencephalon

This part of the forebrain develops into:
- The thalamus
- The hypothalamus

These are areas of grey matter found deep within the brain near the base of the cerebral hemispheres.

The *thalamus* (Fig. 10.10) is a relay centre for many kinds of sensory impulses and helps to integrate them. It is also involved in the processing of motor impulses from the cerebral cortex.

The *hypothalamus* plays an important part in regulating the autonomic nervous system (see page

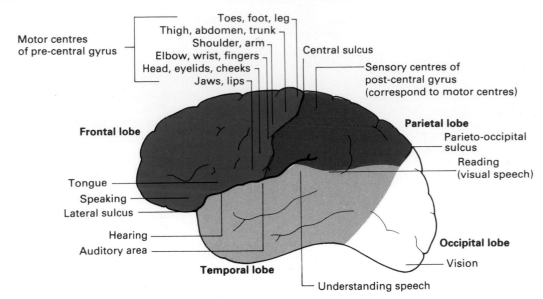

Fig. 10.9 The lateral surface of the cerebrum, showing the lobes and the main nerve centres.

110). It also controls the pituitary gland (see page 120), which is found immediately below it. It is linked to the posterior pituitary directly by nerve fibres, but controls the anterior pituitary by secreting hormones into blood vessels which travel between the two structures.

The midbrain

The midbrain lies between the forebrain and the hindbrain. It is about 2 cm in length and consists of two stalk-like bands of white matter called the *superior cerebral peduncles*, which convey impulses passing to and from the brain and spinal cord, and four small prominences called the *quadrigeminal bodies*, which are concerned with sight and hearing reflexes. The *pineal body*, which develops from the forebrain, lies between the two upper quadrigeminal bodies. This often becomes calcified in later life and can therefore be seen on skull x-rays.

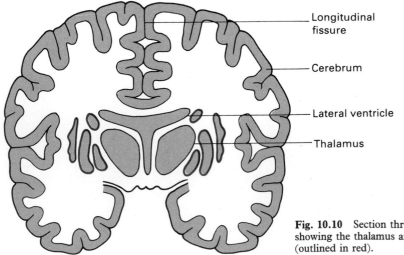

Fig. 10.10 Section through the cerebrum, showing the thalamus and the basal ganglia (outlined in red).

The hindbrain

The hindbrain has three parts:
- The *pons*, which lies between the midbrain above and the medulla oblongata below. It contains fibres which carry impulses upwards and downwards and some which communicate with the cerebellum.
- The *medulla oblongata*, which lies between the pons above and the spinal cord below. It contains the centres which control the heart and respiration; these are also known as the *vital centres*.
- The *cerebellum*, which projects backwards beneath the occipital lobes of the cerebrum. It is connected to the midbrain, the pons and the medulla oblongata by three bands of fibres called the *superior*, *middle* and *inferior cerebellar peduncles*. The cerebellum is responsible for the co-ordination of muscular activity, the control of muscle tone and the maintenance of posture. It is continuously receiving sensory impulses concerning the degree of stretch in muscles, the position of joints and information from the cerebral cortex. It sends information to the thalamus and the cerebral cortex.

The midbrain, the pons and the medulla have many functions in common and together are often called the *brain stem*. Within the brain stem are a number of areas of grey matter. These include the *cranial nerve nuclei*, which are the starting points for the twelve cranial nerves (see page 111).

The ventricles

The ventricles are linked cavities within the brain which contain cerebrospinal fluid. There are:
- Two *lateral ventricles*, which are found one in each cerebral hemisphere
- The *third ventricle*, which lies just above the hypothalamus
- The *fourth ventricle*, which lies in front of the cerebellum

The lateral ventricles are each connected by an *interventricular foramen* to the third ventricle, which is in turn connected to the fourth ventricle by the *cerebral aqueduct*.

Each lateral ventricle contains a *choroid plexus*, which is responsible for the manufacture of cerebrospinal fluid (see page 109).

The blood supply to the brain

The blood supply to the brain is very important; damage due to lack of oxygen occurs after only a few minutes if the blood supply is cut off. It is described in Chapter 19.

The Spinal Cord (Fig. 10.11)

The spinal cord is continuous with the medulla oblongata above. It commences at the foramen magnum, a large hole in the base of the skull, and terminates at the level of the first lumbar vertebra; it

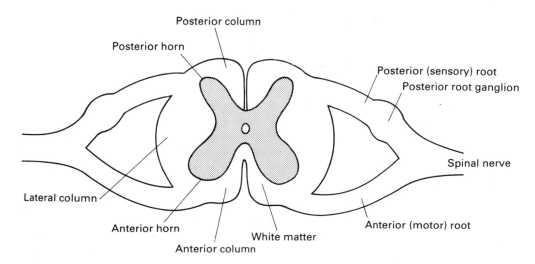

Fig. 10.11 Section through the spinal cord.

is about 45 cm in length. At its lower end it tapers off into a conical shape called the *conus medullaris* from the end of which a fibrous cord known as the *filum terminale* descends to the coccyx.

The spinal cord gives off nerves in pairs throughout its length. Each nerve is composed of two roots:

- An *anterior*, *ventral* or *motor root*, which emerges from the front of the spinal cord
- A *posterior*, *dorsal* or *sensory root*, which emerges from the back of the spinal cord

Each posterior root possesses a swelling known as a *ganglion*, where the cell bodies of the peripheral sensory nerves are found (see page 116). The anterior and posterior roots join as they leave the vertebral column through the intervertebral foramina to form the *spinal nerves*.

The spinal cord varies somewhat in thickness, swelling out in both the cervical and lumbar regions where it gives off the large nerve supply to the upper and lower limbs. The cord is cleft back and front, so that it is divided into right and left sides like the cerebrum.

The cord, like the medulla, consists of white matter on the surface and grey matter in the centre.

The white matter

The white matter of the spinal cord consists of fibres running between the cord and the brain only, not to the body tissues. It contains:

- *Motor fibres* running down from the motor centres of the cerebrum and the cerebellum to the motor cells of the cord
- *Sensory fibres* running up the cord from the sensory cells of the cord to the sensory centres of the brain

The white matter can be divided into the *posterior* (*dorsal*), *lateral* and *anterior columns*.

The grey matter

The grey matter, on cutting across the cord, has an H-shaped pattern, with two portions projecting forwards, one on either side, called the *anterior* or *ventral horns*, and two portions projecting backwards, one on either side, called the *posterior* or *anterior horns*. Like grey matter in the brain, the grey matter in the spinal cord consists of cell bodies.

Injuries to the spinal cord

The spinal cord may be injured in accidents. Partial injuries can produce weakness, abnormal sensations (paraesthesiae), decreased ability to feel pain or temperature or disturbances of the urinary sphincter, depending on where in the cord and at what level the injury occurs. If the cord is divided by the injury, paralysis of the affected part will occur, its extent again depending on the level at which the injury occurred. Paralysis of the legs and all areas below the waist is referred to as *paraplegia* (Fig. 10.12).

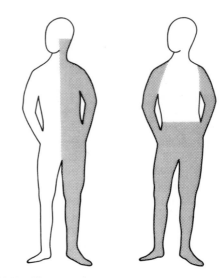

Fig. 10.12   The area of paralysis in paraplegia.

The Motor System

The motor system (Fig. 10.13) is concerned with movement of various parts of the body. As already mentioned (see page 101), the motor area of the cerebrum is situated at the back of the frontal lobe in front of the central sulcus in an area called the precentral gyrus (see Fig. 10.9). Different groups of cells in this area are concerned with different parts of the body. At the bottom of the gyrus is a large area for the head and eye; above that is a large area for the hand and arm, then a small area for the trunk and a large area for the leg extending over the top of the cerebral hemisphere. There is considerable overlap between these areas. The number of cells concerned with a particular part of the body is not proportional to the size of that part; parts which can undertake a

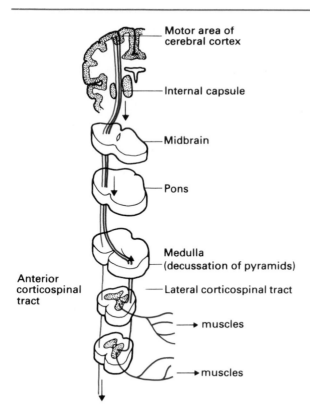

Fig. 10.13   The motor system.

great deal of fine movement such as the hand and arm parts will require a larger area of cell bodies than a part such as the trunk which, although greater in size, does not carry out as much detailed movement. Just in front of the motor area in the pre-central gyrus lies the *pre-motor area*, which is concerned with co-ordinating patterns of movement (Fig. 10.14).

The motor area receives impulses from many other parts of the brain, including the sensory area. From the cortex impulses are sent to the spinal cord, the motor nuclei in the brain stem, the basal ganglia, the cerebellum and the pons.

The motor system can be divided into two main pathways:
- *The corticospinal* or *pyramidal tract*, which is concerned with voluntary movements
- *The extra-pyramidal system*, which is concerned with movements such as the maintenance of body posture

The corticospinal tract

Beginning from cell bodies in the motor area, the corticospinal fibres pass downwards in a fan shape. They then pass through the *internal capsule*, which lies between the thalamus and the basal ganglia at the base of the cerebral hemispheres. All the motor fibres serving one side of the body are gathered close together in the internal capsule, so that even a small amount of damage there can cause extensive paralysis in the affected side; if the whole of one side of the body is affected this is known as *hemiplegia* (Fig. 10.15).

The fibres then pass down through the midbrain and pons to the medulla oblongata, where they form a long narrow projection at the front called a *pyramid*. At the base of the medulla most of the motor fibres cross over to the other side at the *decussation* of the pyramids, so that fibres that arose in the left cerebral hemisphere will now be on the right side of the spinal cord and will supply the right side of the body. The fibres then pass down the spinal cord on each side as the *lateral corticospinal tract*, which is found in the lateral column of white matter. The fibres which did not cross to the opposite side at the decussation of the pyramids pass down the spinal cord as the *anterior corticospinal tract*, which is found in the anterior column of white matter, and eventually cross to the opposite side in the spinal cord. All the way down the spinal cord the motor fibres leave the corticospinal tract and pass to the anterior horn of the grey matter, where they form a synapse with the cell bodies situated there. The fibres then emerge from the front of the spinal cord as the anterior root and join the corresponding posterior root of sensory fibres to form a mixed spinal nerve. These peripheral nerves end in branches to various areas, including muscles, where the motor fibres divide into branches and each branch ends in a motor end-plate attached to an individual muscle fibre.

The term *upper motor neurone* describes the motor fibre within the central nervous system as far as its synapse with an anterior horn cell. A *lower motor neurone* describes an anterior horn cell and its fibre that travels in a spinal nerve.

The extrapyramidal system

The extrapyramidal system controls all the movements that are not controlled by the corticospinal tracts. It involves many parts of the brain, including

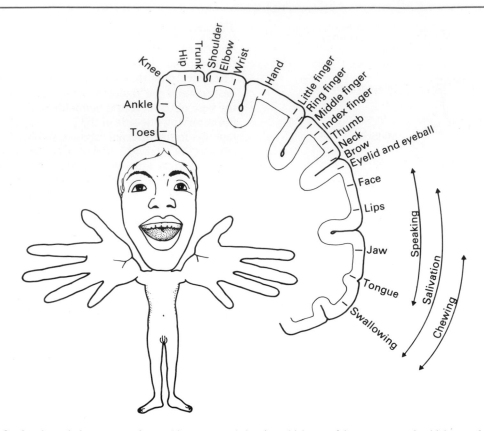

Fig. 10.14   Section through the pre-central gyrus (the motor area) showing which area of the cortex controls which part of the body. The figure shown is proportioned according to the amount of cerebral cortex devoted to control of each part of the body. Note that more cortical tissue is devoted to controlling those parts capable of skilled, complex movement, such as the hands and the mouth.

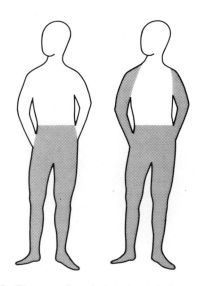

Fig. 10.15   The area of paralysis in hemiplegia.

the cerebrum, the cerebellum, the basal ganglia and various areas of the brain stem. The main function of the extrapyramidal system is co-ordination of muscle movement in the maintenance of body posture, so that movements can be performed accurately while still keeping the desired posture.

The Sensory System

The sensory system is concerned with receiving and interpreting the impulses which are constantly stimulating it. Many of these do not reach the level of consciousness because the nervous system deals with them automatically. Examples are information regarding the blood pressure, the rate of the heart beat, and the degree of tone in the muscles.

Sensory impulses are transmitted to the central nervous system from the special sense organs (the ears, eyes, nose and tongue) and from receptors in the skin and deeper parts of the body (Fig. 10.16). The sensory nerves in the skin have receptors which are sensitive to touch, pain, heat and cold. From deeper structures nerves give information about the position of the joints in space and the degree of contraction of the muscles. These are called *proprioceptor nerves*. Deeper structures also have nerves which convey a sense of pain.

The cell bodies of sensory nerves are found in the posterior root ganglia which lies just outside the spinal cord (see Fig. 10.11).

Nerve fibres carrying the sensation of touch and proprioception enter the spinal cord through the posterior root and pass up the posterior column of white matter to the medulla, where there is a synapse. The second nerve crosses to the other side of the body and runs up to the thalamus, where a third neurone originates which carries the sensation to the sensory cortex. This lies at the front of the parietal lobe, immediately behind the motor area (see Fig. 10.9). As with the motor area, the different groups of cells in the sensory area are concerned with different areas of the body.

Pain and temperature fibres follow a different pathway. The nerve synapses in the spinal cord in the posterior horn of the grey matter. The second neurone crosses immediately to the opposite side and passes upwards in the lateral columns of white matter to the thalamus. A third neurone conveys the information from the thalamus to the sensory cortex.

Sensory information arriving in the brain is compared with a body image that has been learnt through experience. However, the wrong conclusion may occasionally be reached: if you cross your middle and index fingers and place a pencil between the two, there is a sensation that two pencils are being held because in order to stimulate those two areas simultaneously it would normally be necessary to use two pencils.

If a sensory nerve is stimulated somewhere along its length, it is normally assumed that the sensation is originating in the receptor at the furthest point. This can give rise to what is generally known as *referred pain*. For example, a prolapsed intervertebral disc may press on a nerve root and send impulses into the spinal cord, but the pain is felt in the area from which the nerve comes—if it is a lumbar disc the affected area will be the back of the

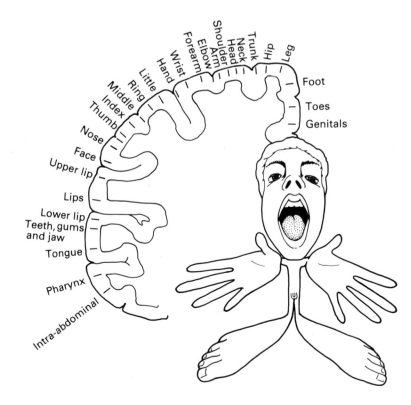

Fig. 10.16 Section through the post-central gyrus (the sensory area) showing which area of the cortex receives sensory information from which part of the body. The figure shown is proportioned according to the amount of cerebral cortex devoted to receiving sensory information from each part of the body.

leg. One of the most distressing examples of referred pain follows amputation of a limb, when pain is felt in a limb which is no longer there; it may take a long time for the body image to be modified.

The Meninges

The meninges are the protective membranes covering the central nervous system (Fig. 10.7). There are three layers:

- The dura mater
- The arachnoid mater
- The pia mater

The dura mater

This is the outer layer. It is a tough fibrous membrane which has two layers. The outer layer lines the inner surface of the skull, forming the periosteum. At the foramen magnum this layer is continuous with the periosteum on the outer surface of the skull. The inner layer of dura projects inwards in certain places to form a double layer, which separates parts of the brain and helps to maintain them in position. The *falx cerebri* is one such fold, which is found between the two cerebral hemispheres; another is the *tentorium cerebelli*, which is found between the cerebrum and the cerebellum. The two layers of the dura are mostly in contact with one another, but are separated when they enclose large veins known as the *venous sinuses*. The inner layer of dura mater also encloses the spinal cord and continues down as far as the sacrum.

The *sub-dural space* lies between the dura mater and the arachnoid mater. However, these two layers are usually in close contact and the space between them only becomes apparent if something, e.g. a collection of blood, enters it.

The arachnoid mater

The arachnoid mater is a delicate membrane which lies immediately beneath the dura and dips down with it between the main portions of the brain. It accompanies the dura as a covering to the spinal cord and extends to the sacrum.

At various places the arachnoid mater protrudes through the dura mater to form the *arachnoid villi* or *granulations*. These lie close to the venous sinuses of the skull.

The *sub-arachnoid space* lies between the arachnoid mater and the pia mater and is filled with cerebrospinal fluid. Between the cerebellum and the medulla oblongata the space is comparatively large and is known as the *cisterna magna*.

The pia mater

The pia mater is a thin, vascular membrane which is in contact with the surface of the brain and spinal cord and dips into all the convolutions.

Damage to the meninges may occur due to inflammation (meningitis) or due to injury. A blow on the head, which may not fracture the skull, may be sufficient to cause bruising, swelling or haemorrhage, and a collection of blood may be formed between the meninges. This will also occur if a blood vessel supplying the brain bursts. These collections of blood are described in relation to the space which they occupy; for example, a sub-dural haemorrhage is found in the sub-dural space, between the dura mater and the arachnoid mater, and a sub-arachnoid

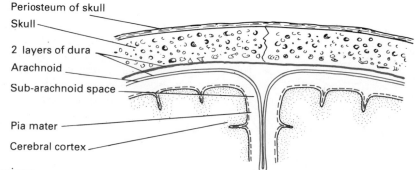

Fig. 10.17 The meninges.

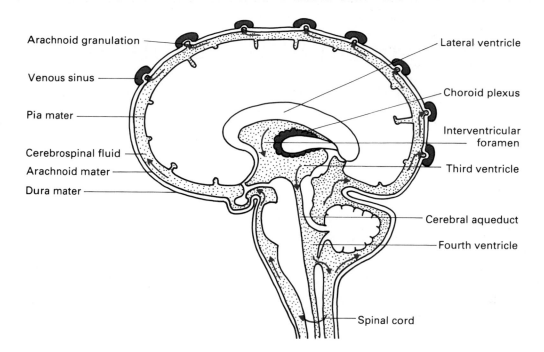

Arachnoid granulation
Venous sinus
Pia mater
Cerebrospinal fluid
Arachnoid mater
Dura mater

Lateral ventricle
Choroid plexus
Interventricular foramen
Third ventricle
Cerebral aqueduct
Fourth ventricle
Spinal cord

Fig. 10.18 Section through the brain and spinal cord to show the circulation of the cerebrospinal fluid.

haemorrhage occurs in the sub-arachnoid space, between the arachnoid mater and the pia mater.

The Cerebrospinal Fluid

The cerebrospinal fluid (CSF) is a clear, colourless liquid which fills the sub-arachnoid space and the ventricles of the brain. It is secreted by the choroid plexuses in the ventricles, and passes from the two lateral ventricles through the interventricular foramina to the third ventricle, and then through the cerebral aqueduct into the fourth ventricle. There are three small openings in the roof of the fourth ventricle through which the cerebrospinal fluid passes into the sub-arachnoid space, in which it circulates around the outside of the brain and spinal cord. It is finally absorbed through the arachnoid granulations into the venous sinuses (Fig. 10.18).

The cerebrospinal fluid is similar to blood plasma in composition, although it contains a smaller amount of protein. There are about 120–150 ml of fluid altogether at a pressure of 60–150 mm of water. It usually contains 0.1–0.4 g/l of protein and about 2.5–5.3 mmol/l of glucose. These amounts may be altered in disease.

The main function of the cerebrospinal fluid is to protect the brain and spinal cord by forming a water cushion between the delicate nerve tissues and the walls of the bony cavities in which they lie. In addition, it enables the pressure within the skull to be kept constant and it carries away waste and toxic substances.

Some babies are born with a condition in which there is a block in the normal circulation of cerebrospinal fluid. Since this usually develops before the joints in the skull (the sutures) close, the head becomes much larger than normal as the soft bones of the skull are pushed apart. If the disorder is severe, the cortex of the brain can be compressed. The condition is known as *hydrocephalus*. Surgical treatment consists of inserting a tube to shunt the cerebrospinal fluid into another part of the body where it can be absorbed, usually the right atrium of the heart.

—11—
The Peripheral and Autonomic Nervous Systems

Objectives: After studying Chapter 11 you should be able to:

1   List the functions of the cranial nerves.
2   Explain the distribution of the spinal nerves.
3   Discuss the actions of the autonomic nervous system.
4   Draw, label and describe the functions of a reflex action.
5   Discuss the control of micturition.
6   Explain how nerve fibres regenerate.

The Peripheral Nervous System

The peripheral nervous system consists of 12 pairs of cranial nerves and 31 pairs of spinal nerves.

The cranial nerves

The cranial nerves originate or terminate within the brain. Some are motor nerves which supply voluntary muscles, some are sensory nerves and others are mixed nerves. They are arranged symmetrically and most supply structures within the head and neck. The exception is the vagus nerve, which supplies organs within the abdominal and thoracic cavities. Some of the cranial nerves also carry fibres of parasympathetic nerves of the autonomic nervous systems; the cranial nerves which do this are the oculomotor, facial, glossopharyngeal and vagus nerves.

The spinal nerves

The spinal nerves emerge from the spinal cord along its entire length (Fig. 11.1). A spinal nerve consists of a large number of nerve fibres, tightly packed together, some of which are myelinated and some are not. As has already been mentioned in Chapter 10, the motor fibres leave from the anterior roots of the cord while the sensory fibres enter the posterior roots. The cell bodies of the sensory fibres are in an enlarged part of the nerve, called a *ganglion*, which lies very close to the point where the two nerve roots join to form a mixed spinal nerve.

The spinal nerves are divided into groups according to the region of the cord from which they arise. There are:
- Eight pairs of cervical nerves, one emerging above the first cervical vertebra and one emerging below each remaining cervical vertebra
- Twelve pairs of thoracic nerves
- Five pairs of lumbar nerves
- Five pairs of sacral nerves
- One pair of coccygeal nerves

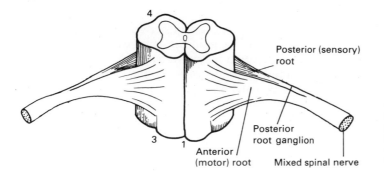

Fig. 11.1   Section of the spinal cord, showing a pair of spinal nerves arising from it. 1 and 2 = fissures dividing the right and left sides of the cord; 3 and 4 = smaller fissures at the side, where the nerves arise.

Table 11.1   The cranial nerves.

Name	Type	Function and distribution
1. Olfactory nerve	Sensory	The nerve of smell. Starts in the nose and passes to the olfactory bulb
2. Optic nerve	Sensory	The nerve of sight. Starts in the retina and passes to the lateral geniculate body
3. Oculomotor nerve	Motor	Arises in the midbrain and ends in the muscles which move the eye
4. Trochlear nerve	Motor	As for the third cranial nerve
5. Trigeminal nerve	Motor and sensory	Supplies the muscles of mastication and has three sensory branches— ophthalmic, maxillary and mandibular
6. Abducent nerve	Motor	Arises in the pons and ends in one of the muscles moving the eye
7. Facial nerve	Motor and sensory	Supplies the muscles of facial expression and carries sensory branches from the tongue
8. Vestibulocochlear nerve	Sensory	Branches from the ear and the cochlea give hearing and the sense of balance
9. Glossopharyngeal nerve	Motor and sensory	The nerve of taste. Also sends motor fibres to the pharynx
10. Vagus nerve	Motor and sensory	Supplies the digestive tract, controlling both secretion and movement
11. Accessory nerve	Motor	Supplies the muscles of the neck, most of the pharynx and the soft palate
12. Hypoglossal nerve	Motor	Supplies the tongue

Each nerve, apart from the first cervical nerve, emerges through the intervertebral foramen below the vertebra of the same number. For example, the third thoracic spinal nerve (sometimes referred to as T3) emerges below the third thoracic vertebra. However, since the spinal cord ends at the level of the first lumbar vertebra, the size of each section of the spinal cord is smaller than the size of the corresponding vertebra. Therefore, the nerve roots from the lower end of the spinal cord have to travel downwards before they can leave through the appropriate intervertebral foramina. The lumbar, sacral and coccygeal nerve roots have the farthest to travel; they hang down from the end of the spinal column, surrounding the filum terminale, and are together known as the *cauda equina* (Latin for 'horse's tail').

Each spinal nerve divides into two main branches soon after leaving the cord:

- The *posterior* (*dorsal*) *branch* or *ramus* supplies the

muscles and skin of the back of the head and neck and trunk
- The *anterior (ventral) branch* or *ramus* is longer and supplies the limbs and the sides and back of the trunk

In addition small meningeal branches supply the meninges and the ligaments of the vertebral column. In certain sections of the spinal cord there is also a fourth branch which forms part of the autonomic nervous system.

In certain regions the anterior branches of a group of spinal nerves join up again to form a network of nerves called a *plexus*. From each plexus emerge a number of nerves which supply various parts of the body. Because the spinal nerves may split and join up with other spinal nerves within the plexus, the nerves which emerge may contain fibres from different sections of the spinal cord.

The cervical nerves

The cervical nerves combine to form two plexuses.

The *cervical plexus* is formed from the anterior branches of the first four cervical nerves (C1 to C4). It supplies the neck and shoulder and gives rise to the *phrenic nerve*, which supplies the diaphragm.

The *brachial plexus* is formed from the anterior branches of the last four cervical nerves and the first thoracic nerve (C5 to C8 and T1), together with small branches from C4 and T2. It gives off three main nerves—the radial, median and ulnar nerves (Fig. 11.2).

The *radial nerve* runs round the back of the humerus and down the outer side of the forearm. It supplies the extensor muscles of the elbow, wrist and hand. It is vulnerable to injury from pressure in the armpit and where it runs along the humerus. Injury to it causes wrist-drop, when the wrist joint is flexed and cannot be extended. This may result from the use of badly padded crutches, with no hand rest, pressing in the armpit, or from pressure by the edge of the operation table on the nerve against the humerus if the patient's arms are allowed to hang down during an operation.

The *ulnar* and *median nerves* run down the inner side and middle of the upper limb, respectively, and supply the flexor muscles of the wrist and hand. The ulnar nerve crosses in the groove between the back surface of the medial epicondyle of the humerus and the olecranon. When knocked here, a tingling pain passes down the nerve to the hand, a sensation known as 'knocking the funny-bone'.

Injury to the ulnar or median nerve causes exten-

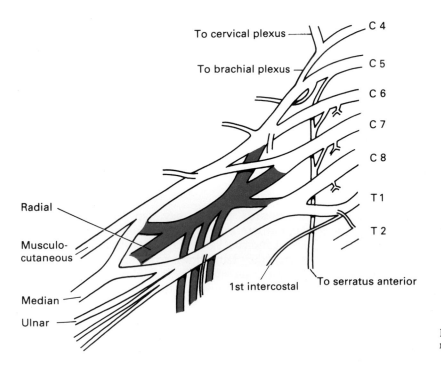

Fig. 11.2 The brachial plexus and the main nerves arising from it.

sion of the wrist and gives rise to a 'claw-like' hand due to the action of the unopposed extensor muscles.

A fourth smaller nerve, the *musculocutaneous nerve*, supplies the flexors of the elbow joint—the biceps and brachialis muscles.

The thoracic nerves

The first thoracic nerve is involved in the brachial plexus. The others supply the muscles of the chest and the main part of the abdominal wall.

The lumbar nerves (Fig. 11.3)

The anterior branches of the first four lumbar nerves (L1 to L4) form the *lumbar plexus*, which gives off one main nerve, the *femoral nerve*. This runs down beside the psoas muscle, under the inguinal ligament, into the front of the thigh and supplies the muscles there. The lumbar plexus also gives off branches to the lower pelvic wall.

The sacral nerves (Fig. 11.4)

The anterior branches of the sacral nerves and the fourth and fifth lumbar nerves form the *sacral plexus*, which gives off one large nerve, the *sciatic nerve*. This is the largest nerve in the body. It leaves the pelvis through the sciatic notch, and runs across the back of the hip joint and down the back of the thigh, supplying the muscles there. Intramuscular injections are usually given into the large muscles of the buttock and thigh and a knowledge of the position of the sciatic nerve is necessary if damage to

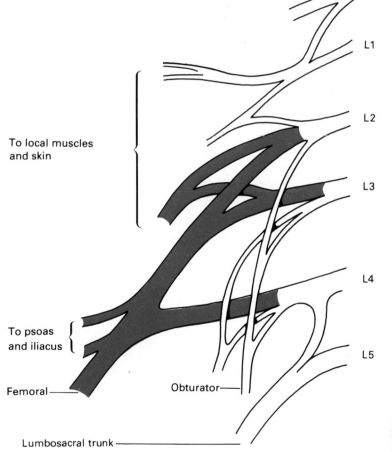

Fig. 11.3 The lumbar plexus and the main nerves arising from it. * This trunk joins the sacral plexus.

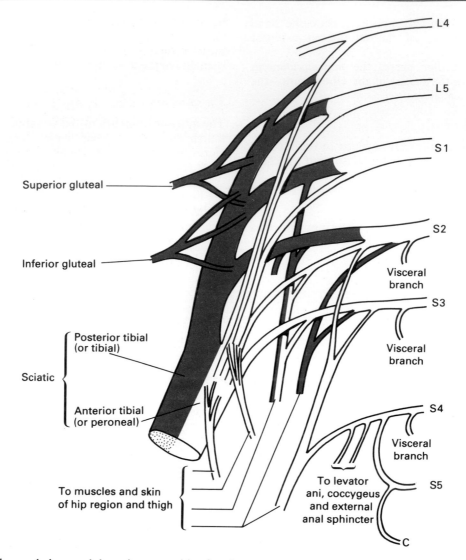

Fig. 11.4 The sacral plexus and the main nerves arising from it.

the nerve is to be avoided during such a procedure. The sciatic nerve divides above the knee into two main branches:

- The *peroneal nerve*, which supplies the muscles of the front of the leg and the foot
- The *tibial nerve*, which supplies the muscles of the back of the leg

The sciatic nerve therefore supplies the whole of the leg below the knee except for a small sensory branch from the femoral nerve.

The sacral nerves also give off branches to the autonomic nervous system.

The coccygeal nerve

The coccygeal nerve, together with branches from the lower sacral nerves, forms a small plexus on the back of the pelvic cavity, supplying the tissues in that area, including the external sphincter of the anus, the skin, the external genitals and the perineum.

The autonomic nervous system

The autonomic nervous system supplies nerves to all the internal organs of the body and the blood vessels. It is so named because it is self-controlled ('auto' means 'self') and not under the control of the will. The functioning of the internal organs normally takes place without any conscious knowledge. The autonomic nervous system is controlled from centres in the brain via the hypothalamus. Although the will does not normally affect this system, sometimes the emotions can.

Most of the nerve fibres in the autonomic nervous system travel outwards from the central nervous system to the organs of the body. Such fibres are called *efferent fibres*. They are of two types:

- *Motor fibres*, supplying the involuntary muscles of the walls of organs such as the stomach, intestines, bladder, heart and blood vessels
- *Secretory fibres*, supplying the glands such as the liver, pancreas and the kidney

There are some fibres which carry information from the organs to the central nervous system. These are called *afferent fibres*. Because they are so few in number, the internal organs are almost insensitive. As a result disease may attack and destroy such organs without causing pain. Any pain which does occur is usually due to inflammation of the lining membrane of the cavity in which they lie; for example, tuberculosis or pneumonia may affect the lung tissue without any pain, but as soon as the pleura is involved sharp pain is felt. In the same way it hurts to cut through the abdominal wall, but a piece of bowel brought to the surface of the abdomen (e.g. as in a colostomy) may be handled without causing the patient any pain.

The overall function of the autonomic nervous system seems to be to maintain the internal environment of the body and to control various aspects of the body's functions such as the activity of the gut, the secretion of sweat and the heart rate.

The autonomic nervous system consists of two parts:

- The sympathetic nervous system
- The parasympathetic nervous system

The sympathetic nervous system (Fig. 11.5)

The sympathetic nervous system consists of:

- A double chain of ganglia running down the sides of the vertebral column inside the trunk and abdomen

- Fibres running from the spinal cord to the ganglia (*pre-ganglionic fibres*)
- Fibres running from the ganglia to various parts of the body (*post-ganglionic fibres*)

The pre-ganglionic fibres emerge from the spinal cord in the thoracic and first two lumbar nerves. They pass from the spinal nerve to a ganglion in the chain through a short branch known as the *white ramus communicans* (the pre-ganglionic fibres are myelinated and so appear white). In the ganglion chain, most pre-ganglionic fibres synapse with a post-ganglionic nerve cell. The post-ganglionic fibres then leave the ganglion chain. Some return to the spinal nerve via the *grey ramus communicans* (the post-ganglionic fibres are not myelinated and so appear grey). These fibres are known as the *parietal branches*; they travel with the spinal nerve to supply the blood vessels, the sweat and sebaceous glands, and the muscles which raise the hairs of the skin, making them 'stand on end'.

Some of the fibres do not re-enter the spinal nerve, but instead supply nearby internal organs; these are known as the *visceral branches*.

In certain regions where there are many organs requiring a nerve supply there are additional ganglia between the two chains, linked up by nerve fibres with the chains and with one another, giving off nerves to the neighbouring organs; these networks are called plexuses. Examples are the *cardiac plexus*, which lies behind the heart in the thoracic region, and the *solar plexus*, which lies just below the diaphragm, where the stomach, liver, kidneys, spleen and pancreas are all found.

Nerve impulses are transmitted across the synapse between the pre- and post-ganglionic fibres by the release of acetylcholine, whereas at the end of the post-ganglionic fibre, the transmitter substance is *noradrenaline*, which bridges the gap between the nerve and the muscle fibre. The sympathetic nerve fibres are therefore described as being *adrenergic*.

Noradrenaline is also produced by the *adrenal medulla* when it is stimulated by the sympathetic nervous system. The adrenal medulla also secretes adrenaline. Both these substances act as hormones and pass directly into the bloodstream; the effects they produce are similar to those produced by stimulating the sympathetic nervous system.

The parasympathetic nervous system

The parasympathetic nervous system consists of fibres which originate either in some of the cranial

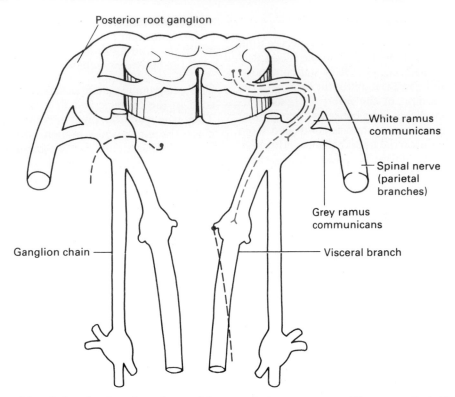

Fig. 11.5   Section of the spinal cord to show the pathways of the sympathetic nervous system. The pre-ganglionic fibres are shown in blue, the post-ganglionic fibres in red.

nerves or from the sacral spinal nerves. There are two neurones as in the sympathetic nervous system, but in the parasympathetic nerves the ganglia often lie in or near the organs supplied and the post-ganglionic fibres are therefore very short. An example is the vagus nerve (the tenth cranial nerve), which supplies the heart with parasympathetic fibres; the ganglion and post-ganglionic fibres lie in the cardiac muscle.

When a nerve impulse reaches the end of a post-ganglionic fibre the chemical transmitter *acetyl-choline* is released. These nerves are therefore described as being *cholinergic*.

There is no endocrine gland which augments the activity of the parasympathetic system as there is with the sympathetic system.

The functions of the autonomic system

All the internal organs have a double nerve supply—sympathetic and parasympathetic. The two sets of nerves have opposite actions, one stimulating and the other checking the activity of the organ. The arrangement is similar to that in a motor car, with an accelerator pedal to make it move faster and a brake pedal to check it.

The sympathetic nerves have a stimulating and quickening effect on the heart and on the respiratory system and cause dilation of the bronchial tubes, increasing the air intake, but they have a checking effect on digestion, stopping the secretion of digestive juices from the salivary glands and throughout the alimentary canal, and checking the peristaltic action in its wall. These nerves are stimulated in association with the experience of strong emotion, such as fear, anger and excitement, and they help to enable the body to respond to the stress. They provide the muscles with a better supply of blood which is rich in oxygen, which enables the individual to run away when frightened or to fight when angry. On the other hand, they are responsible for the arrest of the digestion of food in strong emotion and thus may produce vomiting and emptying of the bowel.

Table 11.2   The effects of stimulation of the autonomic nervous system on various organs.

Organ	Sympathetic stimulation	Parasympathetic stimulation
Skin	↑ Sweat secretion ↑ Smooth muscle contraction	No parasympathetic supply
Eyes	Pupils dilate	Pupils constrict Accommodation for near vision ↑ Lacrimation
Mouth	↓ Saliva secretion	↑ Saliva secretion

Blood vessels to:
  Skin ⎱
  Head ⎰
  Muscles
  Abdominal organs
	Constriction
	Dilation
	Constriction
		In general, no parasympathetic supply. Opposite effect caused by reduction in sympathetic stimulation

Genitalia	Constriction	Dilation
Heart	Speeds	Slows
Bronchi	Dilation	Constriction

Stomach:
  Glands
  Muscle wall
  Sphincters
	↓ Secretion
	Relaxation
	Constriction
		↑ Secretion
		Contraction
		Relaxation

Liver	Mobilization of glycogen	
Gall bladder		Sphincter relaxation

Bowel:
  Muscle wall
  Sphincters
	Relaxation
	Contraction
		Contraction
		Relaxation

Urinary bladder:
  Muscle wall
  Sphincters
	Relaxation
	Constriction
		Contraction
		Relaxation

The parasympathetic nerves have exactly opposite effects. They stimulate the digestive system and produce both a copious flow of digestive juices and peristaltic action. The vagus slows the heart, reducing the circulation, and has a checking effect on the respiratory system, contracting the bronchial tubes. These nerves are stimulated by pleasant emotions. As a result, happiness and a contented mind tend to improve the digestion. The scientist Pavlov was able to show this in a dog with a gastric fistula (a connection between the stomach and the skin which allowed the production of gastric juice to be monitored). When the dog was shown a bone which pleased him, gastric juice began to pour into the stomach due to parasympathetic stimula-

tion through the vagus nerve. The bringing of a cat into the room angered the dog and the flow was checked, the sympathetic nerves being stimulated. Pavlov also noticed that if a bell was rung before the dog's food was brought in each day, after a time the ringing of the bell without bringing the food would cause a flow of gastric juice. This is termed a *conditioned response*. The animal had learned to associate the two things, so that either would produce the same response. It is the same with human beings. The ringing of a dinner bell will cause secretion of digestive juices, as will the smell and sight of pleasant, well-served food. Therefore serving foods appetizingly and choosing dishes which will give the person as much pleasure as possible will aid the digestion process. This is particularly important for patients whose appetite is poor.

Control of micturition

The muscles of the bladder are influenced by both the sympathetic and the parasympathetic nervous systems. The parasympathetic system causes the bladder muscle to contract and the internal sphincter to relax and allow the passage of urine. However, the external sphincter is under the control of the will after the first few years of life and can remain contracted; micturition then only occurs when this sphincter is voluntarily relaxed.

The sympathetic system relaxes the bladder muscle and allows the bladder to fill. It also contracts the internal sphincter. As urine passes into the bladder, the pressure inside the organ increases and then, after a little time, the muscles relax slightly and the pressure drops again. This increase and decrease in the internal pressure continues until there is 200–300 ml of urine in the bladder. The pressure is then such that the stretch and tension receptors in the wall are stimulated and the desire to pass urine is felt.

Reflex Actions

A reflex action is the result of the stimulation of motor neurones as a result of stimuli brought in by sensory neurones from the tissues without any conscious effort. These incoming stimuli will only produce sensation if they are also passed on to the sensory centres of the brain. Sensory stimuli are pouring into the cord and brain from the tissues all the time. If they reach the sensory centres of the cortex of the cerebrum and stimulate them they produce sensations of which we are conscious. If they stimulate motor cells in the spinal cord they produce a reflex action; for example, the touch of something hot on the skin causes immediate withdrawal of the part, a tap on the patella ligament causes contraction of the quadriceps extensor muscle and produces the 'knee-jerk', and the stroking of the sole of the foot causes the toes to be drawn down.

Some reflexes occur entirely within the spinal cord. The stimulus is brought into the spinal cord by sensory fibres in the posterior root, is transmitted across the grey matter by connector or *association fibres* to the motor cells in the anterior horn, and passed out along the motor fibres through the

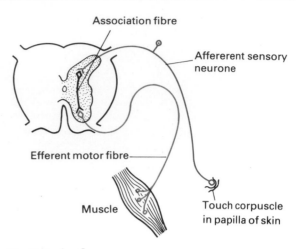

Fig. 11.6   A reflex arc.

anterior root, and on to the structures, e.g. the muscles, which bring about the action. This pathway is known as a *reflex arc* (Fig. 11.6).

Although these simple reflex arcs do not involve the brain, the cerebrum can have an inhibiting effect on a reflex action. If we touch something hot the natural reflex is to withdraw. On the other hand, if we pick up a hot plate with our dinner on it, appreciating the value of the plate and the dinner, we can continue to hold the plate and put it safely down at the expense of burnt fingers; the reflex is inhibited voluntarily. If we have been warned and expect the plate to be hot, this control is more easily established. Even with reflexes over which we do not have voluntary control, e.g. the knee-jerk and the drawing down of the toes on tickling the sole of the foot, there is still some inhibiting effect from the brain; if the nerve pathways from the brain to the anterior horn cell are destroyed by injury or disease, the reflex action is much more marked.

Actions which are in the first place voluntary can become reflex; for example, standing is in the first place a voluntary act which is carried out by the exercise of the will, but once we have learnt to keep our balance, using the sensations from the skin of our feet, from muscles and joints, and the sensory organs of balance including visual impulses, we can stand without voluntary effort unless disease affects the sensory nerves.

Reflex action may occur at three different levels in the nervous system:
● The spinal reflex, e.g. the knee-jerk
● Reflexes occurring at the base of the brain, e.g.

sneezing, coughing, vomiting, and walking (which involves the cerebellum)

- Reflexes occurring in the cerebrum, and involving use of the association fibres of the brain, e.g. salivating at the smell of fish and chips and 'goose pimples' at the anticipation of some exciting event

Degeneration and Regeneration of Nerve Fibres

When a peripheral nerve is cut, the fibres which are no longer connected to the cell body *degenerate*. Immediately the nerve is severed conduction of nerve impulses stops. The myelin sheath degenerates into fatty droplets and these and the degenerated axon are removed by phagocytosis.

Within twenty-four hours of the injury the part of the axon still joined to the cell body begins to put out new processes, first forming buds and then fine fibres, which grow at a rate of about 1 mm per day towards the structure the nerve supplied; this process is known as *regeneration*.

Sympathetic fibres regenerate most rapidly, so improvement in skin colour and control of blood vessels is an early sign of regeneration. Sensory fibres return next and motor fibres last.

Regeneration is only possible when the cell body is intact. The neurilemma (nerve sheath) is also an important factor. Since nerve sheaths only occur in the peripheral nervous system and not the central nervous system, regeneration is thought to only occur with peripheral nerves. Regeneration is also inhibited in the central nervous system by the formation of scar tissue by the supporting glial cells.

—12—
The Endocrine Glands

Objectives: After studying Chapter 12 you should be able to:

1   Define a hormone and a target structure.
2   List ways in which hormone secretion is controlled.
3   Describe the position and functions of the pituitary gland (hypophysis) and explain how its hormone secretion is regulated.
4   Describe the thyroid gland and summarize its functions.
5   Describe the position and functions of the parathyroid and adrenal glands.
6   Describe briefly the role of the thymus and pineal glands.

The second major control system of the body is the *endocrine system*. However, these two systems do not function independently of one another. They are integrated by the connections which exist between the hypothalamus of the brain and the pituitary gland of the endocrine system. In addition, the adrenal medulla, part of the endocrine system, is controlled by the autonomic nervous system. The main role of the endocrine system is to modify metabolism.

The *endocrine glands* are organs producing secretions called *hormones*, which are poured directly into the bloodstream from the glandular cells. It is for this reason that they are also known as *ductless glands*.

The glands are scattered around the body and have no direct anatomical connections with each other. However, they behave in a similar way in that they all pour their secretions into the blood and so can be thought of as one system. They provide a slower-acting control and co-ordination of body function than is provided by the nervous system and are specially concerned with growth and maintenance of the body and with reproduction.

Hormones are organic compounds manufactured by the endocrine glands from substances carried in the blood. They are mostly made from proteins, but some are steroids (a type of lipid). The hormones are then carried by the bloodstream to other parts of the body, where they have a specific effect. As the hormones circulate around the body they come into contact with all the cells, but not all cells respond to them. Each hormone has its *target structures* and only these will respond.

The functions of the endocrine glands are closely interrelated. Initially the functions of the hormones they produce were deduced by observing the effects of disease, destruction or overgrowth of the glands. In recent years various hormones have been isolated, obtained in pure form, analysed and in some cases successfully synthesized.

The endocrine glands secrete their hormones continuously, but the quantity secreted can be increased or decreased according to body needs. Control of hormone secretion occurs in several different ways:

● Nerve cells produce chemical substances which are carried to the gland and cause secretion.
● The gland responds to impulses from the autonomic nervous system.
● One gland produces a hormone which affects a second gland. The second gland produces its hormone, which influences the secretion of the first gland. This is called a 'feedback' mechanism.
● The gland responds to blood levels of substances other than hormones.

The Pituitary Gland

The *pituitary gland* or *hypophysis* lies in the hypophyseal fossa of the sphenoid bone at the base of the skull. It is attached by a stalk of neural tissue to the *hypothalamus*, part of the forebrain that is found at the base of the cerebrum (Fig. 12.1).

The pituitary gland consists of an *anterior lobe* (the *adenohypophysis*), and a *posterior* or *neural lobe* (the *neurohypophysis*). The anterior lobe is an endocrine gland, while the posterior lobe is derived from the brain and consists of nervous tissue; it is connected directly to the hypothalamus and acts as a releasing

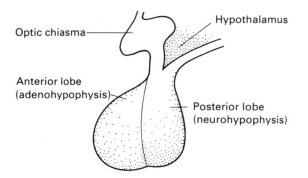

Fig. 12.1 Section through the pituitary gland, showing its relationship to the hypothalamus.

station for hormones produced there. The two lobes are essentially two different endocrine glands and are commonly called the anterior and posterior pituitary glands.

The anterior lobe

The anterior lobe of the pituitary gland is sometimes referred to as the 'master gland' of the endocrine system because it has an important role in regulating the function of other glands. It produces a number of hormones:

- Thyroid-stimulating hormone (TSH)
- Adrenocorticotrophic hormone (ACTH)
- Growth hormone (GH)
- Follicle-stimulating hormone (FSH)
- Luteinizing hormone (LH)
- Prolactin

Thyroid-stimulating hormone

This hormone influences all aspects of thyroid gland function including the stimulation of the uptake of iodine by the gland for conversion into thyroid hormones, and the manufacture of the hormones and their release into the bloodstream. Through its action on the thyroid gland, TSH is involved in the regulation of metabolic rate, the breakdown of fat and the increase of the water content of certain tissues.

Adrenocorticotrophic hormone

This hormone regulates the development and secretion of the cortex of the adrenal glands.

Growth hormone

This hormone exerts its influence mainly on the hard tissues of the body, though there is some effect on the soft tissues. It controls the rate of growth and maintains the size of the body once maturity has been reached. In particular, it controls the rate of growth in epiphyses and other ossification centres of the skeletal system.

Oversecretion of this hormone causes overgrowth of the long bones in children (gigantism) and acromegaly in adults. In acromegaly the bones cannot increase in length because the epiphyseal plates have closed, so that instead the bones become thicker and coarser; the lower jaw, hands and feet are particularly affected. Undersecretion of growth hormone in children produces short stature. People who are very short or very tall due to undersecretion or oversecretion of this hormone are usually of normal intelligence.

Metabolic effects of growth hormone include the stimulation of the synthesis of proteins from amino acids. During fasting the hormone helps to minimize the breakdown of protein to amino acids, to inhibit the use of glucose by all but the nerve cells, and to act with the hormone glucagon to stimulate the breakdown of fat and its release into the blood as fatty acids and ketone bodies; these latter substances act as an alternative energy supply when glucose is in short supply.

Follicle-stimulating hormone

This controls the maturation of ovarian follicles in the female and the production of sperm in the male.

Luteinizing hormone

This causes changes in the female which lead to the formation of the corpus luteum in the ovary (see page 246); it also helps to prepare the breasts during pregnancy for the secretion of milk. In the male it acts on the testes and controls the secretion of the male sex hormone, testosterone.

Prolactin

This is one of several hormones involved in the production of milk by the breasts. It does not appear to have a function in males.

Secretion of hormones from the anterior lobe of the pituitary gland may be regulated by *negative feed-*

Table 12.1   The action of pituitary hormones.

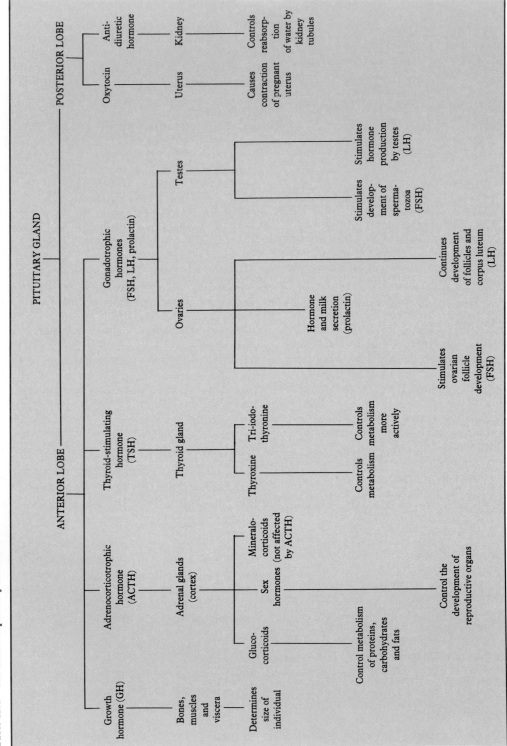

back from target glands, by regulatory hormones from the hypothalamus or by both methods. TSH, ACTH, FSH and LH are controlled by feedback from their target glands: as the pituitary hormones are produced, the target glands are stimulated to produce more hormones, which in turn inhibit the production of the pituitary hormones. However, this regulation does not operate for GH or prolactin because their target organs are not other endocrine glands.

Several regulatory hormones are released by the hypothalamus, some of which are releasing hormones and some inhibiting hormones. Secretion of growth hormone is controlled by inhibiting hormones from the hypothalamus, but the remaining pituitary hormones are controlled by the release of an appropriate stimulating hormone. In this way the nervous system, via the hypothalamus, plays an important part in controlling the endocrine system.

The posterior lobe

The posterior lobe of the pituitary gland releases two hormones. However, it is important to note that these are produced in the hypothalamus and only stored in, and released from, the posterior lobe of the pituitary. The hormones are:
- Oxytocin
- Antidiuretic hormone (ADH)

Oxytocin

This hormone exerts its effects mainly in pregnancy and labour. It causes the unstriped muscle of the pregnant uterus and the cells around the ducts of the breasts to contract, and also promotes a generalized contraction of unstriped muscle throughout the body.

Antidiuretic hormone

This hormone, which is also known as vasopressin, causes an increase in the reabsorption of water by the kidney tubules so that less urine is excreted. Undersecretion of ADH causes less water to be reabsorbed and excessive amounts of very dilute urine are excreted, a condition known as diabetes insipidus. ADH also causes a small amount of constriction of the blood vessels with consequent small rise in the blood pressure.

The Thyroid Gland

The thyroid gland is situated at the front and sides of the neck, at the level of lower cervical and first thoracic vertebrae (Fig. 12.2). It consists of two lobes, one on either side, joined by a narrower portion called the *isthmus*, which crosses in front of the trachea just below the larynx. The gland is formed of a number of closed-in areas called *follicles* containing a yellow semi-fluid material called *colloid* and surrounded by cells (Fig. 12.3). The cells produce a hormone called *thyroxine*, which may be released directly into the bloodstream if it is required or may be linked to a protein substance to form *thyroglobulin*, which is then stored in the colloid. The amino acid tyrosine and the mineral iodine are both essential for the formation of thyroxine.

The function of thyroxine is to regulate metabolism in the tissues. It stimulates the breakdown of food molecules in the cells and increases the production of adenosine triphosphate (ATP). Together with growth hormone it ensures proper development of the brain. It also increases urine production, protein breakdown and the uptake of glucose by the cells. The thyroid also produces a second hormone, *tri-iodothyronine*, which has a more immediate, though similar, effect to thyroxine.

Undersecretion of thyroid hormones in a child produces the condition of thyroid cretinism, which if untreated results in mental retardation and short stature. In an adult, undersecretion produces the condition known as myxoedema. In both these conditions the skin is dry and coarse and the hair is dry, coarse and lank. The metabolic rate is lowered so the patient is obese, has a low body temperature and feels cold.

Oversecretion of the thyroid hormones produces thyrotoxicosis, a condition in which there is an increase in the metabolic rate. The individual is anxious and nervous and has a fast pulse rate. The skin is fine and moist, the patient feels the heat, and loses weight in spite of having a good appetite. He may or may not have protruding eyeballs, a condition known as exophthalmos.

Any enlargement of the thyroid gland is known as goitre; this may be present with or without hyperthyroidism or myxoedema. The presence of a goitre may cause pressure on the trachea or on the nerve to the larynx, causing hoarseness.

Another hormone produced by the thyroid gland is *thyrocalcitonin*. This hormone is produced by cells which lie alongside the follicles (parafollicular cells)

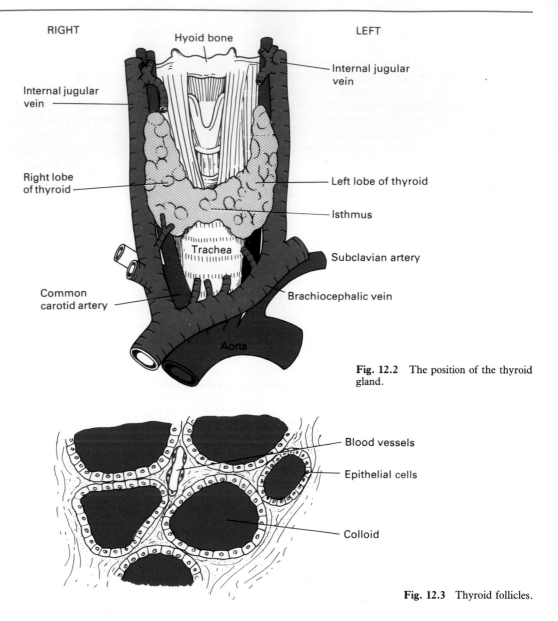

RIGHT

LEFT

Hyoid bone

Internal jugular vein

Internal jugular vein

Right lobe of thyroid

Left lobe of thyroid

Isthmus

Trachea

Subclavian artery

Common carotid artery

Brachiocephalic vein

Aorta

Fig. 12.2 The position of the thyroid gland.

Blood vessels

Epithelial cells

Colloid

Fig. 12.3 Thyroid follicles.

of the thyroid and is concerned with the maintenance of the blood calcium levels. It lowers the calcium level when it is raised above normal (i.e. 2.5 mmol/l) and is thought to act by inhibiting the removal of calcium from bones.

The Parathyroid Glands

The parathyroid glands usually lie between the posterior borders of the lobes of the thyroid gland and its capsule. They are about the size of a pea and there are usually four, two behind each lobe. (This number occasionally varies.)

The parathyroid glands produce a hormone called *parathormone*, which regulates the distribution and metabolism of calcium and phosphorus in the body. Parathormone maintains the level of calcium in the blood in three ways:

- It increases the release of calcium from bone
- It causes the kidney to increase reabsorption of calcium

• It increases reabsorption of calcium from the digestive tract

Vitamin D is also necessary for the absorption of calcium.

Oversecretion of parathormone causes too much calcium to be moved from the bones into the blood, from which it is excreted in the urine. The bones become porous and brittle and the increased level of calcium in the urine may cause the formation of kidney stones (renal calculi).

Undersecretion of parathormone causes low blood calcium levels resulting in the muscular rigidity and spasm seen in the condition known as tetany. This complication may occasionally be seen after surgery on the thyroid gland in which the parathyroid glands have inadvertently been removed. Calcium is given to correct this condition.

The Adrenal Glands

The adrenal (or suprarenal) glands lie above and in front of the upper end of each kidney, behind the peritoneum (Fig. 12.4). They are surrounded by loose connective or areolar tissue in the form of a tough transparent layer which is found between and around most organs of the body. This areolar tissue consists of a loose network of fibres, some made of a coarse material which will not stretch very much called collagen, and some elastic fibres, with fat cells lying between the fibres. Each gland consists of two quite separate endocrine glands: the outer part,

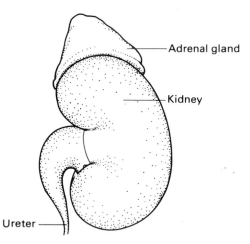

Fig. 12.4   The position of the adrenal gland.

called the *cortex* and the inner part, called the *medulla*.

The adrenal cortex

The cortex is subdivided into three zones:
• The outer zone, which produces the mineralo-corticoids
• The central zone, which produces the gluco-corticoids
• The inner zone, which produces the sex hormones

The mineralocorticoids

These are steroid hormones that regulate electrolyte levels. *Aldosterone* is an important mineralocorticoid which has a regulatory effect on the relative concentrations of minerals in the body fluids, particularly sodium and potassium. It therefore also affects the water content of the tissues.

The glucocorticoids

These hormones are important in carbohydrate metabolism. They increase the conversion of protein to glucose in the liver (*gluconeogenesis*) and decrease the utilization of glucose by the cells, thus increasing the blood sugar level. *Cortisone, cortisol (hydrocortisone)* and *corticosterone* are the primary glucocorticoids. They may be given as drugs to people who have chronic inflammatory and allergic responses, such as in rheumatoid arthritis, because in large amounts they inhibit the inflammatory and repair mechanisms of the body.

Oversecretion of the cortical hormones results in several disorders. Cushing's disease is due mainly to overproduction of the glucocorticoids. There is excess fatty tissue on the trunk and face but not the limbs and sodium is retained so there is oedema, increased plasma volume and a raised pH (alkalosis).

Sex hormones

Androgens (male hormones) and oestrogens (female hormones) are produced in minute quantities in both sexes by the adrenal cortex. They affect the development and function of the reproductive organs and the physical and temperamental characteristics of men and women. Their effects become noticeable when there is oversecretion; for example, an adrenal tumour in a woman may produce secondary masculine characteristics such as the growth of hair on the face and deepening of the voice.

Sex hormones are also produced by the testes (see page 241) and the ovary (see page 245).

Undersecretion of all the cortical hormones results in a condition known as Addison's disease, which produces symptoms of anaemia, muscular weakness, low blood pressure, low sugar level, and a bronze colour in the skin and mucous membranes.

The adrenal medulla

The medulla of the adrenal glands produces two hormones—*adrenaline* and *noradrenaline*—which have effects similar to that obtained by stimulating the sympathetic nervous system. Control of the medulla is via pre-ganglionic neurones of the sympathetic nervous system, without interruption, and response to stimulation is therefore very rapid, creating a set of conditions in which the body is prepared for 'fight or flight'. Adrenaline increases the strength and rate of the heart beat, causes dilation of arteries supplying the heart and skeletal muscles but constriction of other arteries, increases the rate and depth of respiration, increases the blood sugar level by promoting the breakdown of liver glycogen, and stimulates the general metabolic activity of cells.

The Thymus Gland

The thymus gland lies in the lower part of the neck and chest, between the lungs and over the heart. It varies in size with age: it grows until the child is two years of age and then shrinks, so that in the adult only fibrous remnants are found. When fully developed it is greyish-pink in colour and consists of two or three lobes. Its structure resembles that of a lymph node and it is involved in the regulation of immune mechanisms in the body. It is thought that a substance is released from the thymus into the blood to enable the lymphatic tissue elsewhere in the body to produce antibodies. It may also supply new lymphocytes which can react against new substances with which the body may come in contact.

The Pineal Body

The pineal body is a small reddish body about the size of a cherry stone lying behind the third ventricle of the brain. Its function is unclear, but tumours of this gland may be associated with sexual malfunction, so it is thought to be part of the endocrine system. In later life it becomes calcified and acts as a useful landmark in x-rays of the skull.

The pancreas

The pancreas also acts as an endocrine gland, producing the hormones *insulin* and *glucagon*. It is described in more detail on page 227.

SECTION 6
The Special Senses

Colour Plates 20 and 21 relate to this section. The plates are between pages 134 and 135.

—13—
Taste and Smell

Objectives: After studying Chapter 13 you should be able to:

1 Draw a diagram of the tongue indicating the main sensory areas of sweet, salt, sour and bitter.
2 State where the receptors for smell are to be found.
3 State the significance of injury to olfactory cell bodies.
4 Discuss briefly the relationship between the senses of taste and smell.

The sense of taste and the sense of smell complement each other and some 'tastes' are in fact 'smells'. Think of how 'tasteless' food is when you have a cold; the inflamed nasal mucosa and increased nasal secretions prevent the smell receptors being stimulated, causing a 'lack of flavour'.

Taste

Receptors for taste (taste buds) are found mainly on the tongue, but some are thought to be found in other parts of the mouth too. There are four types of taste receptors—those for (Fig. 13.1):
- Saltiness
- Sweetness
- Sourness
- Bitterness

The receptors are spread widely, but unevenly, over the tongue. Some main areas on the tongue have been identified as follows:
- The anterior part has mainly receptors for sweetness.
- The lateral part has mainly receptors for saltiness and sourness.
- The posterior part has mainly receptors for bitterness.

The taste buds are not nervous tissue, although they

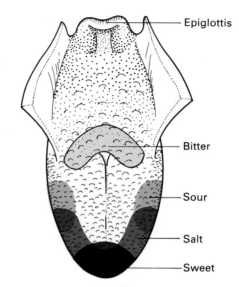

Fig. 13.1 The taste regions of the tongue.

are connected to a nerve supply (Fig. 13.2). When damaged they can be replaced. The nerve supply to the taste buds is from two nerves: the *lingual nerve* supplies the anterior two-thirds of the tongue, and the *eleventh cranial nerve* (the *accessory nerve*) the posterior third.

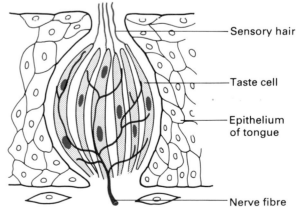

Fig. 13.2 A taste bud.

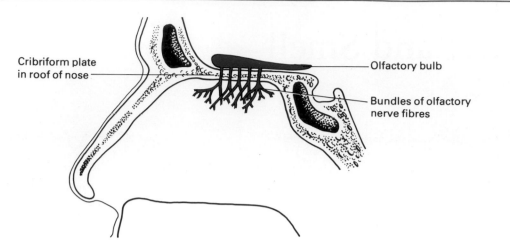

Fig. 13.3 Location of the olfactory epithelium.

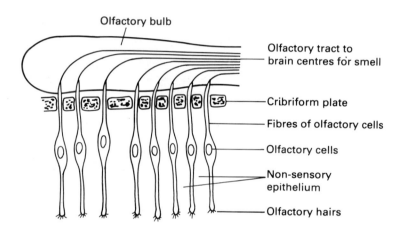

Fig. 13.4 The detailed structure of the olfactory epithelium.

Taste not only gives pleasure, but also acts as a protective measure against the consumption of unpleasant and possibly poisonous substances. It is also an important factor in the stimulation of digestive juices.

Smell

Receptors for smell are to be found in the *olfactory epithelium* high up in the nasal cavity. As air passes over the receptors, the substances in the atmosphere stimulate them (Figs. 13.3 and 13.4).

The receptors react very quickly to different stimuli, and sometimes allow different smells to be identified at the same time. However, some odours 'mask' others—a fact that is made use of in 'air fresheners'.

The olfactory cells are nervous tissue; their cell bodies are actually in the olfactory epithelium. For this reason injury to, or irritation of, the epithelium (by recurrent infections or exposure to toxic air pollution) may destroy the cell bodies and the cells will die, causing a reduced ability to smell.

The nerve supply to the olfactory epithelium is from the *first cranial nerve* (the *olfactory nerve*).

—14—
The Ear

Objectives: After studying Chapter 14 you should be able to:

1 Describe the external ear.
2 Describe the middle ear.
3 Describe the inner ear.
4 Draw a diagram to illustrate your description.
5 Describe the mechanism of hearing.

The ear is the organ of hearing and also plays an important part in the maintenance of balance (Fig. 14.1). It is divided into:

- The external ear
- The middle ear
- The inner ear

The external ear, the middle ear and the cochlea of the internal ear are concerned with *hearing*; the semicircular canals, the utricle and the saccule of the internal ear are concerned with *balance*.

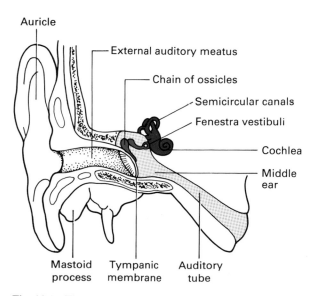

Auricle

External auditory meatus

Chain of ossicles

Semicircular canals

Fenestra vestibuli

Cochlea

Middle ear

Mastoid process

Tympanic membrane

Auditory tube

Fig. 14.1 The ear.

The Structure of the Ear

The external ear

The external ear has two parts: the auricle and the external auditory meatus. The *auricle* or *pinna* projects from the side of the head. It is composed of a thin piece of elastic fibrocartilage, covered with skin, and funnels sound waves towards the external auditory meatus.

The *external auditory meatus* is a tubular passage about 4 cm long leading into the temporal bone. The outer one-third has walls of cartilage and the inner two-thirds walls of bone; the canal is curved, running first forwards and upwards, then backwards and upwards and finally forwards and slightly downwards. These curves may be straightened in order to view the eardrum with an otoscope by a gentle pull on the auricle; in adults the pull is upwards and backwards, in children backwards only and in infants downwards and backwards. The differences in the angles of traction needed are due to the shape of the ear at different developmental stages. The inner end of the meatus is closed by the *tympanic membrane* or *ear drum*.

The skin lining the cartilaginous part of the meatus contains hair follicles and numerous glands which secrete *cerumen*, a waxy substance which forms ear wax. This protects the canal from foreign bodies by trapping dust and other particles, but the cerumen may itself block the canal if it accumulates, and will then require removal by syringing.

The middle ear

The middle ear is a small space within the temporal bone. The tympanic membrane separates it from the external ear and its medial wall is formed by the lateral wall of the internal ear. The cavity is lined with mucous membrane and is filled with air which enters from the pharynx through the *auditory tube*. This keeps the air pressure equal on both sides of the tympanic membrane.

The middle ear contains a chain of three tiny

bones, called *ossicles*, which transmit the vibrations of the tympanic membrane across to the internal ear. The three ossicles are named the *malleus*, the *incus* and the *stapes*. The tympanic membrane is thin and semi-transparent and the handle of the malleus, the first of the ossicles, is firmly attached to its inner surface. The incus articulates with the malleus and with the stapes. The base of the stapes is attached to the fenestra vestibuli, which leads to the internal ear. The posterior wall of the middle ear has an irregular opening which leads into the *mastoid antrum*, a cavity in the temporal bone. This in turn leads to a number of *mastoid air cells*, which are air-filled cavities within the bone. Like the nasal sinuses, these may become infected.

The internal ear

The internal ear lies in the petrous part of the temporal bone. It consists of two parts—the *bony labyrinth*, which contains the *membranous labyrinth*.

The bony labyrinth (Fig. 14.2)

The bony labyrinth is divided into three parts:
● The vestibule
● The cochlea
● The semicircular canals

The *vestibule* joins the middle ear through two openings: the *fenestra vestibuli* (or *oval window*), which is filled by the base of the stapes, and the *fenestra cochlea* (or *round window*), which is filled by fibrous tissue. The vestibule connects directly with the semicircular canals via a posterior opening and the cochlea via an anterior opening.

The *cochlea* is concerned with hearing (Fig. 14.3). It is a spiral tube which makes two and three-quarter

turns round a central pillar of bone called the *modiolus*. The tube is divided lengthwise into three separate tunnels by two membranes, the *basilar membrane* and the *vestibular membrane*, which stretch from the modiolus to the outer wall. The outer tunnels are known as the *scala vestibuli* above and the *scala tympani* below. These tunnels are filled with perilymph and they join at the top of the modiolus. The lower end of the scala tympani is closed by the fibrous fenestra cochlea. The middle tunnel is called the cochlear duct. It is filled with endolymph and forms part of the membranous labyrinth (see below).

The *semicircular canals* are three in number. They lie above and behind the vestibule in three different planes of space, one vertical, one horizontal and one transverse.

The membranous labyrinth

The membranous labyrinth is contained within the bony labyrinth. It is smaller but similar in shape. It is filled with a fluid known as *endolymph*, and between the membranous labyrinth and the bony walls is a fluid known as *perilymph*. It consists of:
● The utricle
● The saccule
● The semicircular ducts
● The cochlear duct

The *utricle* and *saccule* are two small sacs found within the vestibule, and are joined together by a connecting duct. The three semicircular ducts are continuous with the utricle. Where they join, the membranous and bony labyrinths are enlarged to form the *ampullae*. The saccule is found between the utricle and the cochlear duct.

The *semicircular ducts* are similar in shape to the

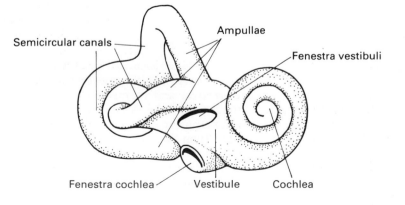

Fig. 14.2   The bony labyrinth.

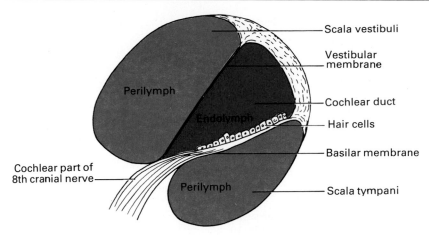

Fig. 14.3 Section through the cochlea.

semicircular canals and lie within them, but are only a quarter of the diameter. They contain endolymph, which is continuous with that in the utricle.

The utricle, saccule and semicircular ducts all contain special cells with hair-like processes (hair cells). These cells are connected to nerve fibres. When the position of the head changes, the endolymph moves, stimulating the hair cells, and nerve impulses are sent along the nerve fibres. These travel in the vestibular part of the vestibulocochlear nerve (the eighth cranial nerve) to the brain. This information helps in the maintenance of balance and posture, though in the light the eyes play a more important part in supplying information about the position of the head.

The *cochlear duct* is a spiral tube within the bony canal of the cochlea. Its roof is formed by the vestibular membrane, its floor by the basilar membrane, and its outer wall by the bony wall of the cochlea. Within the cochlea duct are hair cells attached to nerve fibres that travel to the brain in the cochlear part of the vestibulocochlear nerve. These cells are involved in the mechanism of hearing (see below).

The Mechanism of Hearing

The *sound wave* is a wave of vibration of the air set up by the vibration of an object. The vibration of a fiddle-string or the vocal cord, for instance, sets up vibration of the air in contact with it producing waves of vibration which spread out in all directions, like the ripples set up in a still pond when a pebble is thrown into it.

To produce sound, vibrations must be within certain rates. The human ear is stimulated only by vibrations at rates between 30 and 30 000 per second. The slow vibrations produce low notes and the quick vibrations produce high ones. It is for this reason that a man's voice is lower than a woman's, for his vocal cords are longer and vibrate more slowly, while the woman's are shorter and vibrate more quickly. It is the rapid growth in the larynx and the consequent lengthening of the boy's vocal cords at puberty which cause the breaking of the voice.

Sound waves travel at a speed of 340 m per second. They travel much more slowly than light rays; hence a flash of lightning is seen before thunder (the noise made by the lightning) is heard, and the farther away the storm the longer the interval between the two.

Sound waves are normally carried by air, but they can also pass through solid bodies; in fact, a solid carries sound more readily than air. Thus, putting an ear to the ground, it is possible to hear footsteps at a greater distance than through the air.

The process of *hearing* involves the transmission of vibrations from the air through various structures to the inner ear (Fig. 14.4). The air in the external ear vibrates and causes the tympanic membrane to vibrate. This sets the ossicles and fenestra vestibuli vibrating, which in turn causes vibration of the perilymph. As fluid is incompressible, the perilymph can vibrate only if the fenestra cochlea is able to bulge outwards as the fenestra vestibuli bulges inwards. Hence the need for two windows in the internal ear. Vibration of the perilymph gives rise to vibration of the endolymph, and this affects

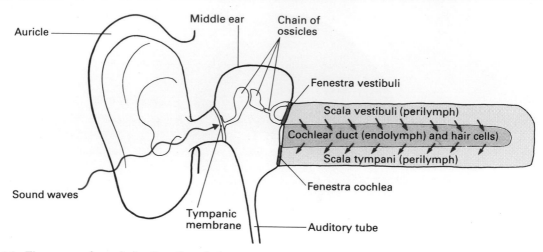

Fig. 14.4   The passage of sound vibrations through the ear.

the little hairs which jut into it and stimulates the endings of the vestibulocochlear nerve. The nerve carries the stimulus to the centre of hearing in the temporal lobe of the brain, where it is appreciated and interpreted.

The appreciation of sound will result from any stimulus brought by the nerve to the centre of hearing, but the meaning given to the sound will depend on previous experience and the power of reasoning.

The loss or impairment of hearing may lead to social isolation and possible personality changes.

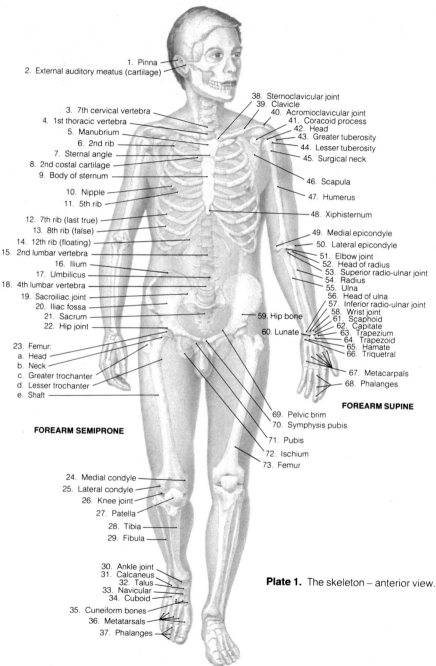

1. Pinna
2. External auditory meatus (cartilage)

3. 7th cervical vertebra
4. 1st thoracic vertebra
5. Manubrium
6. 2nd rib
7. Sternal angle
8. 2nd costal cartilage
9. Body of sternum
10. Nipple
11. 5th rib
12. 7th rib (last true)
13. 8th rib (false)
14. 12th rib (floating)
15. 2nd lumbar vertebra
16. Ilium
17. Umbilicus
18. 4th lumbar vertebra
19. Sacroiliac joint
20. Iliac fossa
21. Sacrum
22. Hip joint

23. Femur:
a. Head
b. Neck
c. Greater trochanter
d. Lesser trochanter
e. Shaft

FOREARM SEMIPRONE

24. Medial condyle
25. Lateral condyle
26. Knee joint
27. Patella
28. Tibia
29. Fibula

30. Ankle joint
31. Calcaneus
32. Talus
33. Navicular
34. Cuboid
35. Cuneiform bones
36. Metatarsals
37. Phalanges

38. Sternoclavicular joint
39. Clavicle
40. Acromioclavicular joint
41. Coracoid process
42. Head
43. Greater tuberosity
44. Lesser tuberosity
45. Surgical neck

46. Scapula

47. Humerus

48. Xiphisternum

49. Medial epicondyle
50. Lateral epicondyle
51. Elbow joint
52. Head of radius
53. Superior radio-ulnar joint
54. Radius
55. Ulna
56. Head of ulna
57. Inferior radio-ulnar joint
58. Wrist joint
59. Hip bone
61. Scaphoid
62. Capitate
60. Lunate
63. Trapezium
64. Trapezoid
65. Hamate
66. Triquetral

67. Metacarpals
68. Phalanges

FOREARM SUPINE

69. Pelvic brim
70. Symphysis pubis

71. Pubis
72. Ischium
73. Femur

Plate 1. The skeleton – anterior view.

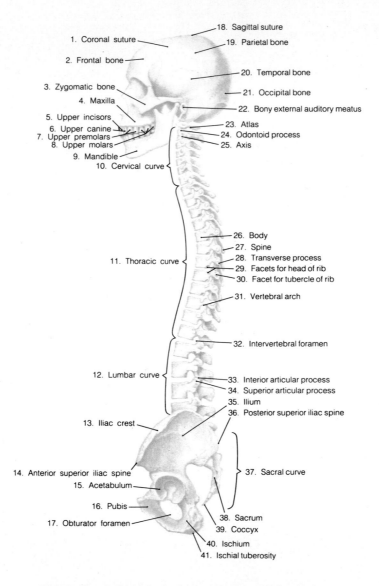

1. Coronal suture
2. Frontal bone
3. Zygomatic bone
4. Maxilla
5. Upper incisors
6. Upper canine
7. Upper premolars
8. Upper molars
9. Mandible
10. Cervical curve
11. Thoracic curve
12. Lumbar curve
13. Iliac crest
14. Anterior superior iliac spine
15. Acetabulum
16. Pubis
17. Obturator foramen

18. Sagittal suture
19. Parietal bone
20. Temporal bone
21. Occipital bone
22. Bony external auditory meatus
23. Atlas
24. Odontoid process
25. Axis
26. Body
27. Spine
28. Transverse process
29. Facets for head of rib
30. Facet for tubercle of rib
31. Vertebral arch
32. Intervertebral foramen
33. Interior articular process
34. Superior articular process
35. Ilium
36. Posterior superior iliac spine
37. Sacral curve
38. Sacrum
39. Coccyx
40. Ischium
41. Ischial tuberosity

Plate 2. The skull, vertebral column and pelvis – left lateral view.

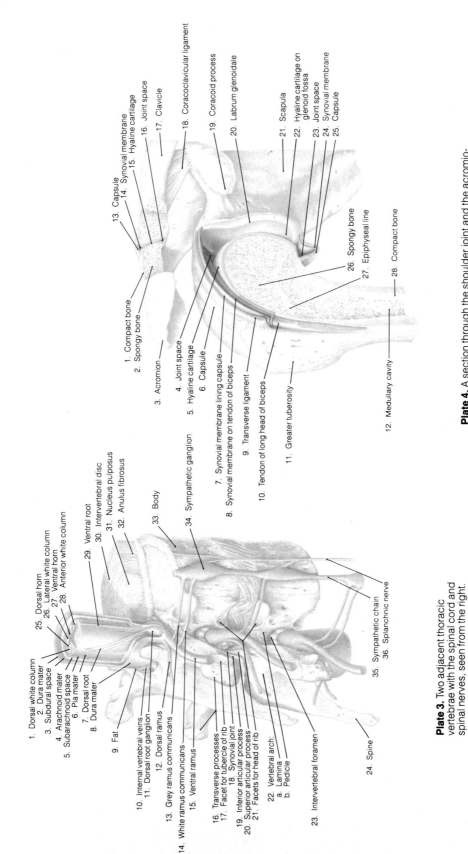

1. Dorsal white column
2. Dura mater
3. Subdural space
4. Arachnoid mater
5. Subarachnoid space
6. Pia mater
7. Dorsal root
8. Dura mater

9. Fat

10. Internal vertebral veins
11. Dorsal root ganglion
12. Dorsal ramus
13. Grey ramus communicans

14. White ramus communicans
15. Ventral ramus

16. Transverse processes
17. Facet for tubercle of rib
18. Synovial joint
19. Inferior articular process
20. Superior articular process
21. Facets for head of rib

22. Vertebral arch:
    a. Lamina
    b. Pedicle

23. Intervertebral foramen

24. Spine

25. Dorsal horn
26. Lateral white column
27. Ventral horn
28. Anterior white column

29. Ventral root
30. Intervertebral disc
31. Nucleus pulposus
32. Anulus fibrosus

33. Body

34. Sympathetic ganglion

35. Sympathetic chain
36. Splanchnic nerve

Plate 3. Two adjacent thoracic vertebrae with the spinal cord and spinal nerves, seen from the right.

13. Capsule
14. Synovial membrane
15. Hyaline cartilage
16. Joint space
17. Clavicle
18. Coracoclavicular ligament
19. Coracoid process
20. Labrum glenoidale
21. Scapula
22. Hyaline cartilage on glenoid fossa
23. Joint space
24. Synovial membrane
25. Capsule

26. Spongy bone
27. Epiphyseal line
28. Compact bone

1. Compact bone
2. Spongy bone

3. Acromion

4. Joint space
5. Hyaline cartilage
6. Capsule
7. Synovial membrane lining capsule
8. Synovial membrane on tendon of biceps
9. Transverse ligament
10. Tendon of long head of biceps
11. Greater tuberosity

12. Medullary cavity

Plate 4. A section through the shoulder joint and the acromio-clavicular joint, approximating to the coronal plane and seen from the front.

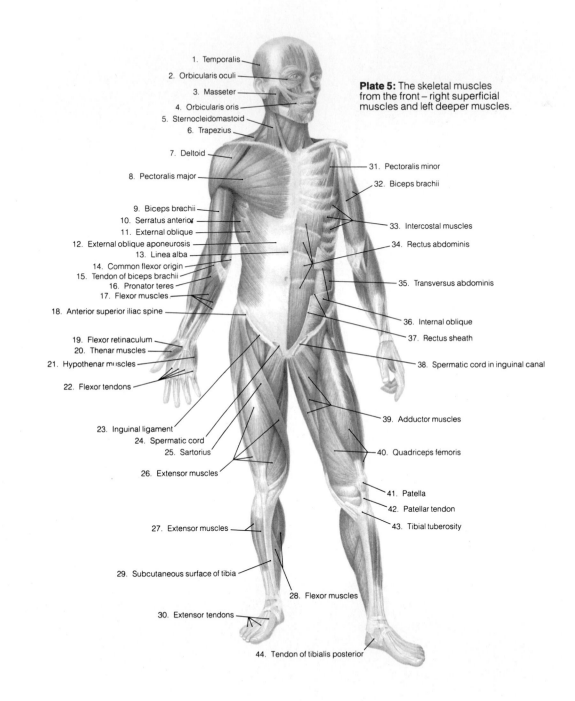

1. Temporalis
2. Orbicularis oculi
3. Masseter
4. Orbicularis oris
5. Sternocleidomastoid
6. Trapezius
7. Deltoid
8. Pectoralis major
9. Biceps brachii
10. Serratus anterior
11. External oblique
12. External oblique aponeurosis
13. Linea alba
14. Common flexor origin
15. Tendon of biceps brachii
16. Pronator teres
17. Flexor muscles
18. Anterior superior iliac spine
19. Flexor retinaculum
20. Thenar muscles
21. Hypothenar muscles
22. Flexor tendons
23. Inguinal ligament
24. Spermatic cord
25. Sartorius
26. Extensor muscles
27. Extensor muscles
29. Subcutaneous surface of tibia
30. Extensor tendons
28. Flexor muscles
44. Tendon of tibialis posterior

31. Pectoralis minor
32. Biceps brachii
33. Intercostal muscles
34. Rectus abdominis
35. Transversus abdominis
36. Internal oblique
37. Rectus sheath
38. Spermatic cord in inguinal canal
39. Adductor muscles
40. Quadriceps femoris
41. Patella
42. Patellar tendon
43. Tibial tuberosity

Plate 5: The skeletal muscles from the front – right superficial muscles and left deeper muscles.

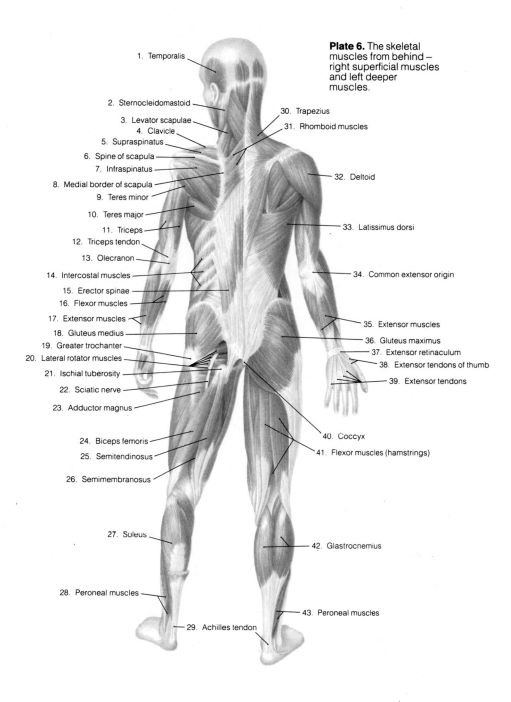

1. Temporalis
2. Sternocleidomastoid
3. Levator scapulae
4. Clavicle
5. Supraspinatus
6. Spine of scapula
7. Infraspinatus
8. Medial border of scapula
9. Teres minor
10. Teres major
11. Triceps
12. Triceps tendon
13. Olecranon
14. Intercostal muscles
15. Erector spinae
16. Flexor muscles
17. Extensor muscles
18. Gluteus medius
19. Greater trochanter
20. Lateral rotator muscles
21. Ischial tuberosity
22. Sciatic nerve
23. Adductor magnus
24. Biceps femoris
25. Semitendinosus
26. Semimembranosus
27. Soleus
28. Peroneal muscles
29. Achilles tendon

Plate 6. The skeletal muscles from behind — right superficial muscles and left deeper muscles.

30. Trapezius
31. Rhomboid muscles
32. Deltoid
33. Latissimus dorsi
34. Common extensor origin
35. Extensor muscles
36. Gluteus maximus
37. Extensor retinaculum
38. Extensor tendons of thumb
39. Extensor tendons
40. Coccyx
41. Flexor muscles (hamstrings)
42. Glastrocnemius
43. Peroneal muscles

Plate 7. The respiratory system.

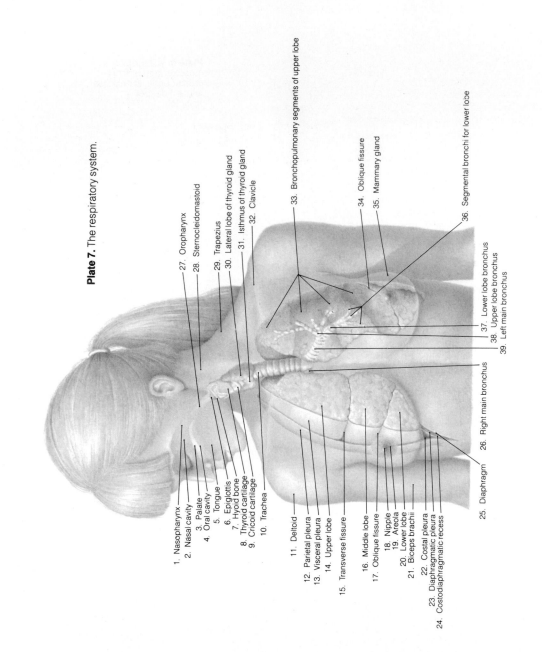

1. Nasopharynx
2. Nasal cavity
3. Palate
4. Oral cavity
5. Tongue
6. Epiglottis
7. Hyoid bone
8. Thyroid cartilage
9. Cricoid cartilage
10. Trachea

11. Deltoid
12. Parietal pleura
13. Visceral pleura
14. Upper lobe
15. Transverse fissure
16. Middle lobe
17. Oblique fissure
18. Nipple
19. Areola
20. Lower lobe
21. Biceps brachii
22. Costal pleura
23. Diaphragmatic pleura
24. Costodiaphragmatic recess

25. Diaphragm
26. Right main bronchus

27. Oropharynx
28. Sternocleidomastoid
29. Trapezius
30. Lateral lobe of thyroid gland
31. Isthmus of thyroid gland
32. Clavicle

33. Bronchopulmonary segments of upper lobe

34. Oblique fissure
35. Mammary gland

36. Segmental bronchi for lower lobe

37. Lower lobe bronchus
38. Upper lobe bronchus
39. Left main bronchus

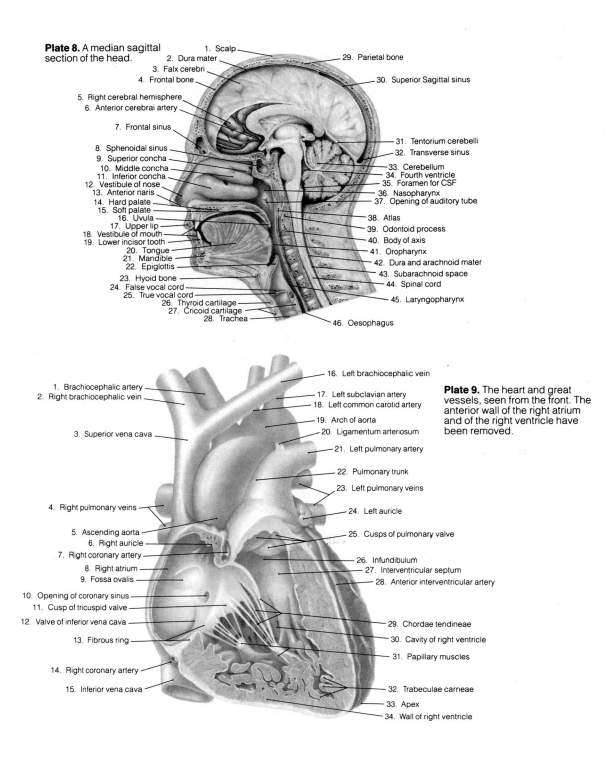

Plate 8. A median sagittal section of the head.

1. Scalp
2. Dura mater
3. Falx cerebri
4. Frontal bone
5. Right cerebral hemisphere
6. Anterior cerebral artery
7. Frontal sinus
8. Sphenoidal sinus
9. Superior concha
10. Middle concha
11. Inferior concha
12. Vestibule of nose
13. Anterior naris
14. Hard palate
15. Soft palate
16. Uvula
17. Upper lip
18. Vestibule of mouth
19. Lower incisor tooth
20. Tongue
21. Mandible
22. Epiglottis
23. Hyoid bone
24. False vocal cord
25. True vocal cord
26. Thyroid cartilage
27. Cricoid cartilage
28. Trachea

29. Parietal bone
30. Superior Sagittal sinus
31. Tentorium cerebelli
32. Transverse sinus
33. Cerebellum
34. Fourth ventricle
35. Foramen for CSF
36. Nasopharynx
37. Opening of auditory tube
38. Atlas
39. Odontoid process
40. Body of axis
41. Oropharynx
42. Dura and arachnoid mater
43. Subarachnoid space
44. Spinal cord
45. Laryngopharynx
46. Oesophagus

1. Brachiocephalic artery
2. Right brachiocephalic vein
3. Superior vena cava
4. Right pulmonary veins
5. Ascending aorta
6. Right auricle
7. Right coronary artery
8. Right atrium
9. Fossa ovalis
10. Opening of coronary sinus
11. Cusp of tricuspid valve
12. Valve of inferior vena cava
13. Fibrous ring
14. Right coronary artery
15. Inferior vena cava

16. Left brachiocephalic vein
17. Left subclavian artery
18. Left common carotid artery
19. Arch of aorta
20. Ligamentum arteriosum
21. Left pulmonary artery
22. Pulmonary trunk
23. Left pulmonary veins
24. Left auricle
25. Cusps of pulmonary valve
26. Infundibulum
27. Interventricular septum
28. Anterior interventricular artery
29. Chordae tendineae
30. Cavity of right ventricle
31. Papillary muscles
32. Trabeculae carneae
33. Apex
34. Wall of right ventricle

Plate 9. The heart and great vessels, seen from the front. The anterior wall of the right atrium and of the right ventricle have been removed.

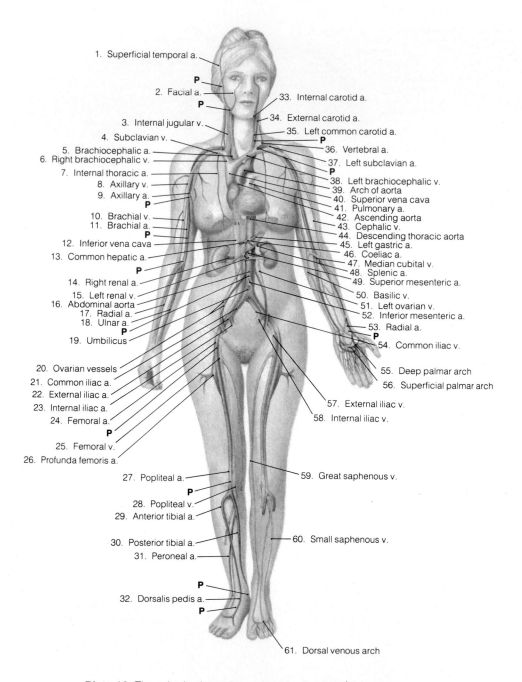

1. Superficial temporal a.
2. Facial a.
3. Internal jugular v.
4. Subclavian v.
5. Brachiocephalic a.
6. Right brachiocephalic v.
7. Internal thoracic a.
8. Axillary v.
9. Axillary a.
10. Brachial v.
11. Brachial a.
12. Inferior vena cava
13. Common hepatic a.
14. Right renal a.
15. Left renal v.
16. Abdominal aorta
17. Radial a.
18. Ulnar a.
19. Umbilicus
20. Ovarian vessels
21. Common iliac a.
22. External iliac a.
23. Internal iliac a.
24. Femoral a.
25. Femoral v.
26. Profunda femoris a.
27. Popliteal a.
28. Popliteal v.
29. Anterior tibial a.
30. Posterior tibial a.
31. Peroneal a.
32. Dorsalis pedis a.

33. Internal carotid a.
34. External carotid a.
35. Left common carotid a.
36. Vertebral a.
37. Left subclavian a.
38. Left brachiocephalic v.
39. Arch of aorta
40. Superior vena cava
41. Pulmonary a.
42. Ascending aorta
43. Cephalic v.
44. Descending thoracic aorta
45. Left gastric a.
46. Coeliac a.
47. Median cubital v.
48. Splenic a.
49. Superior mesenteric a.
50. Basilic v.
51. Left ovarian v.
52. Inferior mesenteric a.
53. Radial a.
54. Common iliac v.
55. Deep palmar arch
56. Superficial palmar arch
57. External iliac v.
58. Internal iliac v.
59. Great saphenous v.
60. Small saphenous v.
61. Dorsal venous arch

Plate 10. The principal arteries and veins. Superficial veins are illustrated in the left upper and lower limbs. deep veins in the right upper and lower limbs. a=artery; v=vein; **P** indicates a pressure point.

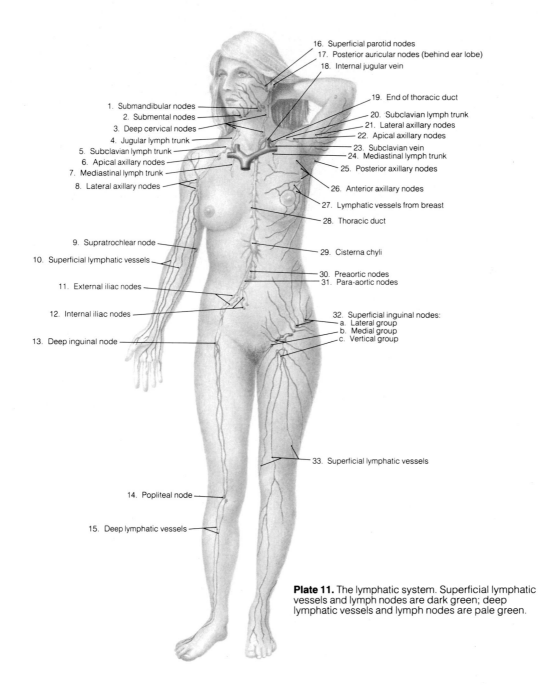

16. Superficial parotid nodes
17. Posterior auricular nodes (behind ear lobe)
18. Internal jugular vein

1. Submandibular nodes
2. Submental nodes
3. Deep cervical nodes
4. Jugular lymph trunk
5. Subclavian lymph trunk
6. Apical axillary nodes
7. Mediastinal lymph trunk
8. Lateral axillary nodes

19. End of thoracic duct
20. Subclavian lymph trunk
21. Lateral axillary nodes
22. Apical axillary nodes
23. Subclavian vein
24. Mediastinal lymph trunk
25. Posterior axillary nodes
26. Anterior axillary nodes
27. Lymphatic vessels from breast
28. Thoracic duct

9. Supratrochlear node
10. Superficial lymphatic vessels

29. Cisterna chyli

11. External iliac nodes

30. Preaortic nodes
31. Para-aortic nodes

12. Internal iliac nodes

32. Superficial inguinal nodes:
   a. Lateral group
   b. Medial group
   c. Vertical group

13. Deep inguinal node

33. Superficial lymphatic vessels

14. Popliteal node

15. Deep lymphatic vessels

Plate 11. The lymphatic system. Superficial lymphatic vessels and lymph nodes are dark green; deep lymphatic vessels and lymph nodes are pale green.

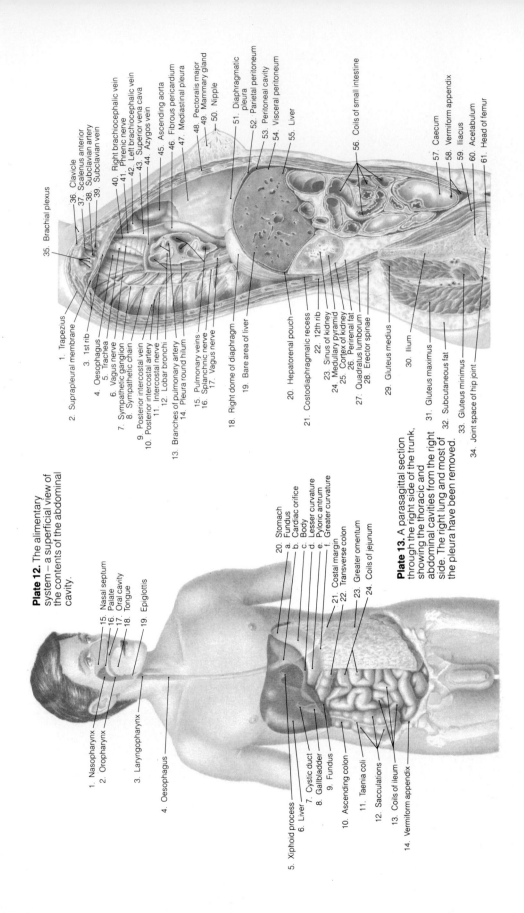

Plate 12. The alimentary system – a superficial view of the contents of the abdominal cavity.

1. Nasopharynx
2. Oropharynx
3. Laryngopharynx
4. Oesophagus
5. Xiphoid process
6. Liver
7. Cystic duct
8. Gallbladder
9. Fundus
10. Ascending colon
11. Taenia coli
12. Sacculations
13. Coils of ileum
14. Vermiform appendix
15. Nasal septum
16. Palate
17. Oral cavity
18. Tongue
19. Epiglottis
20. Stomach
  a. Fundus
  b. Cardiac orifice
  c. Body
  d. Lesser curvature
  e. Pyloric antrum
  f. Greater curvature
21. Costal margin
22. Transverse colon
23. Greater omentum
24. Coils of jejunum

Plate 13. A parasagittal section through the right side of the trunk, showing the thoracic and abdominal cavities from the right side. The right lung and most of the pleura have been removed.

1. Trapezius
2. Suprapleural membrane
3. 1st rib
4. Oesophagus
5. Trachea
6. Vagus nerve
7. Sympathetic ganglion
8. Sympathetic chain
9. Posterior intercostal vein
10. Posterior intercostal artery
11. Intercostal nerve
12. Lobar bronchi
13. Branches of pulmonary artery
14. Pleura round hilum
15. Pulmonary veins
16. Splanchnic nerve
17. Vagus nerve
18. Right dome of diaphragm
19. Bare area of liver
20. Hepatorenal pouch
21. Costodiaphragmatic recess
22. 12th rib
23. Sinus of kidney
24. Medullary pyramid
25. Cortex of kidney
26. Perirenal fat
27. Quadratus lumborum
28. Erector spinae
29. Gluteus medius
30. Ilium
31. Gluteus maximus
32. Subcutaneous fat
33. Gluteus minimus
34. Joint space of hip joint
35. Brachial plexus
36. Clavicle
37. Scalenus anterior
38. Subclavian artery
39. Subclavian vein
40. Right brachiocephalic vein
41. Phrenic nerve
42. Left brachiocephalic vein
43. Superior vena cava
44. Azygos vein
45. Ascending aorta
46. Fibrous pericardium
47. Mediastinal pleura
48. Pectoralis major
49. Mammary gland
50. Nipple
51. Diaphragmatic pleura
52. Parietal peritoneum
53. Peritoneal cavity
54. Visceral peritoneum
55. Liver
56. Coils of small intestine
57. Caecum
58. Vermiform appendix
59. Iliacus
60. Acetabulum
61. Head of femur

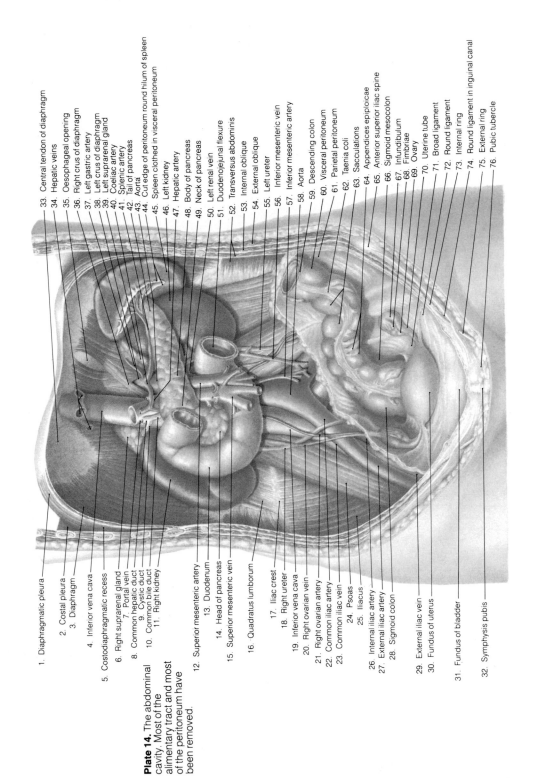

Plate 14. The abdominal cavity. Most of the alimentary tract and most of the peritoneum have been removed.

1. Diaphragmatic pleura
2. Costal pleura
3. Diaphragm
4. Inferior vena cava
5. Costodiaphragmatic recess
6. Right suprarenal gland
7. Portal vein
8. Common hepatic duct
9. Cystic duct
10. Common bile duct
11. Right kidney
12. Superior mesenteric artery
13. Duodenum
14. Head of pancreas
15. Superior mesenteric vein
16. Quadratus lumborum
17. Iliac crest
18. Right ureter
19. Inferior vena cava
20. Right ovarian vein
21. Right ovarian artery
22. Common iliac artery
23. Common iliac vein
24. Psoas
25. Iliacus
26. Internal iliac artery
27. External iliac artery
28. Sigmoid colon
29. External iliac vein
30. Fundus of uterus
31. Fundus of bladder
32. Symphysis pubis

33. Central tendon of diaphragm
34. Hepatic veins
35. Oesophageal opening
36. Right crus of diaphragm
37. Left gastric artery
38. Left crus of diaphragm
39. Left suprarenal gland
40. Coeliac artery
41. Splenic artery
42. Tail of pancreas
43. Aorta
44. Cut edge of peritoneum round hilum of spleen
45. Spleen clothed in visceral peritoneum
46. Left kidney
47. Hepatic artery
48. Body of pancreas
49. Neck of pancreas
50. Left renal vein
51. Duodenojejunal flexure
52. Transversus abdominis
53. Internal oblique
54. External oblique
55. Left ureter
56. Inferior mesenteric vein
57. Inferior mesenteric artery
58. Aorta
59. Descending colon
60. Visceral peritoneum
61. Parietal peritoneum
62. Taenia coli
63. Sacculations
64. Appendices epiploicae
65. Anterior superior iliac spine
66. Sigmoid mesocolon
67. Infundibulum
68. Fimbriae
69. Ovary
70. Uterine tube
71. Broad ligament
72. Round ligament
73. Internal ring
74. Round ligament in inguinal canal
75. External ring
76. Pubic tubercle

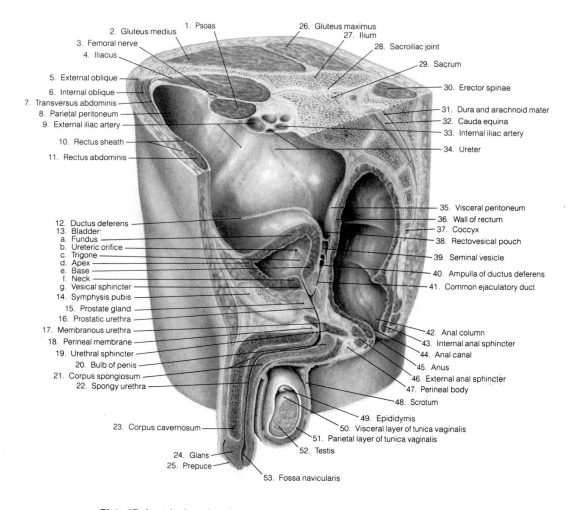

1. Psoas
2. Gluteus medius
3. Femoral nerve
4. Iliacus
5. External oblique
6. Internal oblique
7. Transversus abdominis
8. Parietal peritoneum
9. External iliac artery
10. Rectus sheath
11. Rectus abdominis
12. Ductus deferens
13. Bladder:
   a. Fundus
   b. Ureteric orifice
   c. Trigone
   d. Apex
   e. Base
   f. Neck
   g. Vesical sphincter
14. Symphysis pubis
15. Prostate gland
16. Prostatic urethra
17. Membranous urethra
18. Perineal membrane
19. Urethral sphincter
20. Bulb of penis
21. Corpus spongiosum
22. Spongy urethra
23. Corpus cavernosum
24. Glans
25. Prepuce

26. Gluteus maximus
27. Ilium
28. Sacroiliac joint
29. Sacrum
30. Erector spinae
31. Dura and arachnoid mater
32. Cauda equina
33. Internal iliac artery
34. Ureter
35. Visceral peritoneum
36. Wall of rectum
37. Coccyx
38. Rectovesical pouch
39. Seminal vesicle
40. Ampulla of ductus deferens
41. Common ejaculatory duct
42. Anal column
43. Internal anal sphincter
44. Anal canal
45. Anus
46. External anal sphincter
47. Perineal body
48. Scrotum
49. Epididymis
50. Visceral layer of tunica vaginalis
51. Parietal layer of tunica vaginalis
52. Testis
53. Fossa navicularis

Plate 15. A sagittal section of the male pelvis, seen from the left.

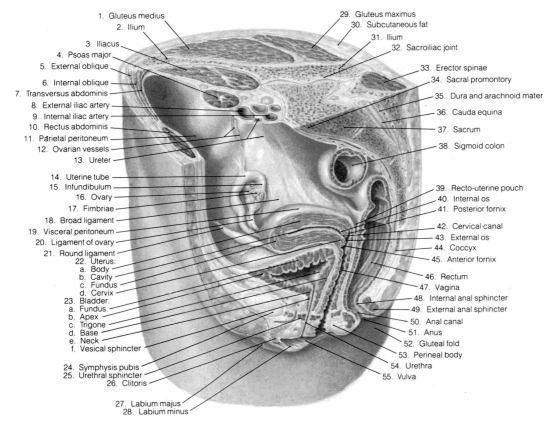

1. Gluteus medius
2. Ilium
3. Iliacus
4. Psoas major
5. External oblique
6. Internal oblique
7. Transversus abdominis
8. External iliac artery
9. Internal iliac artery
10. Rectus abdominis
11. Parietal peritoneum
12. Ovarian vessels
13. Ureter
14. Uterine tube
15. Infundibulum
16. Ovary
17. Fimbriae
18. Broad ligament
19. Visceral peritoneum
20. Ligament of ovary
21. Round ligament
22. Uterus:
 a. Body
 b. Cavity
 c. Fundus
 d. Cervix
23. Bladder:
 a. Fundus
 b. Apex
 c. Trigone
 d. Base
 e. Neck
 f. Vesical sphincter
24. Symphysis pubis
25. Urethral sphincter
26. Clitoris
27. Labium majus
28. Labium minus

29. Gluteus maximus
30. Subcutaneous fat
31. Ilium
32. Sacroiliac joint
33. Erector spinae
34. Sacral promontory
35. Dura and arachnoid mater
36. Cauda equina
37. Sacrum
38. Sigmoid colon
39. Recto-uterine pouch
40. Internal os
41. Posterior fornix
42. Cervical-canal
43. External os
44. Coccyx
45. Anterior fornix
46. Rectum
47. Vagina
48. Internal anal sphincter
49. External anal sphincter
50. Anal canal
51. Anus
52. Gluteal fold
53. Perineal body
54. Urethra
55. Vulva

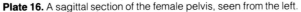

Plate 16. A sagittal section of the female pelvis, seen from the left.

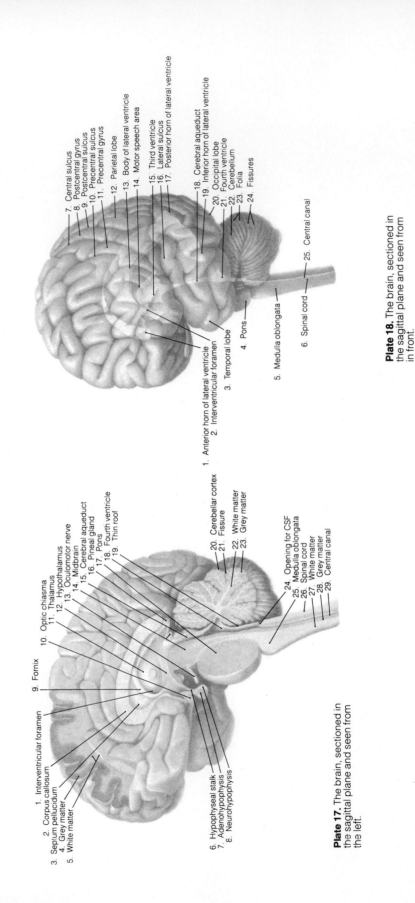

Plate 17 labels:

9. Fornix
10. Optic chiasma
11. Thalamus
12. Hypothalamus
13. Oculomotor nerve
14. Midbrain
15. Cerebral aqueduct
16. Pineal gland
17. Pons
18. Fourth ventricle
19. Thin roof

1. Interventricular foramen
2. Corpus callosum
3. Septum pellucidum
4. Grey matter
5. White matter

6. Hypophyseal stalk
7. Adenohypophysis
8. Neurohypophysis

20. Cerebellar cortex
21. Fissure
22. White matter
23. Grey matter

24. Opening for CSF
25. Medulla oblongata
26. Spinal cord
27. White matter
28. Grey matter
29. Central canal

Plate 17. The brain, sectioned in the sagittal plane and seen from the left.

Plate 18 labels:

7. Central sulcus
8. Postcentral gyrus
9. Postcentral sulcus
10. Precentral sulcus
11. Precentral gyrus
12. Parietal lobe
13. Body of lateral ventricle
14. Motor speech area
15. Third ventricle
16. Lateral sulcus
17. Posterior horn of lateral ventricle

18. Cerebral aqueduct
19. Inferior horn of lateral ventricle
20. Occipital lobe
21. Fourth ventricle
22. Cerebellum
23. Folia
24. Fissures

1. Anterior horn of lateral ventricle
2. Interventricular foramen
3. Temporal lobe
4. Pons
5. Medulla oblongata
6. Spinal cord
25. Central canal

Plate 18. The brain, sectioned in the sagittal plane and seen from in front.

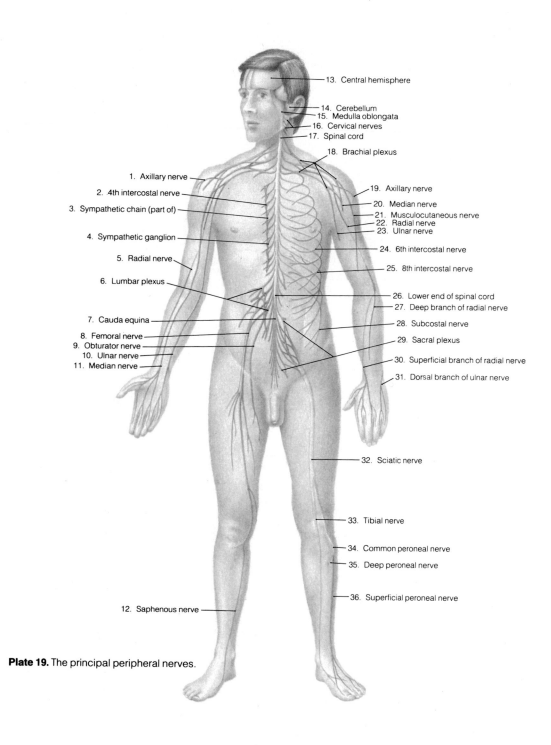

13. Central hemisphere

14. Cerebellum
15. Medulla oblongata
16. Cervical nerves
17. Spinal cord

18. Brachial plexus

1. Axillary nerve

2. 4th intercostal nerve

3. Sympathetic chain (part of)

19. Axillary nerve

20. Median nerve
21. Musculocutaneous nerve
22. Radial nerve
23. Ulnar nerve

4. Sympathetic ganglion

24. 6th intercostal nerve

5. Radial nerve

25. 8th intercostal nerve

6. Lumbar plexus

26. Lower end of spinal cord
27. Deep branch of radial nerve

7. Cauda equina

28. Subcostal nerve

8. Femoral nerve
9. Obturator nerve
10. Ulnar nerve
11. Median nerve

29. Sacral plexus

30. Superficial branch of radial nerve

31. Dorsal branch of ulnar nerve

32. Sciatic nerve

33. Tibial nerve

34. Common peroneal nerve

35. Deep peroneal nerve

36. Superficial peroneal nerve

12. Saphenous nerve

Plate 19. The principal peripheral nerves.

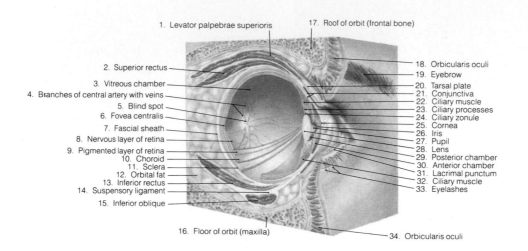

1. Levator palpebrae superioris
2. Superior rectus
3. Vitreous chamber
4. Branches of central artery with veins
5. Blind spot
6. Fovea centralis
7. Fascial sheath
8. Nervous layer of retina
9. Pigmented layer of retina
10. Choroid
11. Sclera
12. Orbital fat
13. Inferior rectus
14. Suspensory ligament
15. Inferior oblique
16. Floor of orbit (maxilla)

17. Roof of orbit (frontal bone)
18. Orbicularis oculi
19. Eyebrow
20. Tarsal plate
21. Conjunctiva
22. Ciliary muscle
23. Ciliary processes
24. Ciliary zonule
25. Cornea
26. Iris
27. Pupil
28. Lens
29. Posterior chamber
30. Anterior chamber
31. Lacrimal punctum
32. Ciliary muscle
33. Eyelashes
34. Orbicularis oculi

Plate 20. A parasagittal section through the pupil of the right eye, seen from the right side.

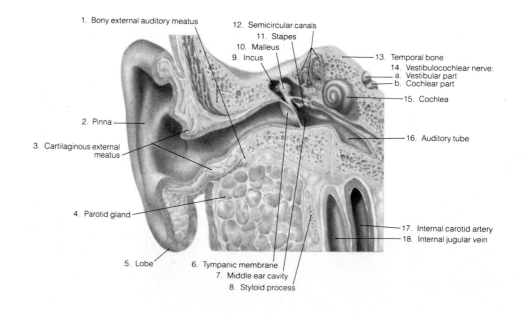

1. Bony external auditory meatus
2. Pinna
3. Cartilaginous external meatus
4. Parotid gland
5. Lobe
6. Tympanic membrane
7. Middle ear cavity
8. Styloid process
9. Incus
10. Malleus
11. Stapes
12. Semicircular canals
13. Temporal bone
14. Vestibulocochlear nerve:
   a. Vestibular part
   b. Cochlear part
15. Cochlea
16. Auditory tube
17. Internal carotid artery
18. Internal jugular vein

Plate 21. The external, middle and internal ear.

—15—

The Eye

Objectives: After studying Chapter 15 you should be able to:

1 Describe the structure of the eye.
2 Describe the protective mechanisms of the eye.
3 Draw diagrams to aid your descriptions.
4 Describe the mechanism of sight.

The eye is the organ of sight and it is situated in the bony orbit, which protects it from injury.

The Structure of the Eye (Fig. 15.1)

The eye is spherical in shape and is embedded in fat. It has three coats:

- An outer, fibrous coat
- A vascular, pigmented coat
- An inner, nervous coat

The outer, fibrous coat

The outer coat has two parts. The posterior part is opaque and is called the *sclera*; it is a firm membrane which preserves the shape of the eyeball. Its external surface is white and forms the white of the eye. The anterior part of the sclera is covered with conjunctiva, which is reflected on to it from the inner side of the eyelid and is continuous with the corneal epithelium covering the cornea. The *cornea* is the anterior part of the fibrous coat. It projects a little from the spherical shape of the eye and is transparent, allowing light rays to enter the eye and bending them to focus on the retina (refraction). Most of the refractory power of the eye is at the

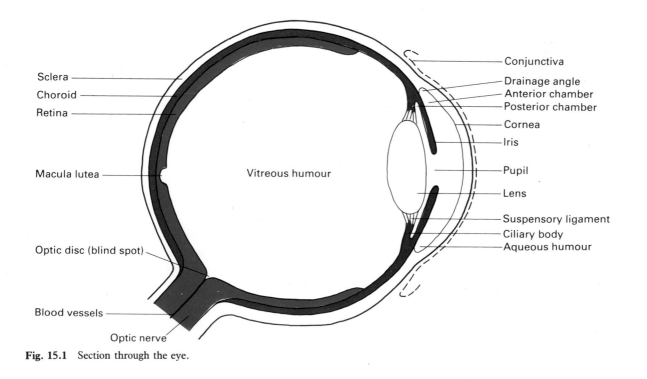

Fig. 15.1 Section through the eye.

Sclera
Choroid
Retina
Macula lutea
Optic disc (blind spot)
Blood vessels
Optic nerve
Vitreous humour
Conjunctiva
Drainage angle
Anterior chamber
Posterior chamber
Cornea
Iris
Pupil
Lens
Suspensory ligament
Ciliary body
Aqueous humour

cornea. Through the cornea the iris and the pupil can be seen.

The vascular, pigmented coat

This middle coat has three parts.

The *choroid* lines all but the front part of the eye. It is dark brown in colour and supplies blood to the other layers of the eye, particularly the retina.

The *ciliary body* is a thickened part of the middle coat containing muscular and glandular tissue. The *ciliary muscles* within the ciliary body control the shape of the lens, enabling it to focus light rays from near or far away as required. They are known as the muscles of *accommodation*. The *ciliary glands* within the ciliary body produce a watery fluid, the *aqueous humour*, which fills the eye in front of the lens and drains into the venous system, through small openings in the angle between the iris and the cornea, known as the *trabecular meshwork* (or *drainage angle*).

The *iris* is the coloured part of the eye. It lies between the cornea and the lens and divides the space between them into anterior and posterior chambers. There is a circular opening in the centre called the *pupil*. The iris contains muscular tissue arranged in circular and radiating fibres; the circular fibres constrict the pupil and the radiating fibres dilate it. The pupil is contracted in bright light to prevent too much light entering the eye and dilated in poor light to allow as much light as possible to reach the retina (Fig. 15.2). The muscular fibres of the iris are under the control of the autonomic nervous system.

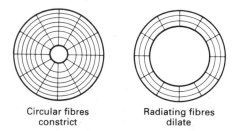

Circular fibres   Radiating fibres
constrict   dilate

Fig. 15.2 Changes in the size of the pupil caused by the muscular fibres of the iris.

The inner, nervous coat

The inner lining of the eye is called the *retina*. It is a delicate membrane adapted for the reception of light rays and contains many nerve cells and fibres. It is made up of two types of light-sensitive receptor cells, *rods* and *cones*, which are thought to have separate functions. The cones are more numerous in the centre of the eye and are responsible for detailed vision and colour perception; the rods are more numerous around the outer edge of the retina and are responsible for vision in conditions of low illumination, such as at night. They contain a pigment called *rhodopsin* or *visual purple*. To synthesize this pigment, vitamin A is required; lack of vitamin A in the diet may result in *night blindness*. Near the centre of the back of the retina there is an oval yellowish area called the *macula lutea* where only cones are present. This is where the visual acuity is best, and the cornea, aqueous humour and lens focus the light from objects onto this area.

The nerve fibres from the rods and cones pass over the inside of the retina to the *optic nerve*, which carries impulses from the eye to the brain. About 3 mm to the nasal side of the macula lutea the optic nerve leaves the eye; this area is called the *optic disc* and because it is insensitive to light it is called the blind spot. An object can only be opposite the blind spot in one eye at a time. To find your blind spot, mark a piece of paper as shown below:

X   ●

Now shut the left eye and, holding the paper at eye level, fix the right eye steadily on the cross. Move the paper slowly backwards and forwards; at a certain point the dot will disappear because light from it is being focused onto the blind spot.

Inside the eye

The eye contains:
- The aqueous humour
- The vitreous humour
- The lens

The *aqueous humour* is a clear watery fluid. It contributes to the refraction of light and plays a part in maintaining the forward curve of the cornea.

The *vitreous humour* is a colourless, transparent, jelly-like substance which maintains the shape of the eyeball. It fills the space between the lens and the back of the eye.

The *lens* is situated immediately behind the iris. It is a transparent, biconvex body enclosed in a transparent, elastic capsule from which ligaments pass to the ciliary body. These *suspensory ligaments* hold the lens in position and are the means by which the ciliary muscles exert pull on the lens, altering its shape for near or far vision.

The Mechanism of Sight

As light rays pass through the transparent cornea, aqueous humour and lens they are bent, a process known as *refraction*. This makes it possible for light from a large area to be focused on a small area of the retina. Parallel light rays striking a convex lens are bent towards a focal point (Fig. 15.3).

An object can only be seen clearly and in focus if light rays from it are refracted onto the macula lutea of the retina. If the light rays are focused in front of or behind the macula lutea, or elsewhere on the retina, the object will not be in focus. When the lens

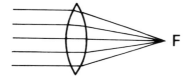

Fig. 15.3 A convex lens, showing how parallel light rays are brought to focus at point F.

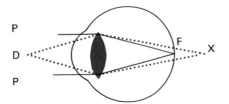

Fig. 15.4 The normal eye at rest, accommodated for distant objects. Parallel rays (P) from a distant object are focused by the lens on the retina at point F. The dotted lines show the diverging rays from a near object (D), which are focused behind the retina at point X.

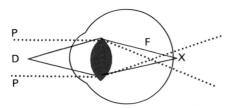

Fig. 15.5 The normal eye during accommodation for near objects. Diverging rays from a near object (D) are focused on the retina at point X by the fatter lens. The dotted lines show the parallel rays (P) from a distant object, which are now focused in front of the retina at point F.

is in its normal resting position, the eye focuses parallel light rays from a distant object onto the retina. However, if the object is less than 7 m away the lens must be made fatter to enable the light from the object to be focused on the retina. This is called *accommodation*. It is brought about by the contraction of the ciliary muscles. In order to focus on distant objects again the ciliary muscles relax, pulling the lens into a more flattened shape (Figs. 15.4 and 15.5).

Some people are naturally *short-sighted (myopic)*. This is usually due to the fact that their eyes are too long, so that the retina is farther from the lens than it should be and parallel light rays from distant objects are focused in front of it when the lens is in its resting position. However, a near object can be seen with the lens at rest (normally used for far sight), but for far sight glasses with concave lenses are necessary. These lenses will spread out the light rays a little before they reach the eye and will therefore throw the focus point farther back (Fig. 15.6).

Others are naturally *long-sighted (hypermetropic)*. This is usually due to the fact that their eyes are too

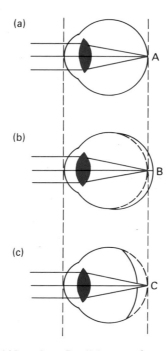

Fig. 15.6 (a) Normal eye. Parallel rays are focused on the retina at A. (b) Myopic eye (short-sighted). The eye is longer from back to front and parallel rays are focused in front of the retina at B. (c) Hypermetropic eye (long-sighted). The eye is shorter from back to front and parallel rays are focused behind the retina at C.

short, so that the retina is too close to the lens and the focusing point lies behind it. In this case a distant object can be seen using the lens in its thicker, more curved state used by the normal person for near sight, as this will bend the light rays more and bring the focusing point forward. However, the lens cannot become any more curved for near sight, and glasses with convex lenses are necessary to bend the light rays from the near object in a little before they reach the eye.

Movement of the eyes

The eye is moved within the orbit by six orbital (or extrinsic) muscles which are ribbon-like and are run between the sclera and the bony orbit. These muscles pull on the eyes and are used to co-ordinate their movement, so that both eyes focus on the same object. No one muscle can act purely on its own: they work together to bring about movement. However, their primary actions are as follows:

- The *superior rectus* moves the eye upwards.
- The *inferior rectus* moves the eye downwards.
- The *medial rectus* moves the eye inwards.
- The *lateral rectus* moves the eye outwards.
- The *inferior oblique* moves the eye upwards and outwards.
- The *superior oblique* moves the eye downwards and outwards.

A weakness in one or more muscles will cause one eye to deviate, a condition known as *strabismus* or, more commonly, as *squint*.

These muscles are supplied by the oculomotor, the trochlear and the abducent nerves (the third, fourth and sixth cranial nerves).

Protection of the Eyes

The eyes are very delicate organs and are protected by the eyebrows, the eyelids and lacrimal apparatus, as well as by the bony orbits in which they lie, embedded in fatty tissue.

The overhanging *eyebrows* protect the eyes from injury and excessive light, while the hairs entangle sweat and prevent it from running into the eyes.

The *eyelids* consist of a plate of fibrous tissue (the *tarsal plate*) covered by skin and lined with mucous membrane. In the tarsal plates are small glands which secrete a fluid that helps prevent the lids sticking together. It also helps the lacrimal fluid to run along the lower tarsal plate to the punctum. The tarsal glands open via the tarsal ducts along the edge of both tarsal plates. The edges of the lids are provided with hairs, the *eyelashes*, which keep out dust, insects and too much light. The transparent mucous membrane which lines the lids continues over the front of the eyeball as far as the corneal margin and is called the *conjunctiva*. This results in the formation of upper and lower conjunctival sacs under the upper and lower lids respectively. Dust and bacteria tend to stick to the moist surface of this membrane, and to keep it clean it is constantly washed by fluid from the lacrimal apparatus.

The *lacrimal apparatus* (Fig. 15.7) consists of:

- The *lacrimal gland*, lying over the eye at the outer side and secreting lacrimal fluid into the upper conjunctival sac

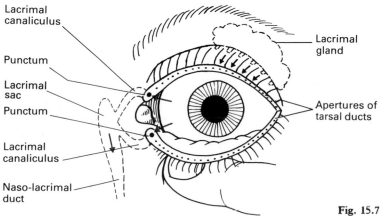

Fig. 15.7   The lacrimal apparatus.

- Two fine canals, called *lacrimal canaliculi*, leading from the inner angle of the lids to the lacrimal sac
- The *lacrimal sac*, which lies at the inner angle of the eyelids in a groove in the lacrimal bone
- The *naso-lacrimal duct*, which runs from the lacrimal sac down to the nose

The opening into the canaliculi can be seen at the inner angle of the eyelids and is called the *punctum*.

The fluid secreted by the lacrimal glands washes over the eyeball and is swept up by the blinking action of the eyelids. The muscles which cause the blink (orbicularis oculi and levator palpebrae superioris) press on the lacrimal sac and contract it, so that as they relax the sac expands and sucks the fluid from the edges of the lids along the fine canals into the sac; from this it runs by gravity down into the nose. Thus the front of the eye is constantly irrigated by a gentle stream of fluid, which keeps it clean and washes away micro-organisms and harmful substances. The fluid is composed of water, salts and an antibacterial substance called *lysozyme*.

As with hearing, visual loss or impairment can cause social isolation.

—16——
The Skin

Objectives: After studying Chapter 16 you should be able to:

1 Describe the structure of the skin.
2 Draw a diagram to aid your description.
3 State the appendages of the skin.
4 State the functions of the skin and appendages.

The skin covers the body and protects the deeper tissues. It contains the endings of many sensory nerves and is important in the regulation of body temperature (Fig. 16.1).

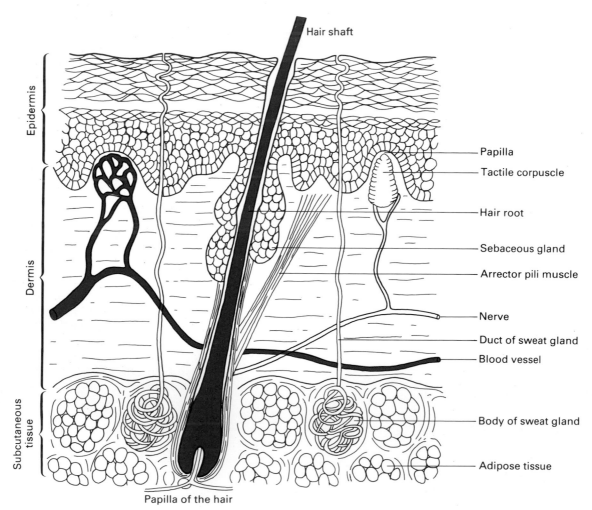

Fig. 16.1 Section of the skin.

The Structure of the Skin

The skin has two layers:
- The epidermis
- The dermis (or corium)

The epidermis

The epidermis forms the outer layer of the skin and consists of stratified epithelium. It is very thick, hard and horny on such areas as the palms of the hands and the soles of the feet, and is much thinner and softer over parts such as the trunk and the inner sides of the limbs. The epidermis has two layers or zones: the outer is called the horny zone and the inner the germinative zone (Fig. 16.2).

The *horny zone* has three layers:
- The *horny layer* (stratum corneum) is the most superficial layer. The cells are flat and scale-like. They have no nuclei and the protoplasm has been replaced by a horny substance called keratin, which is waterproof.
- The *clear layer* (stratum lucidum) is composed of cells with clear protoplasm; some have flattened nuclei.
- The *granular layer* (stratum granulosum) is the deepest layer of the horny zone. It consists of several layers of cells with granular protoplasm; the nuclei can be clearly seen.

The *germinative zone* is found beneath the horny zone and consists of two layers:
- The *prickle cell layer* (stratum spinosum) contains cells of varying shapes, each having short processes, rather like thorns or prickles, joining them together. The nuclei are clearly seen.
- The *basal cell layer* (stratum germinativum) con-

sists of columnar cells arranged on a basement membrane.

The surface scales of the horny layer are constantly being rubbed off by friction and are constantly renewed from below: the deep cells multiply and are pushed up to the surface, developing into scales as they approach it. The epidermis has no blood supply and practically no nerve supply. It is nourished by tissue fluid from the blood vessels in the underlying dermis. It is the epidermis which is raised in a blister.

The basal layer of cells in contact with the dermis contains *melanocytes* (Fig. 16.3). These cells manufacture the pigment which gives the skin its colour. The pigment protects the body from the harmful effects of the sun's rays, but absorbs some of the radiation. The scales of the surface of the epidermis prevent the entrance of bacteria and other micro-organisms into the tissues, since they cannot digest these dried-up cells or make their way through them. Once the epidermis is broken by a cut or prick, infection may enter the tissues and sepsis may follow.

The dermis

The dermis is a tough elastic layer which is very thick in the palms of the hands and the soles of the feet and very thin in the eyelids. It consists of elastic connective tissue, blood vessels, lymphatic vessels and nerves. Numerous conical projections, called *papillae*, extend from the surface of the dermis and protrude into the epidermis. They are most numerous where the skin is most sensitive and in these areas they are arranged in parallel ridges, different in each individual. The surface of the epidermis follows these ridges; this can be clearly seen at the finger-tips, where the ridges form the finger prints.

The *nerve endings* in the skin are for the most part sensory, and are of different varieties to give the various different sensations of which the skin is capable, i.e. the sensations of touch, heat, cold and pain. The nerves of touch end in round bodies known as the touch or *tactile corpuscles* which are stimulated by pressure, and the nerves of heat, cold and pain end in delicate, tree-like branches. A few of the branches of these nerve endings pass into the epidermis. A particular sensation is only experienced if the stimulus touches the skin over the termination of a special nerve ending affected by

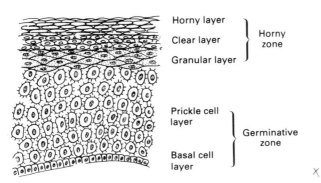

Horny layer ⎫
Clear layer ⎬ Horny zone
Granular layer ⎭

Prickle cell layer ⎫
⎬ Germinative zone
Basal cell layer ⎭

Fig. 16.2 The epidermis.

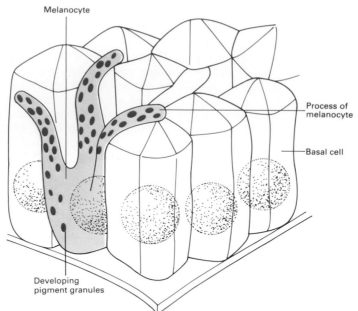

Melanocyte

Process of melanocyte

Basal cell

Developing pigment granules

Fig. 16.3   A melanocyte.

that stimulus. In some parts the nerve endings are so close together that this is not appreciated, but where the nerve endings are less numerous, as over the back of the hand, it is possible to find spots where heat can be felt and others where cold is felt.

The arteries supplying the skin form a network in the subcutaneous tissue. Branches supply the sweat glands and the hair follicles, and fine capillaries also pass into the papillae.

The appendages of the skin

The skin carries the following appendages:
- Sweat glands
- Hairs
- Nails
- Sebaceous glands

The sweat glands

The sweat glands are twisted, tubular glands which lie deep in the dermis or the subcutaneous tissues. They consist of a coiled tube with a duct leading up through the dermis and epidermis to open onto the surface of the skin. Their ducts open in the pores of the epidermis, and the tube is coiled up into a little round ball deep in the skin, called the body of the gland. The sweat glands secrete sweat, which consists of water, salts, and a trace of other waste products. If sweating is profuse and runs off the body the cooling effect is lost. The secretion of sweat is a means of excretion of waste products; some poisons and drugs may be got rid of in this manner. However, its chief importance lies in the fact that the evaporation of sweat uses up body heat, since heat is required to turn water into water vapour (see Chapter 1). The amount of sweat secreted therefore depends on the amount of heat that the body needs to lose. The average amount excreted in 24 hours is 500 to 600 ml. In hot weather and in violent exercise sweating is increased, so that more heat is lost. At these times less urine is passed, so that there is not excessive loss of fluid. In cold weather or rest, less sweat is secreted, so that there is less loss of heat by evaporation; at the same time more urine is secreted by the kidney, so that loss of water is balanced.

Sweat glands are present all over the body, but are larger and more numerous in certain parts, such as the palm of the hand, the sole of the foot, the axillae, groins and forehead.

The hairs

The hairs consist of modified epithelium. They grow from tiny pits in the skin, known as hair follicles. The part of the hair below the skin is called the *root*, while that above the skin is called the *shaft*. The base of each follicle is found in the dermis or the subcutaneous tissues. Here a group of epithelial cells multiply to form the hair. As new cells are made, the older cells are pushed up the root to the surface of the skin. As they travel upwards they manufacture keratin and then die. Thus the shaft of the hair consists of dead cells containing keratin.

Underneath the follicle is a small conical projection called a *papilla* containing blood vessels and nerves which supply the hair.

Hairs are always set obliquely in the skin. Small involuntary muscles known as the *arrector pili* muscles are connected to the hair follicles. They are always on the side towards which the hair leans, so that when they contract the hair stands erect. The skin around the hair is elevated at the same time, which produces the effect known as 'goose-flesh'.

The hairs are constantly being shed and renewed. As long as the root is healthy, fresh hair will grow from it, but if the root is destroyed or its blood supply interfered with, the growth of hair will stop, resulting in baldness. Brushing the hair and massaging the scalp stimulate the blood supply and so promote the health and growth of the hair of the head. Hair is present all over the body except on the palms of the hands and the soles of the feet, but is so fine and sparse as a rule that it cannot be seen. It is longer and more plentiful in the eyebrows, axillae and groins, where it entangles the sweat, preventing it from running downwards and assisting its evaporation.

The nails

The nails are horny plates of modified epithelium which protect the tips of the digits. They grow from a root of typical soft epithelial cells at the base of the nail. This root is embedded in a fold of epidermis. The nails are continuous with the epidermis they grow from, so that there is a continuous barrier to exclude micro-organisms. It is, however, easy for a break in the continuity to occur at the junction between the nail and the epidermis if the nails are not carefully looked after; this is particularly dangerous among nurses, since they are in contact with infection in the course of their work.

Although the ends of the nails are continually being worn away, they also require regular attention.

The sebaceous glands

The sebaceous glands are small saccular glands which secrete an oily substance called *sebum*. They are situated in the angle between the hair follicle and the arrector pili muscle, so that contraction of the muscle has the effect of squeezing sebum from the gland. This lubricates the skin and hair, keeping them soft and pliant, so that they do not readily break. Sebum picks up dust and bacteria, which cling to the oily surface. When the skin is washed with soap and water, the sebum is removed along with the dirt. It may be necessary to replace the oil using an artificial substitute (e.g. hand-cream) if the skin is washed very frequently; this prevents the skin becoming brittle, when it breaks easily, letting bacteria and other micro-organisms enter. The nurse, whose hands are often in soapy water, needs to pay particular attention to this point.

Functions of the Skin

The skin has seven main functions:
- It regulates body temperature.
- It secretes waste products.
- It is the organ of touch and other senses through which the body is made aware of the environment.
- It keeps out bacteria and other micro-organisms by its dry, scaly outer surface.
- It secretes sebum.
- It protects the body by its pigment from the harmful effects of the sun's rays.
- It produces vitamin D through the action of ultraviolet rays on a cholesterol compound that it contains.

The appearance of the skin also has an important role to play in the psychological well-being of a person.

The control of body temperature

Body temperature is a balance between heat gained and heat lost. Man is warm-blooded and the temperature must be maintained around 37°C; a rise or fall of one degree or more affects the normal functioning of the nervous system and of the enzymes. Although many systems are involved in the regulation of body temperature, the skin plays a key role in altering the amount of heat lost from the body.

The main temperature regulating mechanism is in the hypothalamus. It acts on a 'negative feedback' system; if the body temperature rises, mechanisms come into action so that heat is lost from the body; if the body temperature falls, heat is conserved until the temperature approaches normal.

Heat production

Heat production occurs primarily due to metabolic activity. Additional heat is produced by exercise, increased muscle tension, shivering and also by endocrine disorders, infections, trauma and emotion. Heat production is lowest during sleep and highest during muscular activity.

Heat loss

Heat loss occurs through:
- Radiation, conduction and convection of heat from the skin
- Evaporation of sweat
- Respiration
- Excretion of urine and faeces

Radiation is the transfer of heat from one object to another without physical contact between the two. The body radiates heat to every object near it and the heat loss is proportional to the surface area; a large area loses a lot of heat but heat loss can be diminished by reducing the surface area. For example, less heat is lost from the body in a curled-up position than in a stretched-out position, because a smaller surface area is exposed.

Conduction is the transfer of heat from one molecule to another. If one end of a metal rod is placed in the fire, heat will be conducted along it until the whole rod is hot. In the same way, the body will lose heat to any object with which it is in direct contact and which is cooler than the body.

Convection is the transfer of heat from the body to the air, which then rises and is replaced by cooler air, which in turn is heated. Heat loss by convection is reduced by wearing suitable clothing.

Evaporation of sweat from the surface of the skin is continuous and has a cooling effect on the body. It occurs more readily in dry climates, because when the air is humid and already saturated with water vapour, further evaporation cannot occur.

Respiration involves heat loss as the expired air is warm. Similarly, small amounts of body heat are lost through the excretion of warm urine and faeces.

In *hot* conditions, to keep the temperature normal:
- *Heat production is lessened*; the thyroid and adrenal glands do not stimulate so much tissue activity.
- *Heat loss is increased* by dilation of blood vessels in the skin which raises the temperature of the surface of the skin, so that radiation, conduction and convection are increased, and by increased sweating, so that more heat is lost by evaporation.

In *cold* conditions, to keep the temperature normal:
- *Heat production is increased* by an increase in the metabolic activity of the body. Increased activity in the muscles can result in involuntary contractions (shivering).
- *Heat loss is lessened* by the raising of the hairs of the skin to the vertical position due to contraction of the arrector pili muscles. Air is then trapped between the hairs and acts as an insulating layer. In addition, the blood vessels in the skin constrict, reducing the heat lost by radiation, conduction and convection, and less sweat is produced.

—SECTION 7————
The Transport Systems

Colour Plates 9, 10, 11 and 14 relate to this section. The plates are between pages 134 and 135.

SECTION

—17—

The Blood

Objectives: After studying Chapter 17 you should be able to:

1 Describe the composition of blood and its functions.
2 List the stages of the mechanism by which blood clots.
3 Explain, briefly the ABO and Rhesus blood groups.
4 Describe the humoral and the cellular immune responses.
5 Explain the difference between active and passive immunity.

The circulatory system is the main transport system of the body by which food, oxygen, water and all other essentials are carried to the tissue cells and their waste products are carried away. Since most of the cells of the body have no contact with the external environment they depend entirely on this transport system for the provision of these substances and for the removal of waste or unwanted materials. However, the cells themselves are not in direct contact with the circulating blood but only with the tissue fluid that surrounds them. The composition of the tissue fluid is maintained by an exchange of substances with the blood.

The circulatory system has three parts:
- The blood, which is the fluid in which materials are carried to and from the tissues
- The heart, which is the pump which propels the blood around the body
- The blood vessels, which are the routes by which the blood travels to and through the tissues, and back to the heart

The Composition of Blood

The blood is a thick red fluid; it is bright red in the arteries, where it is rich in oxygen, and a dark purplish-red in the veins, where it has less oxygen, having given up some of its oxygen to the tissues (which causes the colour change) and received waste products from them. It is slightly alkaline, with a pH of 7.4. This is a homeostatically controlled characteristic; the pH varies very little during life, as the cells of the body can live only if the pH is within normal limits.

The blood forms 5–7% of the body weight, so that the average volume is 4–5 litres.

Although apparently fluid, blood actually consists of a fluid and a solid part. When examined under the microscope it is seen to contain large numbers of *blood cells*. These form the solid part, while the liquid in which they float is the fluid part and is called *plasma*. The cells form 45% and the plasma 55% of the total volume.

Plasma

The plasma or fluid part of the blood is a straw-coloured watery fluid, similar to the fluid seen in an ordinary blister. It consists of:
- *Water*, which forms over 90% of the whole
- *Mineral salts*, including chlorides, phosphates and carbonates of sodium, potassium and calcium. The chief salt present is sodium chloride. The correct balance of various salts is necessary for the normal functioning of the body tissues. Mineral salts form about 0.9% of the whole
- *Plasma proteins*, including albumin, globulin, fibrinogen and prothrombin. Plasma proteins form about 7% of the whole
- *Foodstuffs* in their simplest forms, including glucose, amino acids, fatty acids, glycerol and vitamins
- *Gases* in solution, mainly oxygen, carbon dioxide and nitrogen
- *Waste products* from the tissues, including urea, uric acid and creatinine
- *Antibodies* and *antitoxins*, which protect the body against bacterial infection
- *Hormones* from the ductless glands
- *Enzymes*

Water

The water in plasma provides fresh water to renew the water in the fluid which bathes all the body cells and that within the cells. Sixty per cent of the body weight is water; therefore an average man weighing 70 kg contains approximately 46 litres of water. Of this 46 litres, approximately 29 litres are found within the cells (*intracellular fluid*) and 17 litres are outside the cells (*extracellular fluid*). The extracellular fluid is divided between the blood vessels (3 litres) and the fluid bathing the cells, called the *interstitial fluid* (14 litres).

Mineral salts

The salts in the plasma are necessary for the building of protoplasm. They also act as buffer substances, neutralizing acids or alkalis in the body and maintaining the blood at the correct pH. Blood is always slightly alkaline in health, with a pH of 7.4 (see Chapter 1). The mineral salts in plasma are mostly in the form of ions. In plasma there are approximately 155 mmol/l of positively charged ions, mainly sodium (Na^+), balanced by 155 mmol/l of negatively charged ions, mainly chloride (Cl^-) and bicarbonate (HCO_3^-). This is referred to as the *electrolyte balance*. A similar situation is found in the interstitial fluid. In the intracellular fluid potassium replaces sodium as the main positively charged ion, and phosphate ions and ionized proteins replace chloride as the negatively charged ions.

Plasma proteins

The proteins which plasma contains give the blood the sticky consistency, called *viscosity*. The viscosity of the blood assists in the maintenance of the blood pressure. The plasma proteins cannot pass through the walls of the blood vessels and so exert an osmotic pressure (see Chapter 1). This prevents too much fluid passing through the capillary walls into the tissue spaces. If there is a deficiency of protein, as in some kidney diseases where protein is continually lost as albumin in the urine, the osmotic pressure of the plasma is lowered and excess fluid escapes into the tissues. This excess fluid is called *oedema*.

Most of the plasma proteins are formed in the liver. However, one type of globulin known as *immunoglobulin* is produced by plasma cells, which are part of the immune system (see page 153). Fibrinogen and prothrombin are both necessary for the clotting of blood. Plasma without fibrinogen is called *serum*; this can be seen as the yellow fluid which oozes from a cut after a clot has formed.

Foodstuffs

Foodstuffs, in the form of glucose, amino acids, fatty acids and glycerol, are absorbed from the alimentary tract into the blood. They are the end-products of carbohydrate, protein and fat breakdown or metabolism.

Gases in solution

Most of the oxygen in the blood is combined with haemoglobin in the red blood cells. However, a small amount is found in the plasma. In contrast, only a small amount of carbon dioxide is bound to haemoglobin; most of it is carried in the plasma as bicarbonate ions.

Waste products

Urea, uric acid and creatinine are the waste products from *protein metabolism*. Urea is made in the liver; the other waste products are made in the liver and elsewhere in the body.

Antibodies and antitoxins

These are complex protein substances which provide protection against infection and neutralize poisonous bacterial toxins.

Hormones

The plasma transports hormones from the gland which secretes them to the rest of the body, including their target organ. Many hormones bind to proteins in the plasma.

Enzymes

Enzymes are chemical substances produced by the body, which produce chemical changes in other substances without themselves entering into the reaction.

The blood cells

The cells found in the blood are of three types:
● Red blood cells (erythrocytes)

- White blood cells (leucocytes)
- Platelets (thrombocytes)

Red cells

The red cells or erthyrocytes are minute disc-shaped bodies, concave on either side (Fig. 17.1). This shape greatly increases the surface area available for the passage of gases in and out of the cell. They are very numerous—there are about 5×10^{12} red cells per litre of blood. They are very small, having a diameter of only 7.2 micrometres (μm). They have no nucleus, but contain a special protein known as *haemoglobin*. This is a pigment and is yellow in colour, though the overall effect of these numerous yellow bodies is to make the blood red. Haemoglobin contains a little iron; this iron is essential to normal health, though the total amount in the whole body is said to be only sufficient to make a 2-inch nail.

Haemoglobin can combine with oxygen. As the red cells pass through the capillaries of the lungs, oxygen from the air diffuses through the alveolar and capillary walls into the blood, where it combines with haemoglobin in the red cells, forming oxyhaemoglobin. Oxyhaemoglobin is brighter in colour than haemoglobin and this makes the oxygenated blood bright red. Since red cells pass through the lungs in one or two seconds it is necessary that they should have a large surface area to increase the amount of oxygen that can enter them in this short time; this is provided by their biconcave shape. They are also very elastic and are able to change shape easily when passing through very small blood vessels. As the red cells pass through other parts of the body oxygen is released from the haemoglobin and diffuses out of the blood into the tissues, and the haemoglobin becomes a dull colour (reduced haemoglobin), making the blood a dark purplish-red.

Haemoglobin can also transport small amounts of carbon dioxide from the tissues to the lungs, where it is expired. However, most of the carbon dioxide is transported in the plasma.

The function of red cells is therefore to carry oxygen to the tissues from the lungs and to carry away some carbon dioxide. These functions are dependent on the amount of haemoglobin they contain. If there is a lack of haemoglobin, either because the red cells are reduced in number or because each one does not contain the normal quantity of haemoglobin, the individual suffers

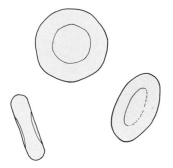

Fig. 17.1 Red blood cells (seen from three different angles).

from *anaemia*. The amount of haemoglobin in the blood is normally 2.2 mmol/l.

Red cells are produced in the red bone marrow of spongy bone, which is found in the extremities of the long bones and in flat and irregular bones. In childhood the red bone marrow also extends throughout the shaft of the long bones, as children have greater need for the production of red cells.

Red cells pass through various stages of development in the bone marrow. They begin as *erythroblasts*, which are large cells containing nuclei and a small quantity of haemoglobin. These develop into *normoblasts*, which are smaller cells with more haemoglobin and smaller nuclei. The nucleus then disintegrates and disappears and the cytoplasm contains fine threads, at which stage the cells are called *reticulocytes*. Finally, the threads disappear and the fully mature erythrocyte passes into the bloodstream. In health almost all red cells in the blood should be erythrocytes, with only an occasional reticulocyte.

Many factors are necessary for the normal formation of red blood cells:
- *Protein* is required for the manufacture of protoplasm.
- *Iron* is needed for the production of haemoglobin. As the red cells become worn out and are broken down, the iron is stored and used again; very little iron is excreted. However, a certain amount of iron must be taken in the diet. A man requires about 90–180 μmol iron per day; women require about 320 μmol to make good the menstrual loss and the depletion of iron reserves which occur during pregnancy, labour and lactation. Iron-containing foods are red meat, egg-yolk, green vegetables, peas, beans and lentils.

- *Vitamin B₁₂* (cyanocobalamin) is necessary for the maturation of red blood cells. It is usually found in adequate quantities in the diet in temperate climates. It can be absorbed from the small intestine only when it has been combined with the *intrinsic factor*, which is secreted by the stomach. Together these two substances are known as the *anti-anaemic factor* (or *haemopoietic factor*). Vitamin B₁₂ is stored in the liver and passed on to the bone marrow as necessary. It is also known as the *extrinsic factor*.
- Other factors which are necessary in small quantities are vitamin C, folic acid (one of the vitamin B complex), the hormone thyroxine, and traces of copper and manganese.

Red blood cells live in the circulation for about 120 days, after which they are ingested by the cells of the reticulo-endothelial system in the spleen and lymph nodes. Here the haemoglobin is broken down into its component parts—haem and globin—which are carried to the liver. The globin is returned to the protein stores or is excreted in the urine after being broken down further. The haem is further split into iron, which is stored and used again, and pigment, which is converted by the liver into bile pigments and is excreted in the faeces. Red cell production and breakdown usually proceed at the same rate, so the number of cells remains constant.

Production of red blood cells is regulated by the level of oxygen in the tissues. If the level is low there is an increased production of cells. Low oxygen level stimulates the kidney to produce a substance which enters the blood and converts an inactive plasma protein to an active substance called *erythropoietin*. Erythropoietin is then carried in the blood to the bone marrow where it stimulates the production of red cells.

High erythropoietin levels and a resulting increase in the number of red cells may occur in athletes, whose tissues are regularly depleted of oxygen during strenuous exercise, and those who live at high altitudes, where the pressure of oxygen in the air is low.

White cells

The white cells, or leucocytes, are larger than the red cells, measuring between 10 and 20 μm in diameter, and they are less numerous. There are 7–10 × 10⁹ per litre of blood, though this number increases considerably to 30 × 10⁹ per litre when infection is present in the body. This increase is known as *leucocytosis*.

The leucocytes are of three different types (Figs. 17.2 and 17.3):

- Polymorphonuclear leucocytes

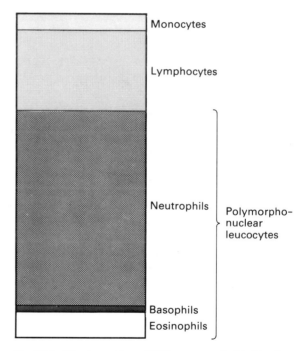

Fig. 17.2 The proportions of different types of white blood cells.

 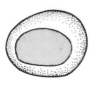 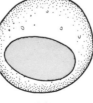

(a)   (b)   (c)

Fig. 17.3 White blood cells. (a) A polymorphonuclear leucocyte. (b) A lymphocyte. (c) A monocyte.

- Lymphocytes
- Monocytes

Polymorphonuclear leucocytes are also known as *granulocytes* because of the granular appearance of the cytoplasm. The nucleus gradually develops several lobes, hence the name ('poly' being Greek for 'many' and 'morph' being Greek for 'form'). These cells make up about 70% of the total white cells. They are made in the red bone marrow and survive for about 21 days. Granulocytes can be further classified according to their staining properties. *Neutrophils* (65% of the total white cells) absorb both acid and alkaline dyes. They have the ability to ingest small particles, e.g. bacteria and cell debris; the foreign material is then digested by the enzymes contained in the many lysosomes in the cells. This ability is called *phagocytosis* and the cells are sometimes known as *phagocytes*. They have amoeboid movement (see page 30) and can pass out of the bloodstream through the capillary walls to accumulate where there is infection. *Eosinophils* (4% of the total white cells) absorb acid dyes and stain red. An increase in their number occurs during allergic states such as asthma, and during infestation with worms. *Basophils* (1% or less of the total white cells) absorb alkaline or basic dyes and stain blue. They produce heparin and histamine.

Lymphocytes make up about 25% of the total white cell count. They are made in the bone marrow of the embryo but during fetal life some pass to the thymus gland, where they are transformed into *T-lymphocytes*, and others become *B-lymphocytes*, having matured possibly in the spleen. Both types of lymphocyte then pass to lymphatic tissue, which is present in the lymph nodes, spleen and other organs. They show some amoeboid movement but are not actively phagocytic. They are concerned in the immune reaction.

Monocytes make up about 5% of the total white cell count. They are the largest of the white blood cells and have a horse-shoe-shaped nucleus. They both show amoeboid movement and are phagocytic, and are part of the reticulo-endothelial system (see page 25).

Platelets

Platelets or thrombocytes are even smaller than red blood cells and are made in the bone marrow. There are about 250×10^9 per litre of blood. They are necessary for the normal cessation of capillary bleeding—haemostasis.

The Clotting of Blood

If a blood vessel wall is damaged, the damaged tissue cells or damaged platelets activate a series of reactions involving various *clotting factors* and resulting in the production of an enzyme *thromboplastin* (or *prothrombin activator*). In the presence of this enzyme, and when adequate amounts of calcium are also present, *prothrombin*, a protein normally present in the plasma, is converted into a new substance called *thrombin*. Thrombin is also an active enzyme, which acts on *fibrinogen*, another of the normal plasma proteins, to produce an insoluble thread-like substance called *fibrin*. The fibrin threads trap blood cells to form a clot (see Table 17.1). After some time the clot shrinks and serum is released. Contraction of the clot helps bring the damaged edges of the blood vessel together.

Factors affecting clotting

Prothrombin is made in the liver and the fat-soluble vitamin K is necessary for its manufacture. Vitamin K is present in green vegetables and is also manufactured in the intestine by bacterial action. It can only be absorbed from the intestine into the blood in the presence of bile. If bile is not present, as in some forms of jaundice, the amount of prothrombin in the blood may be reduced and the tendency to bleed is increased.

Heparin is a chemical normally present in blood in

Table 17.1 Stages in clot formation.

1.	Damaged platelets or tissue cells release	thromboplastin
2.	Thromboplastin + prothrombin + calcium →	thrombin
3.	Thrombin + fibrinogen →	fibrin
4.	Fibrin + cells →	clot

minute amounts. It is formed in the liver and also released by basophils and mast cells. It prevents blood clotting in the vessels and is therefore called an *anticoagulant*.

The Functions of Blood

The functions of blood are:
- To carry food to the tissues
- To carry oxygen to the tissues in the form of oxyhaemoglobin
- To carry water to the tissues
- To carry away waste products to the organs which excrete them
- To fight bacterial infection and remove foreign material through the white cells and antibodies
- To provide the materials from which glands make their secretions
- To distribute enzymes and the secretions of ductless glands
- To help distribute heat evenly throughout the body, and so regulate the body temperature
- To arrest haemorrhage through clotting

Blood Groups

Blood from one individual cannot always be safely mixed with that of another. This fact became evident with the introduction of blood transfusion, which at first sometimes cured but sometimes killed the patient. This was due to the fact that blood is of four basic groups. If blood of differing groups is mixed, the red blood cells may become sticky and form clumps; this is termed *agglutination*. It results in the destruction of red cells. In addition, the kidneys are severely damaged by having to excrete excessive quantities of pigment from the destroyed red cells.

Blood groups are named according to the presence or absence of substances called *agglutinogens*, which are found on the surface of the red blood cells. There are two types of agglutinogen, called A and B. If A is present, the blood is said to be group A, and if B is present the blood is said to be group B. If both A and B are present, the blood is said to be group AB, and if neither agglutinogen is present the blood is said to be group O. However, blood plasma contains antibodies called *agglutinins*, which can cause agglutination of red cells. There are two types of agglutinins, called anti-A and anti-B. An individual's plasma contains all agglutinins that will not affect his own red cells. Therefore, the plasma of group A blood contains anti-B agglutinin, the plasma of group B blood contains anti-A agglutinin, the plasma of group AB blood contains no agglutinins, and the plasma of group O blood contains both anti-A and anti-B agglutinins (see Table 17.2). Because group AB blood has no agglutinins in the plasma and therefore cannot cause any red cells to agglutinate, patients with blood belonging to this group will probably be able to receive blood from any other group; group AB is therefore known as the *universal recipient*. Group O blood contains no agglutinogens on the red cells and therefore they cannot be agglutinated by the agglutinins in any plasma. Blood belonging to this group can therefore probably be given to a patient belonging to any group, and it is known as the *universal donor*.

When a person requires a blood transfusion it is necessary first to find out what blood group he belongs to and then to choose blood from a donor with a compatible blood group (see Table 13); for example, a person with blood group B could receive blood from a donor of either blood group B or blood group O. Samples of the recipient's and the donor's blood are mixed together to see whether agglutination occurs. This needs to be done as it is now known that many other systems of grouping exist in addition to the ABO groups, and even within the ABO groups, many sub-groups are found. Thus agglutination may occur even though donor blood of the correct ABO group is being used. If no agglutination occurs, the two samples of blood are said to be *compatible*, and the donor blood can be given to the recipient.

Table 17.2 The agglutinogens and agglutinins associated with blood groups.

Blood group	Agglutinogen on red cells	Agglutinin in plasma	Possible transfusions
A	A	Anti-B	Groups A and O
B	B	Anti-A	Groups B and O
AB	A and B	Neither	Any group
O	None	Anti-A and anti-B	Group O only

Rhesus factor

In addition to the ABO group, there is another factor present on the red cells of about 85% of the Caucasian population. It is an agglutinogen called the *rhesus (Rh) factor*. Those who possess the factor are said to be rhesus positive (Rh+), and the remaining 15% are said to be rhesus negative (Rh−). Although anti-rhesus factor agglutinins are not normally found in the plasma, if a Rh− person receives the blood of an Rh+ donor, this stimulates the production of anti-Rh agglutinins called *anti-D*. If a second Rh+ transfusion were given later, the transfused cells would be agglutinated by the anti-D and destroyed (haemolysed) with serious or fatal results to the recipient.

The rhesus factor can also cause difficulty during pregnancy (Fig. 17.4). If an Rh− mother is carrying an Rh+ fetus there should be no problems with the first pregnancy. However, if at delivery some of the fetal blood cells enter the maternal circulation, she will produce anti-D and destroy the fetal cells. This will not have any immediate effect, but should a second Rh+ pregnancy occur, the anti-D in her blood will cross the placenta to the fetus and destroy its red cells. The fetus is unlikely to survive without medical intervention. To prevent this occurrence it is now usual practice for an Rh− mother to be given an injection of anti-D immediately after delivery of a Rh+ baby. This will destroy any fetal Rh+ cells which have entered her circulation and prevent her developing her own anti-D. The injected anti-D will have disappeared before her next pregnancy. It is also important that Rh− women of child-bearing age are not sensitized to form anti-D by being given a blood transfusion of Rh+ blood.

Immunity and the Immune Response

When a foreign body is introduced into the body the immediate response is the production of a substance which will react with it and render it harmless. The foreign substance capable of producing such a response is called an *antigen*, and the substances produced in response to the antigen are called *antibodies*. Examples of antigens are micro-organisms, such as bacteria, and foreign tissues, such as transplanted organs. The reaction that occurs may be called an antigen–antibody reaction. Some antigens provoke a powerful response; others produce a weak reaction only in some people and none at all in others.

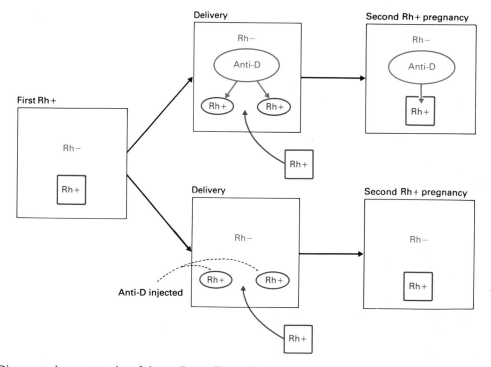

Fig. 17.4 Diagrammatic representation of rhesus disease. The top line represents the events in two Rh pregnancies, the second fetus developing rhesus disease due to the action of anti-D formed during delivery of the first fetus. The second line represents the prevention of rhesus disease by giving the mother an anti-D injection when the first fetus is delivered.

The main cells involved in immunity are the *lymphocytes*, a type of white blood cell, and *macrophages*, which are part of the reticulo-endothelial system. There are two types of immune response:

- The humoral immune response, involving B-lymphocytes
- The cellular immune response, involving T-lymphocytes

The humoral immune response

The humoral immune reaction involves the production of antibodies and is the major defence against bacterial infection. A particular type of B-lymphocyte can only be activated by a particular antigen, and there are thousands of different B-lymphocytes responding to different antigens. When an antigen enters the body it activates a B-lymphocyte, which rapidly reproduces. Some of the daughter cells develop into *plasma cells*, which then produce *antibodies* and secrete them into the blood, lymph and tissue fluid; these are substances which are able to 'mop up' the antigens. Just as one particular antigen activates one B-lymphocyte, the antibodies produced are only able to mop up that particular antigen.

Many of the lymphocytes die after antibody has been produced, but a sufficient number remain so that there will be a quick reaction to another invasion by the same antigen.

The humoral immune response is enhanced by the *complement* system. This system is a series of reactions of plasma proteins (which are normally inactive) and is stimulated by antibody/antigen interactions. It enables the B-lymphocytes and the antibodies to be more effective against the antigen.

The cellular immune response

T-lymphocytes can actively destroy all cells which are not recognized as self, i.e. belonging to the individual. These may be foreign cells, as in a tissue graft or organ transplant, or they may be cells of the body whose surface has been changed so that they are no longer recognized as belonging to self. This type of immune reaction is also a defence against viral infections. Viruses live and multiply within cells of the body and do not activate B-lymphocytes. However, the surface of infected cells is altered, which renders them unrecognizable as self and they are therefore destroyed by T-lymphocytes.

The daughter cells of T-lymphocytes circulate round the body. When a foreign cell is encountered some lymphocytes destroy the cell while others release chemical substances which attract phagocytic cells such as macrophages to the area. Some of the T-lymphocytes remain in the circulation after the encounter, as do B-lymphocytes, so that there can be a quick response to further invasions.

Disordered immune responses

Autoimmune diseases result from the reaction of antibodies with normal body components. Two of the most common are haemolytic anaemia, in which there are antibodies to red blood cells, and rheumatoid arthritis, but there are many others.

Some disordered immune reactions are known as *allergies*. This type of reaction is similar to the humoral immune reaction described above but occurs when certain weak antigens such as pollen, feathers, some foods, dust or cat fur give rise to antibody production. The resulting antigen–antibody reaction causes the release of histamine, which provokes spasm in smooth muscle, dilation of capillaries and increased capillary permeability. These effects may be local or more widespread. It is not fully understood why some individuals are more susceptible to allergies than others but some may have very violent reactions to events such as bee stings, with release of so much histamine that the blood pressure falls rapidly, severe shock follows and death can occur.

Immunity

Immunity may be *active*, when cells in the body make an antibody, or *passive*, when the antibody has been produced in the cells of another person and given to the individual.

Active immunity

Active immunity may be achieved in several ways. Natural active immunity is gained by having the disease, after which the specific antibody-producing B-lymphocytes remain in the blood ready to prevent another attack of the same disease. This type of immunity is also developed by what are called subclinical infections, in which the body is exposed to small numbers of micro-organisms insufficient to give rise to any definite symptoms, but sufficient enough to stimulate antibody production. Artificial active immunity is sometimes induced to prevent people getting diseases which would be serious or fatal. This can be brought about by administering one of the following (depending on the micro-organism concerned):

- Killed micro-organisms
- Chemical poisons produced by the micro-organism (toxins) that have been rendered harmless (toxoids)
- Live micro-organisms that have been rendered harmless (attenuated)

These *vaccines* will not produce the disease but will still act as antigens, producing an antibody response, and so active immunity is built up. Diseases commonly prevented using vaccines are whooping cough, diphtheria, measles, poliomyelitis and tuberculosis.

Passive immunity

Natural passive immunity is gained by the baby before birth as some antibodies are passed from the mother to the fetus via the placenta. Artificial passive immunity is useful in the prevention of disease or in its treatment—the antibodies are produced in another human or in an animal and are injected into the person at risk. Passive immunity is always short-lived as the antibodies are destroyed after a short time.

The reticulo-endothelial system (mononuclear phagocytic system)

A number of different types of phagocytic cells make up the reticulo-endothelial system. These cells are widespread throughout the body. Their ability to move about and to phagocytose foreign matter such as bacteria makes them an important defence against infection.

The cells of the system occur in the following parts of the body:

- Connective tissue, where they are called *macrophages* or *histiocytes*
- Blood, where they are called *monocytes*
- Lining blood vessels of the bone marrow, spleen and liver and parts of the suprarenal gland and the anterior lobe of the hypophysis
- In the lymph nodes, lymph follicles of the small intestine and the tonsils
- The meninges, where they are called *meningiocytes*

Macrophages are also involved in the immune response, as some antigens need to be processed by macrophages before they can activate a humoral or cellular immune response.

—18—

The Heart and Blood Vessels

Objectives: After studying Chapter 18 you should be able to:

1 Draw and label a diagram showing the structure of the heart.
2 Describe the function of each of the valves in the heart.
3 List the sequence of events in the cardiac cycle.
4 Name the types of blood vessels and state the differences between them.
5 Describe briefly the factors concerned in the maintenance of blood pressure.

The Structure of the Heart

The heart is a hollow, muscular, cone-shaped organ (Fig. 18.1); it lies between the lungs in a block of tissue called the *mediastinum*, behind the body of the sternum, with two-thirds of its bulk on the left side. The circular base of the cone is directed upwards and to the right. The apex points downwards, forwards and to the left, and is usually found at the level of the fifth intercostal space (the space below the fifth rib) about 9 cm from the midline. The heart measures about 12 cm from base to apex, about 9 cm in width and is about 6 cm from anterior to posterior.

The heart is divided from base to apex by a muscular partition called the *septum*. The two sides of the heart normally have no communication with each other (Fig. 18.2). Additionally, each side is divided into an upper and lower chamber. The upper chamber on each side, the *atrium*, is smaller and is a receiving chamber into which the blood flows from veins—the *inferior vena cava* and the *superior vena cava* on the right, and the *pulmonary*

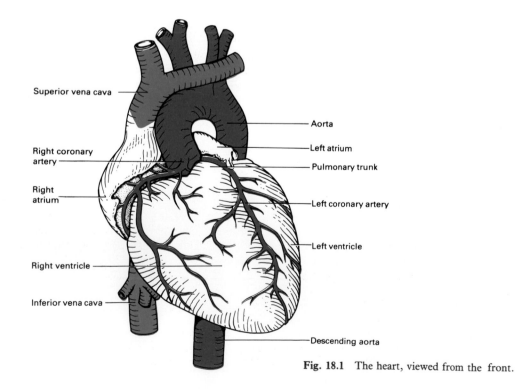

Superior vena cava

Right coronary artery

Right atrium

Right ventricle

Inferior vena cava

Aorta

Left atrium

Pulmonary trunk

Left coronary artery

Left ventricle

Descending aorta

Fig. 18.1 The heart, viewed from the front.

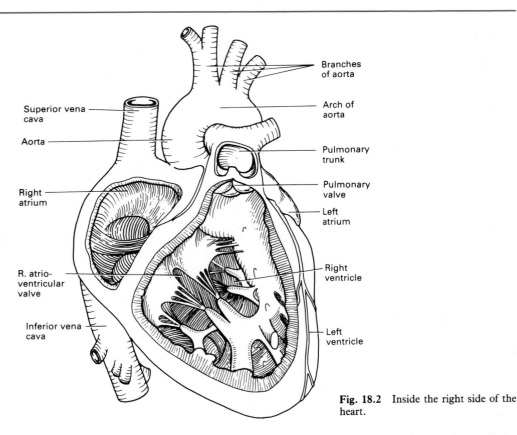

Fig. 18.2 Inside the right side of the heart.

veins on the left side of the heart. The lower chamber, the *ventricle*, is the discharging chamber from which the blood is pumped into the arteries—the *pulmonary trunk* on the right and the *aorta* on the left side of the heart. Each atrium communicates with the ventricle below it on the same side of the heart through an opening guarded by an *atrio-ventricular valve*.

The heart is composed of cardiac muscle (see Chapter 4), the *myocardium*, on the action of which the circulation of the blood depends. The myocardium varies in thickness, being thickest in the left ventricle, thinner in the right ventricle and thinnest in the atria.

The atria and ventricles are lined with a thin, glistening membrane called the *endocardium*. This consists of a single layer of endothelial cells and is continuous with the valves and with the lining of the blood vessels.

The heart and the first part of the large vessels at the top of the heart are covered by *pericardium*. This has two layers:

- The outer layer or *fibrous pericardium* is securely anchored to the diaphragm, the outer coats of the great vessels and the posterior surface of the sternum and therefore maintains the heart in its position in the chest. Because of its fibrous nature it also prevents over-distension of the heart.
- The inner layer, the *serous pericardium* consists of two layers. The inner part is known as the *visceral layer* or *epicardium* and covers the surface of the myocardium. The outer or *parietal layer* lines the fibrous pericardium. The layers are normally in close contact and are moistened by fluid; this prevents any friction as the heart continually contracts and relaxes. The space between the two layers of serous pericardium is known as the *pericardial cavity*. In inflammatory conditions, such as pericarditis, large amounts of fluid may collect within the pericardial cavity, preventing the normal action of the heart, and may be aspirated.

The blood supply to the heart muscle

Oxygenated blood is supplied to the heart muscle by the right and left coronary arteries. These are the first branches from the aorta after it leaves the left ventricle. They give off branches to all parts of the myocardium. There are a number of places within the heart muscle where these two arteries join or *anastomose*. Most of the blood returns from the myocardium in veins which join together to form the *coronary sinus*. This empties into the right atrium.

The valves of the heart

The heart has valves to prevent the blood from flowing in the wrong direction (Fig. 18.3). There are four main valves:

- The right atrio-ventricular valve (the tricuspid valve)
- The left atrio-ventricular valve (the mitral valve)
- The aortic valve
- The pulmonary valve

The right atrio-ventricular valve

The right atrio-ventricular (or tricuspid) valve lies between the right atrium and the right ventricle. It consists of three triangular flaps or cusps, each consisting of a double layer of endocardium strengthened with fibrous tissue. A number of fine, tendinous cords, called *chordae tendineae*, which originate in the papillary muscles in the wall of the ventricle, are attached to the undersurface of the cusps. When the ventricle contracts the blood is pushed back towards the atrio-ventricular opening

but is prevented from entering the atrium by the shape of the valve; as the blood flows into the cusps from below it tends to close the valve. The contraction of the papillary muscles exerts tension on the chordae tendineae, which prevents the valve cusps from turning inside out and being carried into the right atrium.

The left atrio-ventricular valve

The left atrio-ventricular (or mitral) valve has only two cusps. Otherwise its structure is similar to that of the right atrio-ventricular valve. It prevents the backflow of blood into the left atrium during contraction of the left ventricle (Fig. 18.4).

The aortic valve (Fig. 18.5)

The aortic valve consists of three cusps which surround the entrance into the aorta from the left ventricle. The cusps are half-moon-shaped (semilunar) and are fixed by their curved edges to the wall of the aorta; the straight edge is free so that pockets are formed facing into the aorta. As the blood is pumped from the left ventricle into the aorta the cusps lie flat against the vessel wall; as the ventricle relaxes, the blood flows back, filling the pockets. These bulge out, meeting in the centre and blocking the opening completely, thus preventing blood flowing back into the ventricle. The coronary

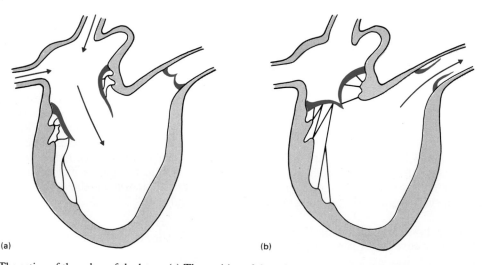

(a)   (b)

Fig. 18.3 The action of the valves of the heart. (a) The position of the valves during contraction of the atrium and relaxation of the ventricle. (b) The position of the valves during contraction of the ventricle and relaxation of the atrium. The arrows indicate the direction of the blood flow.

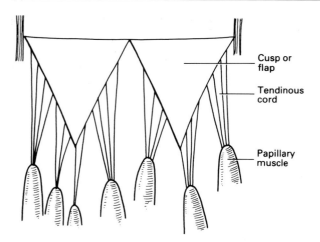

Fig. 18.4 A diagrammatic representation of the left atrio-ventricular valve (the mitral valve) laid open.

arteries, which supply the heart muscle with oxygenated blood, arise from the aorta just above the edges of the cusps of the aortic valve.

The pulmonary valve

The pulmonary valve guards the opening from the right ventricle into the pulmonary trunk. It is similar in structure and action to the aortic valve.

Other valves of the heart

The opening of the coronary sinus in the right atrium is protected by a thin, semi-circular valve called the *valve of the coronary sinus*. This prevents backflow of blood into the sinus during contraction

of the right atrium. There is also an imperfect valve guarding the opening from the inferior vena cava into the right atrium; it is called the *valve of the inferior vena cava*.

The Cardiac Cycle

The heart is a pump the purpose of which is to drive the blood into and through the arteries. The right side of the heart pumps blood into the pulmonary circulation and the left side pumps blood into the systemic circulation. The blood in the right side of the heart does not mix with the blood in the left.

The flow of blood through the heart (Fig. 18.6)

Blood from the systemic circulation of the body is returned to the right atrium through the two large veins, the superior and inferior venae cavae. The right atrium contracts and blood passes from the right atrium through the right atrio-ventricular valve into the right ventricle, which then contracts, sending the blood through the pulmonary valve and into the pulmonary trunk. The pulmonary trunk divides into the right and left pulmonary arteries which carry the blood to the lungs. Here gaseous exchange occurs (see page 192). The blood from the lungs is collected into four pulmonary veins, which return the blood to the left atrium. The left atrium contracts, simultaneously with the right atrium, and the blood is driven through the left atrio-ventricular valve into the left ventricle. This chamber contracts, simultaneously with the right ventricle, and sends the blood into the aorta, the main artery of the body.

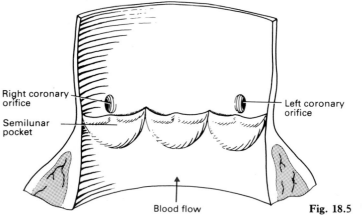

Fig. 18.5 The aortic valve laid open.

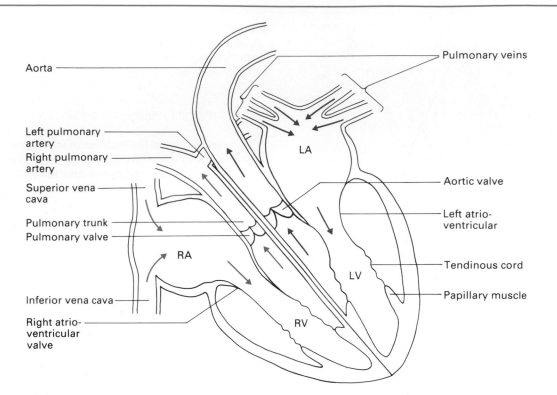

Fig. 18.6   The flow of blood through the heart. LA = left atrium; LV = left ventricle; RA = right atrium; RV = right ventricle.

The heart beat

The heart contracts about 70 to 80 times each minute throughout life, though the rate varies with age, emotion, exercise and other influences. Each beat is a cycle of events which lasts about 0.8 seconds(s) (Fig. 18.7).

Blood pours into the right and left atria from the great veins; they then contract simultaneously, emptying their contents into the ventricles. Atrial contraction lasts about 0.1 s. The ventricles then begin to contract and the atrio-ventricular valves are closed by the rising pressure; the closure of these valves causes the *first heart sound*, which can be heard through a stethoscope placed over the apex of the heart and has been likened to the sound 'lubb'. Ventricular contraction continues, lasting for 0.3 s in all. When the pressure in the ventricles is greater than that in the arteries the pulmonary and aortic valves are forced open, and blood flows into the aorta and pulmonary trunk. As the ventricles relax and the pressure in them decreases, the pressure in the great vessels forces the aortic and pulmonary valves to close, causing the *second heart sound*. This

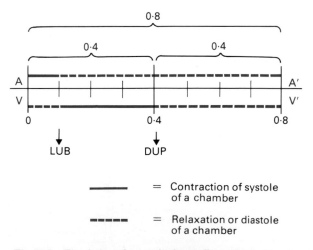

Fig. 18.7   The timing of events in the cardiac cycle. A–A′ = the contraction and relaxation of the atria; V–V′ the contraction and relaxation of the ventricles. The complete cycle takes 0.8 s, of which 0.4 s are occupied by contraction of the atria and then the ventricles. The remaining 0.4 s are occupied by relaxation of all chambers of the heart. (Note 0.8 s is the length of one heart beat if the pulse rate is 75 per minute.)

can be heard over near the end of the second right rib and has been likened to the sound 'dup'. During ventricular contraction the atria are relaxed. Following ventricular contraction the whole heart is relaxed for approximately 0.4 s. During this time blood is flowing into both atria and through the open atrio-ventricular valves into the ventricles.

The phase of the cardiac cycle in which contraction occurs is known as *systole*, and the phase of relaxation is known as *diastole*.

The conducting mechanism of the heart (Fig. 18.8)

Cardiac muscle, unlike skeletal muscle, has the property of being able to contract rhythmically independent of any nerve supply. The autonomic nervous system modifies the speed of the heart beat, but if the heart is cut off from its nerve supply it can continue to beat. The electrical impulse to contract arises in an area of specialized tissue near the entry of the superior vena cava into the right atrium called the *sino-atrial node*—also known as the pacemaker of the heart. The impulse then passes across both atria in more or less concentric rings to the *atrio-ventricular node* situated in the septum near the junction of the right atrium and ventricle. After a slight pause the impulse spreads down the *atrio-ventricular bundle* (or *bundle of His*), which runs in the septum in two strands—the right and left bundles. The strands break up into a network of fibres (the *Purkinje fibres*), from which branches pass to all parts of the ventricles.

The sino-atrial node produces impulses at a rate of about 70–74 per minute. Each impulse produces

contraction of first the atria and then the ventricles, i.e. a complete heart beat. The ventricles are able to contract independently of the atria and they do this if the conducting mechanism is affected by disease, but they will contract much more slowly (about 40 beats per minute). This condition is known as heart block and may be serious as the tissues of the body are unlikely to receive an adequate blood supply. In other types of disease, some impulses pass down through the atrio-ventricular bundles but some do not, so the ventricles contract once to every two or three atrial contractions; this condition is known as partial heart block.

The cardiac output

The amount of blood pumped out by the ventricles with each contraction is about 70 ml. This is known as the *stroke volume*. If the heart is beating 70 times per minute, the volume of blood pumped out each minute will be 70 × 70 ml, which is 4900 ml or approximately 5 litres. This is called the *cardiac output*.

During exercise the heart rate speeds up considerably, by shortening the period of diastole, and the stroke volume increases. The cardiac output may thus rise to three or four times its level at rest.

Nervous control of the heart rate (Fig. 18.9)

The heart is innervated by the autonomic nervous system. The vagus nerve (the tenth cranial nerve) slows the heart rate and causes decreased power of contraction by conveying impulses to the sino-atrial node. The sympathetic nerves speed the heart rate and increase the force of contraction. This dual innervation of the heart is co-ordinated by the cardiac centre in the medulla oblongata in the brain.

The heart rate is also controlled reflexly by two sets of receptors:
- *Pressure receptors*, or baroreceptors, are sensitive to changes in blood pressure. They are found in the *carotid sinuses* of the carotid arteries and in the arch of the aorta. If the blood pressure increases, the sympathetic nerves are depressed and the heart rate slows, thus helping to lower the blood pressure.
- *Chemoreceptors* are sensitive to the amount of oxygen present in the blood. Like the pressure receptors they are found in the *carotid bodies* of the carotid arteries and in the arch of the aorta. When the level of oxygen in the blood falls,

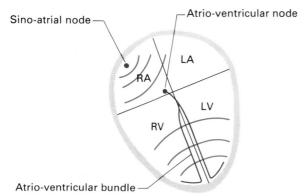

Fig. 18.8 A diagrammatic representation of the conducting mechanism of the heart.

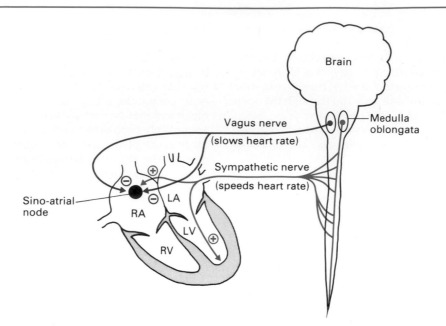

Fig. 18.9   Nervous control of the heart rate. RA = right atrium; RV = right ventricle; LA = left atrium; LV = left ventricle.

impulses are conveyed to the cardiac centre and the heart rate is accelerated to increase the blood supply, and therefore the oxygen supply, to the tissues.

Impulses from these receptors travel to the brain via the glossopharyngeal (the ninth cranial) nerve.

In health the heart rate varies considerably:
- Rest slows the heart rate and exercise quickens it.
- Increasing age slows the heart rate; infants have a heart rate of 120–140 beats per minute at birth and it slows throughout life and into old age.
- Women have a slightly faster heart rate than men.
- Emotions and excitement speed the heart rate.

In disease, conditions such as fever, haemorrhage, shock and hyperthyroidism speed the heart rate, while heart block and increased pressure on the brain slow it. Certain drugs can also speed or slow the heart rate.

The electrocardiogram (Fig. 18.10)

The electrical changes which occur in heart muscle as it beats are large enough to be recordable from the surface of the body producing an electrocardiogram (ECG). The P wave is due to atrial contraction. There is then a short interval while the impulse

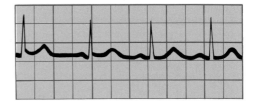

Fig. 18.10   An electrocardiogram.

travels through the atrio-ventricular node to the atrio-ventricular bundle. The QRS complex is due to contraction of the ventricular muscle fibres, and the T wave signifies the end of ventricular contraction.

Disorders of the conducting system of the heart and damage to the myocardium produce characteristic changes on the ECG.

The Blood Vessels

Contraction of the ventricles sends the blood to all parts of the body through a complicated series of tubes called *arteries*. These branch into tiny vessels called *arterioles*, which in turn are continuous with a network of microscopic vessels named *capillaries*. Blood is then collected into tiny vessels called

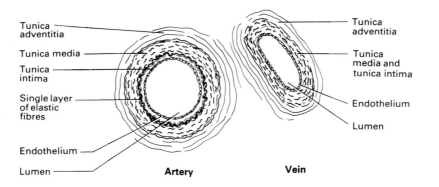

Fig. 18.11 Structure of an artery and a vein.

venules, which unite to form *veins* (Fig. 18.11). These join one another to form large veins, which finally return the blood to the heart.

Structure of the blood vessels

Arteries are thick-walled vessels that, in the systemic circulation, carry oxygenated blood away from the left ventricle (Fig. 18.12). In the pulmonary circulation, the pulmonary trunk, which divides into two pulmonary arteries, carries deoxygenated blood from the right ventricle to the lungs.

All arteries have three coats:

- The *outer coat*, or *tunica adventitia*, which consists of collagenous and elastic fibres
- The *middle coat*, or *tunica media*, which consists mainly of unstriped muscle together with elastic fibres and some collagen fibres
- The *lining*, or *tunica intima*, which consists of a layer of endothelial cells and provides a smooth surface over which the blood can flow without clotting

All parts of the body must have a blood supply and the arteries themselves are no exception. Very tiny blood vessels bring blood to the arterial walls and equally small venules return the blood to the veins.

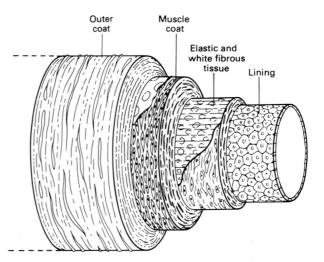

Fig. 18.12 Layers of an artery.

Arterioles have the same three coats as arteries, but the intima and media are relatively thinner and the adventitia relatively thicker than in an artery. There are also more muscle fibres and less elastic fibres.

Capillaries form a network between arterioles and venules. They consist of a single layer of endothelial cells, similar to those which line all other blood vessels (Fig. 18.3).

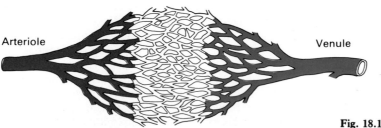

Fig. 18.13 A capillary network.

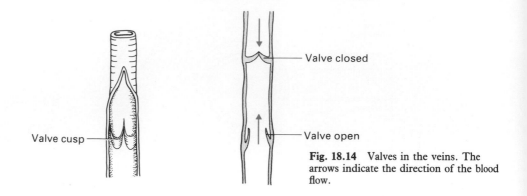

Valve cusp

Fig. 18.14 Valves in the veins. The arrows indicate the direction of the blood flow.

Valve closed

Valve open

Venules and *veins* both have three coats as do arteries, but the middle, muscle coat of a vein is much thinner than that of an artery. Many veins are provided with valves to prevent blood flowing in the wrong direction. Each valve is formed of a double layer of endothelium strengthened by connective tissue and elastic fibres. As in the aortic and pulmonary valves of the heart, the valve cusps are half-moon-shaped and are attached by their curved edges to the wall of the vein (Fig. 18.14).

Veins, like arteries, have their own blood supply.

The Mechanism of Circulation

The pulse

Blood leaving the left side of the heart is rich in oxygen and bright red in colour. When the blood is pumped out of the left ventricle the aorta is already full, so it must distend in order to accommodate the additional blood. As the left ventricle relaxes, the aortic valve closes and the elastic aorta slowly recoils to its original diameter. This recoil of the aorta is very important because it is responsible for continuously driving the blood round the body even when the ventricle is relaxed. The distension and recoil of the aorta sets up a wave of distension and recoil called the *pulse* which travels along all the large arteries; it can be felt with the fingers wherever an artery can be compressed gently against a bone. Since each heart beat produces a pulse, the rate and character of the beat can be judged by the rate and character of the pulse.

The blood pressure

The blood pressure is the force which the blood exerts on the walls of the blood vessels. It varies in the different blood vessels and also with the heart beat. The pressure is greatest in the large arteries leaving the heart, and gradually falls in the arterioles until, when it reaches the capillaries, it is so slight that the least pressure from without will obliterate these vessels and drive the blood out of them; this can be seen by pressing lightly on the nail. It is for this reason that it is so important to change frequently the position of a patient confined to bed, as the tissue carrying the body's weight has little blood circulating through it. In the veins, the pressure is lower still, until in the big veins approaching the heart it is zero. Indeed the pressure here may become negative instead of positive on account of the suction exerted by the heart as its chambers relax (Fig. 18.15).

The pressure in the large arteries varies with the heart beat. It is highest when the ventricle contracts (this is called the *systolic pressure*) and lowest when the ventricle relaxes (the *diastolic pressure*). The pressure of the blood is measured by the height in millimetres (mm) of the column of mercury (Hg) which it will support. The normal arterial pressure is 110–120 mmHg (14.66 kPa–16 kPa) systolic pressure and 65–75 mmHg (8.66 kPa–10 kPa) diastolic pressure. The systolic and diastolic arterial blood pressure can be measured using a sphygmomanometer. The results are often recorded as, for example, 110/70, which is read as '110 over 70'.

The pressure in the superior vena cava in health is 0 to −2 mmHg.

Increasingly, measurement in millimetres of mercury is being superseded by measurement in SI units (see page 12).

The arterial blood pressure is maintained by:
● The cardiac output
● The peripheral resistance
● The total blood volume

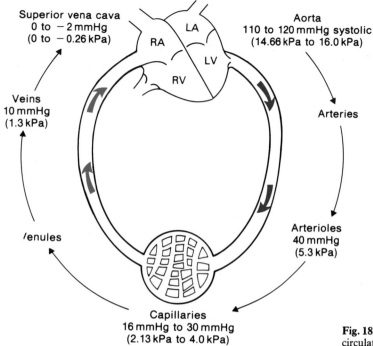

Superior vena cava
0 to −2 mmHg
(0 to −0.26 kPa)

Aorta
110 to 120 mmHg systolic
(14.66 kPa to 16.0 kPa)

RA   LA

LV

RV

Veins
10 mmHg
(1.3 kPa)

Arteries

Arterioles
40 mmHg
(5.3 kPa)

Venules

Capillaries
16 mmHg to 30 mmHg
(2.13 kPa to 4.0 kPa)

Fig. 18.15 Variation in the blood pressure in the systemic circulation.

- The viscosity of the blood
- The elasticity of the arterial walls

The *cardiac output* is the amount of blood pumped out with each ventricular contraction. When the left ventricle contracts, about 70 ml of blood is pushed into the aorta, which is already full, causing it to distend.

The *peripheral resistance* is the resistance offered by the small blood vessels, particularly the arterioles, to the flow of blood. This resistance prevents blood flowing too quickly into the capillaries and in this way helps to maintain the blood pressure in the arteries. The diameter of the arterioles can be altered by the action of the autonomic nervous system and by adrenaline and noradrenaline from the adrenal glands. If the lumen is narrowed the resistance to blood flow is increased and arterial blood pressure is raised. If the lumen is enlarged, more blood will pass through quickly to the capillaries and the arterial blood pressure will be lowered.

The *blood volume* is the total amount of circulating blood. If this is reduced by the loss of blood, as in haemorrhage, or by loss of fluid from the circulation, as in shock, burns or dehydration, the blood pressure will be lowered.

The *viscosity* of the blood is its stickiness. Blood is a viscous fluid which offers two or three times as much resistance as water. The viscosity depends partly on the constituents of the plasma, particularly the plasma proteins, and partly on the number of red cells.

The *elasticity of the arterial walls* allows distension of the aorta when the ventricle contracts and elastic recoil as the ventricle relaxes; this distension and recoil then occur throughout the arterial system, pushing the blood on and maintaining the diastolic pressure (Fig. 18.16). Elasticity may be reduced in atheroma, a degenerative disease of the arteries.

High blood pressure

The blood pressure is said to be high when the systolic pressure is 150 mmHg or more. The diastolic pressure is usually also raised as a general rule (e.g. to 90–120 mm). High blood pressure is dangerous in that the raised pressure causes degenerative lesions in the arteries, which can lead to blockage or rupture of a blood vessel; rupture is particularly likely to occur in the brain and is one of the causes of cerebrovascular accident (a stroke). There is also a strain on the heart which may result

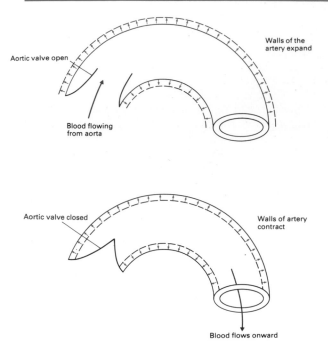

Fig. 18.16 Distension and contraction of aortic wall.

in heart failure, angina or a myocardial infarction (a 'heart attack').

Low blood pressure

The blood pressure is said to be low when the systolic pressure is 100 mmHg or less. It occurs in haemorrhage, shock and collapse, heart failure, and in disease of the adrenal glands. It is dangerous in that it may result in an insufficient supply of blood to the vital centres of the brain.

Blood flow in arterioles and capillaries

Arterioles are supplied by the autonomic nervous system, via which they can be dilated or contracted according to the needs of the tissues. The muscular walls of the arterioles are also affected by hormones from the adrenal glands, particularly adrenaline and noradrenaline, which cause contraction of the muscle fibres in the wall of the arteriole and consequent narrowing of the lumen. Arterioles do not pulsate, but can dilate to carry more blood to an organ which is working and contract so that they carry less blood when an organ is resting. In this way arterioles control the distribution of blood to the various organs of the body. They are also important in the maintenance of arterial blood pressure, as they offer resistance to the outflow of blood from the large elastic arteries.

Capillaries receive blood from the arterioles and pass it to the venules and, as already mentioned, their walls are only one cell in thickness. It is believed that water and other substances in solution which cross capillary walls do this by diffusing between the cells through tortuous, fluid-filled channels or pores.

Exchange of fluid is a balance between the hydrostatic pressure of the blood, which tends to force fluid out of the capillaries by ultrafiltration, and the colloid osmotic pressure of the plasma proteins, which tends to attract it back. At a certain point along a capillary the two pressures will be equal and at this point there will be no movement of fluid in or out of the capillary. Between this point and the arteriole, the hydrostatic pressure will be greater than the colloid osmotic pressure and fluid will leave the capillary. Between the point of balance and the venule, the colloid osmotic pressure will be higher than the hydrostatic pressure and interstitial fluid will enter the capillary by osmosis. The amount of fluid that leaves the capillaries by ultrafiltration is greater than the amount that returns by osmosis. The excess fluid is returned to the blood by the lymphatic system (see Chapter 20).

Few capillary networks run continuously from arterioles to venules; those vessels which do are often referred to as *thoroughfare channels*. The remaining true capillaries are perfused with blood intermittently according to the needs of the tissue for nutrients; muscular pre-capillary sphincters contract and relax to allow more or less blood into the network according to need.

Table 18.1 Fluid movement in the capillaries.

Fluid leaving capillaries by ultrafiltration		Fluid returning to blood via lymphatic system		Fluid entering capillaries by osmosis
20 l/day	=	2–4 l/day	+	16–18 l/day

Small amounts of low molecular weight plasma proteins are able to diffuse out of the capillaries, but cannot return because the concentration inside the capillary is greater than that outside. The return of this protein to the blood to prevent it from accumulating in the tissue spaces is a major function of the lymphatic system.

It should be remembered that, although ultra-filtration and osmosis cause the movement of fluid in and out of the blood, they are not very important mechanisms for the exchange of *solutes* between blood and tissue cells. Solutes are exchanged by diffusion, because of the different concentrations of the individual solutes in the blood and the tissue fluid. This is far quicker and can occur at both the arteriolar and the venous end of the capillaries.

Venous return

Blood is collected up from the capillary network into venules and then into veins. By the time it reaches the veins it has given up most of its oxygen and is a dark purplish colour. The veins contain valves to prevent the blood flowing in the wrong direction.

The return of the venous blood to the heart depends on three factors:
- Suction as the atria relax
- Suction during inspiration, which draws blood towards the heart as well as drawing air into the lungs
- Pressure on the thin-walled veins by contraction of muscles, which would force blood in both directions were it not for the presence of valves, which allow the blood to flow towards the heart only

The force of suction is the most important factor in the maintenance of venous pressure. If the force is lessened, as in heart failure, venous return is impaired and congestion of the venous system occurs.

The Circulation

Objectives: After studying Chapter 19 you should be able to:

1 Describe the systemic circulation.
2 Draw and label diagrams showing the major arteries and veins of the body.
3 Summarize the unique features of the pulmonary, portal and fetal circulations.

The circulation of the blood is divided into two parts:

● The systemic circulation
● The pulmonary circulation

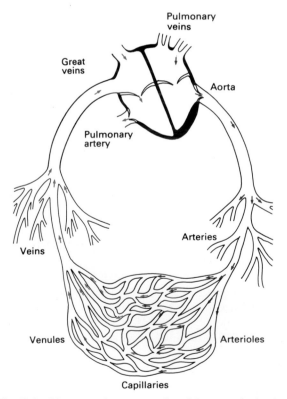

Fig. 19.1 Diagrammatic representation of the systemic circulation. The red arrows represent the flow of oxygenated blood; the blue arrows represent the flow of deoxygenated blood.

The Systemic Circulation

The vessels which carry the blood from the left ventricle throughout the body to the right atrium constitute the systemic circulation (Fig. 19.1).

The arteries

Arteries are named after the bones in the limbs or after the organ they supply (Fig. 19.2). They are usually found on the inner side of a limb where there is only one bone, or between the bones where there are two, and at a joint they would cross the flexor surface. These positions are the safest because the vessels are less likely to be exposed to injury and pressure. The pulse may be felt with the fingers where an artery can be compressed against a bone; firm pressure exerted at such a point may be useful in the control of arterial haemorrhage.

Arteries may subdivide into several branches at the same point or several branches may be given off in succession. Arteries normally end in arterioles and capillaries (see page 163) but sometimes they unite with one another, forming *anastomoses*. For example, in the brain the two vertebral arteries anastomose to form the basilar artery, and the two anterior cerebral arteries both join directly with the anterior communicating artery (see Fig. 19.3). Such an anastomosis may provide an alternative or *collateral* circulation if an artery is occluded by accident or disease; sudden occlusion may be followed by death of the tissue supplied by the artery, but gradual occlusion may allow dilation of the anastomosis and adequate nourishment of the tissue by the alternative route. Some arteries have no anastomoses with other arteries; these are called *end-arteries*. Occlusion of an end-artery will cause death of the tissue supplied by the vessel as a collateral circulation cannot develop. An example is the central artery of the retina; occlusion of this artery causes permanent blindness.

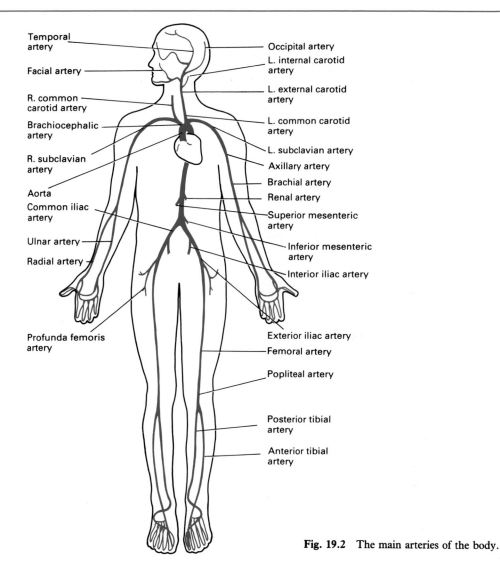

Temporal artery
Facial artery
R. common carotid artery
Brachiocephalic artery
R. subclavian artery
Aorta
Common iliac artery
Ulnar artery
Radial artery
Profunda femoris artery

Occipital artery
L. internal carotid artery
L. external carotid artery
L. common carotid artery
L. subclavian artery
Axillary artery
Brachial artery
Renal artery
Superior mesenteric artery
Inferior mesenteric artery
Interior iliac artery
Exterior iliac artery
Femoral artery
Popliteal artery
Posterior tibial artery
Anterior tibial artery

Fig. 19.2 The main arteries of the body.

The aorta

The aorta is the main artery carrying oxygenated blood to the tissues of the body (Fig. 19.3). It arises from the upper part of the left ventricle, passes upward and to the right (the *ascending aorta*) and then arches backward to the left (the *arch of the aorta*) and passes down through the thorax on the left side of the spine (the *descending thoracic aorta*). It enters the abdominal cavity through an opening of the diaphragm called the aortic hiatus and is then called the *abdominal aorta*. It ends at the lower border of the fourth lumbar vertebra by dividing into the right and left common iliac arteries. Branches from the aorta supply oxygenated blood to the rest of the body.

The ascending aorta. The ascending aorta has two branches, the *right* and *left coronary arteries*, which arise immediately above the cusps of the aortic valve. They supply the heart wall (see page 158).

The arch of the aorta. The arch has three branches arising from the top of the arch:
- The brachiocephalic artery, which divides into the right subclavian artery and the right common carotid artery

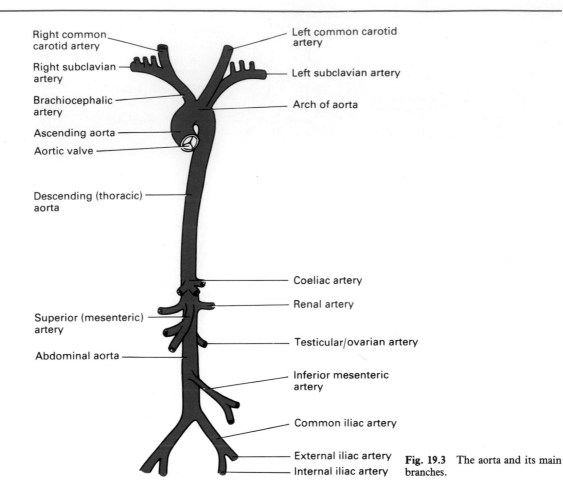

Fig. 19.3 The aorta and its main branches.

- The left common carotid artery
- The left subclavian artery

These supply the head and neck and the upper limb (see below).

The descending thoracic aorta. This part of the aorta is situated in the mediastinum. It supplies the pericardium, bronchi, oesophagus, mediastinum, intercostal muscles and breasts through branches named after the part they supply.

The abdominal aorta. The abdominal part of the aorta begins at the aortic hiatus of the diaphragm, about the level of the last thoracic vertebra. It has many large arteries arising from it to supply the abdominal organs:
- The *phrenic arteries* supply the diaphragm.
- The *coeliac artery* arises just below the aortic

opening in the diaphragm and divides into three branches:
(a) The *left gastric artery*, which supplies the stomach and gives off two or three branches that ascend through the oesophageal opening in the diaphragm and anastomose with the oesophageal arteries
(b) The *common hepatic artery*, which supplies the liver and gives off branches to the duodenum and bile duct as well as a branch to the stomach (the *right gastric artery*)
(c) The *splenic artery*, which divides into many branches to supply the very vascular spleen and also gives off numerous small vessels to supply the pancreas
- The *superior mesenteric artery* and its branches supply all the small intestine, except part of the duodenum, and the first part of the large intestine.

- The *middle adrenal arteries* arise, one on each side of the aorta, opposite the superior mesenteric artery and supply the adrenal glands.
- The *renal arteries* supply the kidneys. The left artery is a little higher than the right because of the positions of the respective kidneys.
- The *ovarian arteries* in the female and the *testicular arteries* in the male supply the organs after which they are named.
- The *inferior mesenteric artery* and its branches supplies the remainder of the large intestine, including the sigmoid colon and rectum.

The abdominal aorta divides into the two *common iliac arteries*. These again divide, at the level of the last lumbar intervertebral disc, into the *internal iliac artery*, which supplies the pelvis, the perineum and the gluteal region, and the *external iliac artery*, which supplies the lower limb (see below).

Blood supply to the head and neck

The *right* and *left common carotid arteries* supply the head and neck. Each divides into two at the level of the thyroid cartilage to form the external and internal carotid arteries. The *external carotid artery* supplies the outer parts of the face and scalp and has many branches such as the facial, temporal, occipital and maxillary arteries. The *internal carotid artery* supplies a large part of the cerebrum, the eyes, the nose and the forehead. At the point where the common carotid artery divides, there is a dilated area called the *carotid sinus* where a large number of sensory nerve endings from the glossopharyngeal (9th cranial) nerve are situated. The sinus reacts to changes in arterial blood pressure and assists in making appropriate changes to return it to normal. A small reddish-brown structure in the wall of the artery behind the division of the common carotid artery is called the *carotid body*; it acts as a chemoreceptor (see page 161).

The *vertebral arteries* arise from the first part of the subclavian arteries and pass upwards in the foramina of the transverse processes of the cervical vertebrae; they enter the skull through the foramen magnum and join together to form the *basilar artery*.

An *anastomosis*, named the *circulus arteriosus* or *circle of Willis* (Fig. 19.4), connects branches of the vertebral arteries and branches of the two internal carotid arteries. This circle is situated at the base of the brain. In front, the two internal carotid arteries divide into the *anterior cerebral* and *middle cerebral arteries*; the anterior cerebral arteries are then joined together by the *anterior communicating artery*. Behind, the basilar artery, formed by the junction of the two vertebral arteries, divides into two *posterior cerebral arteries*, each of which is joined to the internal carotid arteries by the *posterior communicating artery*. This anastomosis increases the likelihood of an adequate blood supply being maintained to the brain if one of the vessels is injured or occluded.

Blood supply to the upper limb

Blood is supplied to the upper limb through one main artery. This is called the *subclavian artery* as far as the outer border of the first rib, the *axillary* as far as the middle third of the humerus, and the *brachial artery* as far as the back of the radius, where it divides into:

- The *radial artery*, which passes along the radial side of the forearm to the wrist, where its pulsation can be felt quite easily, and then crosses into the palm of the hand to unite with the deep branch of the ulnar artery, forming the *deep palmar arch*
- The *ulnar artery*, which runs down the inner side of the forearm to the wrist, which it crosses before joining with branches of the radial artery to form the *superficial palmar arch*

The palmar arches supply the digits. Each arch anastomoses freely with the other so that injury to one allows blood to be brought to the affected part by other vessels.

Blood supply to the lower limb

Blood is supplied to the lower limb through the *external iliac artery*, which crosses the groin and enters the thigh as the *femoral artery*; this in turn becomes the *popliteal artery* at the lower one-third of the thigh. The popliteal artery divides into:
- The *anterior tibial artery*, which runs down the front of the leg on the anterior surface of the interosseous membrane, crosses the front of the ankle joint and supplies the front of the foot as the *dorsalis pedis artery*
- The *posterior tibial artery*, which runs down the back of the leg to the back of the ankle joint and to the sole of the foot, where it forms the plantar arch

The arteries around the ankle joint anastomose freely with one another to form networks of vessels.

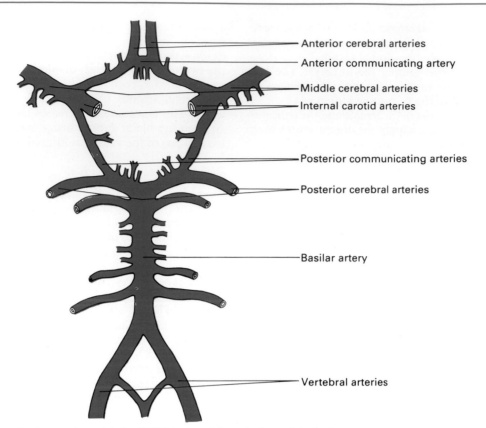

Fig. 19.4   The circulus arteriosus (circle of Willis), viewed from the base of the brain.

The veins

The veins, which return venous blood to the heart, are either *superficial veins*, which vary considerably in position, or *deep veins*, which usually accompany arteries (Fig. 19.5). The arrangement of the systemic veins is more variable from one individual to another than that of the corresponding arteries, and anastomoses occur more frequently. In some areas, such as the pelvis and around the vertebral column, the veins form extensive anastomoses and often do not have valves.

The veins can be described in two groups:
- The veins of the head, neck, upper limbs and thorax, which all end in the superior vena cava
- The veins of the lower limbs, abdomen and pelvis, which all end in the inferior vena cava

Return of blood from the head

The blood from the brain is collected into vessels which are situated between the two layers of the dura mater and are called *venous sinuses* (Fig. 19.6). These in turn empty into the right and left *internal jugular veins* along with blood from the superficial parts of the face and from the neck.

The right and left *external jugular veins* receive blood from the exterior of the cranium and from the deep parts of the face.

At the base of the neck the internal jugular veins join with the subclavian veins to form the *brachiocephalic veins*, which in turn unite to form the *superior vena cava*, through which blood is poured into the right atrium (Fig. 19.7).

Return of blood from the upper limb

The veins of the upper limbs are in two groups (Fig. 19.8):
- The *superficial veins* are immediately under the skin and are *cephalic*, *basilic* and *median veins* and their tributaries.
- The *deep veins* follow the course of the arteries

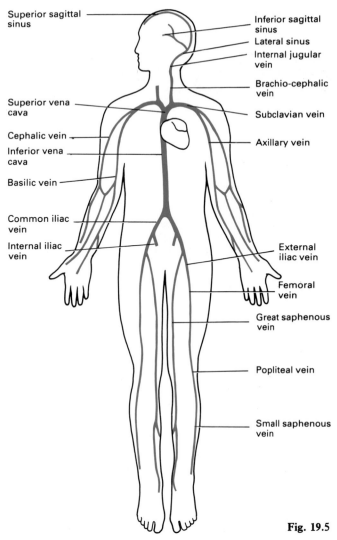

Superior sagittal sinus

Inferior sagittal sinus
Lateral sinus
Internal jugular vein
Brachio-cephalic vein

Superior vena cava

Subclavian vein

Cephalic vein
Inferior vena cava

Axillary vein

Basilic vein

Common iliac vein

Internal iliac vein

External iliac vein

Femoral vein

Great saphenous vein

Popliteal vein

Small saphenous vein

Fig. 19.5 The main veins of the body.

and pour their blood into the *axillary vein*, which is a continuation of the basilic vein, and which becomes continuous with the subclavian vein.

Return of blood from the lower limb

The veins of the lower limb are divided, like those of the upper limb, into superficial veins, which lie under the skin, or deep veins, which accompany the arteries (Fig. 19.9).

The superficial veins are the *small* and *great saphenous veins*, which empty into the *deep popliteal vein* at the back of the knee. The deep veins are the

anterior and *posterior tibial veins*, the *popliteal vein* and the *femoral vein*.

Between the deep and superficial veins of the lower limbs, a number of *perforating veins* exist. These contain valves that prevent blood from flowing from the deep to the superficial veins. If these valves become ineffective, blood can flow from the deep to the superficial veins. This raises the pressure in the superficial veins, causing them to dilate and form varicose veins.

The femoral vein ends at the inguinal ligament by becoming the *external iliac vein*. The *internal iliac vein*, returning blood from the pelvis, unites with

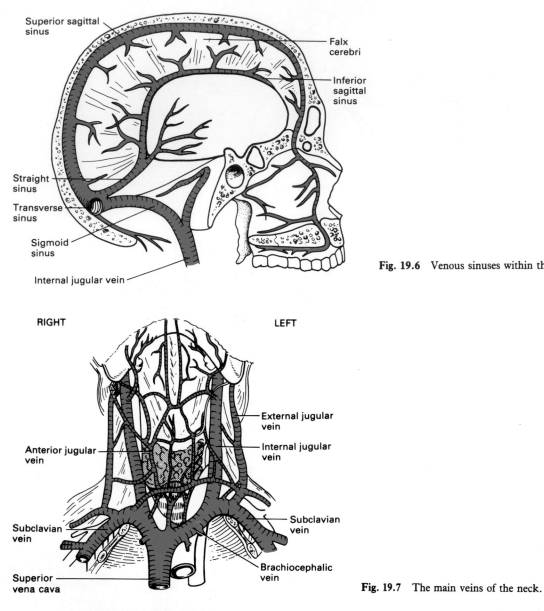

Fig. 19.6   Venous sinuses within the cranium.

Fig. 19.7   The main veins of the neck.

the external iliac vein to become the *common iliac vein*. The left and right common iliac veins then join at the level of the fifth lumbar vertebra to form the inferior vena cava.

Tributaries of the inferior vena cava

After being formed by the common iliac veins, the inferior vena cava receives several tributaries, some important ones being:

- The *renal veins* from the kidneys
- The *ovarian* or *testicular veins* from the reproductive organs, which empty into the inferior vena cava on the right and into the renal vein on the left
- The *hepatic veins*, which return all the blood from the liver, including that from the portal circulation (see below)

The inferior and superior venae cavae carry all the venous blood into the right atrium, except that from

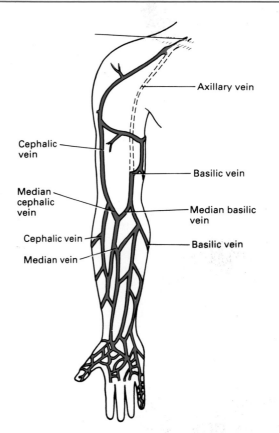

Fig. 19.8 The superficial veins of the upper limb.

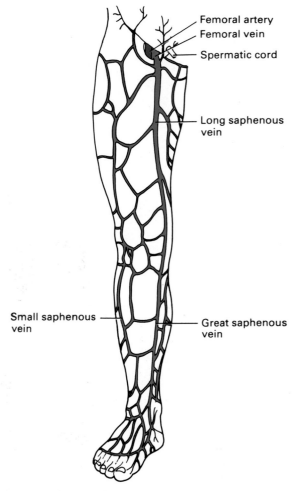

Fig. 19.9 The superficial veins of the lower limb.

the coronary circulation, which is conveyed by the coronary sinus directly into the right atrium.

The portal system

The portal system includes all the veins which drain blood from the abdominal part of the digestive system and from the spleen, pancreas and gall bladder. The blood from these organs, which is rich in foodstuffs, is carried to the liver by the *portal vein*, which ends within the liver in vessels like capillaries, called *sinusoids*. The blood is then conveyed by the *hepatic veins* to the inferior vena cava. Thus, unlike in the rest of the body, blood which returns to the heart via the portal system passes twice rather than once through a network of capillaries—once in the abdominal organ (e.g. the stomach or spleen) and once in the liver.

The liver also receives oxygenated blood and this is conveyed by the hepatic artery.

The Pulmonary Circulation (Fig. 19.10)

The vessels of the pulmonary circulation are concerned with carrying deoxygenated blood from the right side of the heart to the lungs, and oxygenated blood from the lungs back to the left side of the heart. The *pulmonary trunk* carries venous blood from the right ventricle; at the level of the fifth thoracic vertebra it divides into *right* and *left pulmonary arteries*, which then branch and subdivide into progressively smaller arterioles and capillaries to carry blood to the various segments of the lungs. These vessels are the only arteries carrying deoxygenated blood.

The pulmonary capillaries surround the alveoli. During respiration they give up carbon dioxide to

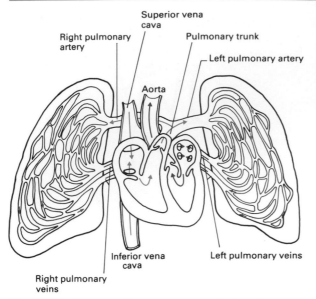

Fig. 19.10 Diagrammatic representation of the pulmonary circulation. The red arrows represent the flow of oxygenated blood; the blue arrows represent the flow of deoxygenated blood.

the air and take up oxygen. They then unite to form the *pulmonary veins*.

The four pulmonary veins return oxygenated blood from the lungs to the left atrium, two vessels from each lung. These are the only veins which carry oxygenated blood.

The Fetal Circulation (Fig. 19.11)

In the fetus, deoxygenated fetal blood is carried to the placenta by the two *umbilical arteries* and oxygenated blood is carried from the placenta to the fetus by the single *umbilical vein*. The blood in the umbilical vein then passes via the *ductus venosus* into the inferior vena cava. Here the oxygenated blood from the placenta and the deoxygenated blood from the abdomen and lower limbs mix before passing into the right atrium of the heart. Because the lungs are not yet responsible for oxygenation of the blood, they do not require a large blood supply, and most of the blood entering the right atrium passes through an opening in the atrial septum called the *foramen*

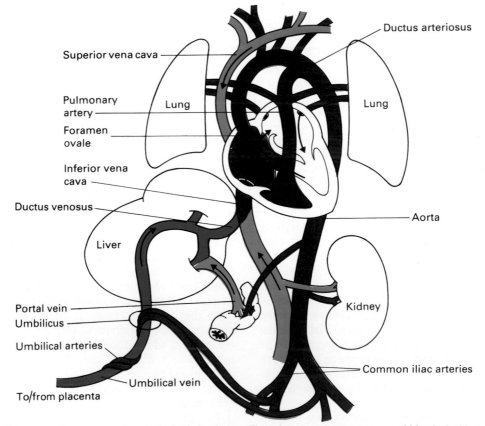

Fig. 19.11 Diagrammatic representation of the fetal circulation. The red areas represent oxygenated blood, the blue areas represent deoxygenated blood, and the purple areas represent mixed blood.

ovale into the left atrium. From here it passes into the left ventricle and is pumped into the aorta. The blood returning to the right atrium through the superior vena cava passes into the right ventricle and pulmonary trunk, after which only a small part of it goes to the lungs; most of it passes through the *ductus arteriosus* directly into the aorta.

At birth the foramen ovale closes, so that blood cannot pass from the right atrium to the left atrium but is directed into the pulmonary trunk and thence to the lungs. The ductus arteriosus also closes shortly after birth.

20

The Lymphatic System

Objectives: After studying Chapter 20 you should be able to:

1   Describe the formation of lymph.
2   List the functions of the lymphatic system.
3   Describe the circulation of lymph from its origin until it is returned to the bloodstream and outline the way in which lymph is propelled along the vessels.
4   Describe the structure and function of the spleen.

As blood passes through the capillaries in the tissues, fluid oozes out through the porous walls and circulates through the tissues themselves, bathing every cell. This fluid is called *tissue* or *interstitial fluid* (Fig. 20.1), as it fills the interstices or the spaces between the cells which form the different tissues. It is straw-coloured fluid similar to the plasma of the blood from which it is derived, although it does not contain proteins of higher molecular weight. It contains large numbers of white cells, particularly lymphocytes, and a few platelets and red cells. While blood circulates only through the blood vessels, tissue fluid circulates around the actual tissue cells. Food, oxygen and water from the bloodstream diffuse through the tissue fluid to each individual cell and its waste products, such as carbon dioxide, urea and water, diffuse through the tissue fluid to the blood.

When blood flows through capillaries, a certain amount of fluid is forced out into the tissues by hydrostatic pressure (see page 166). Some of this fluid passes back through the capillary wall by osmosis, but not all of it. The excess fluid which does not return directly into the bloodstream is collected up and returned to the blood by a second set of vessels—the *lymphatic system*. The fluid which these vessels contain is called the *lymph*. Lymph is therefore similar in composition to tissue fluid.

The lymphatic system consists of:
● Lymphatic capillaries
● Lymphatic vessels
● Lymphatic tissues, particularly nodes and the spleen
● Lymphatic ducts

Lymphatic capillaries

The lymphatic capillaries arise in the spaces between the tissues as fine hair-like vessels with porous walls. These gather up excess fluid from the tissue spaces and unite to form the lymphatic vessels.

Lymphatic vessels

The lymphatic vessels (Fig. 20.2) are thin-walled, collapsible tubes similar in structure to the veins, but carrying lymph instead of blood. They are finer and more numerous than veins and are provided with valves to prevent the lymph flowing in the wrong direction. Lymphatic vessels are found in most tissues except the central nervous system, but are particularly found in the subcutaneous tissues.

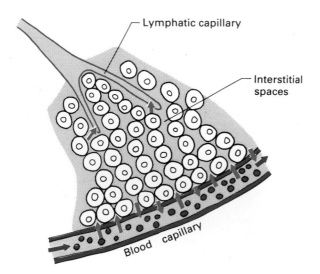

Fig. 20.1   The circulation of tissue fluid. Fluid which has passed out into the interstitial spaces is collected partly by the blood capillary and partly by the lymphatic capillary.

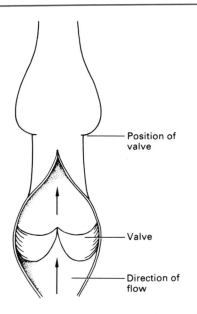

Fig. 20.2   A lymphatic vessel cut open to show a valve.

They pass through one or more lymphatic nodes as they travel towards a lymphatic duct.

Lymph nodes

The lymph nodes (Fig. 20.3) are small bodies varying in size from a pin-head to an almond. Lymphatic

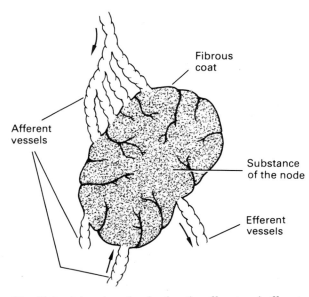

Fig. 20.3   A lymph node, showing the afferent and efferent vessels.

vessels bringing lymph to them are called *afferent vessels*. These enter and divide up within the node and discharge the lymph into the substance of the node. The lymph is then gathered up again into fresh lymphatic vessels called *efferent vessels*. These ultimately empty the lymph into the lymphatic ducts. Some lymph may pass through more than one node.

A lymph node consists mainly of lymphocytes (both B and T) (see page 154) held together by a network of connective tissue, which also forms a capsule for the node.

The functions of the lymph nodes are:
- To filter out bacteria from the lymph as it passes through. Thus when tissues are infected, the nodes through which lymph from the affected part passes may become swollen and tender. If the infection is a mild one, the organisms will be overcome by the cells in the node and the tenderness and swelling will subside. If it is severe, the organisms may cause acute inflammation and destruction of the white cells, causing an abscess to form in the node. If the bacteria are not destroyed by the node they may pass on in the lymph stream and eventually into the blood, causing septicaemia.
- To provide fresh lymphocytes for the bloodstream. The cells of the node constantly multiply and the newly formed cells are carried away in the lymph.

Lymph nodes are for the most part massed together in groups in various parts of the body (Fig. 20.4 and 20.5). Groups in the neck and under the chin filter the lymph from the head, tongue and the floor of the mouth. A group in the axilla filters the lymph from the upper limb and the chest wall. A group in the groin filters lymph from the lower limb and lower abdominal wall. Groups within the thorax and abdomen filter the lymph from the internal organs.

Special areas where lymphatic tissue (like that in a lymph node) is found include:
- The palatine and pharyngeal tonsils
- The thymus gland
- Aggregated lymphatic follicles in the small intestine
- The appendix
- The spleen

These filter tissue fluid or, in the case of the spleen, blood.

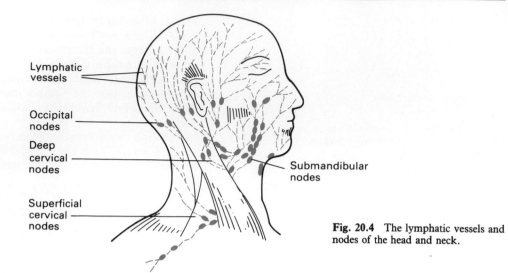

Lymphatic
vessels

Occipital
nodes

Deep
cervical
nodes

Submandibular
nodes

Superficial
cervical
nodes

Fig. 20.4 The lymphatic vessels and nodes of the head and neck.

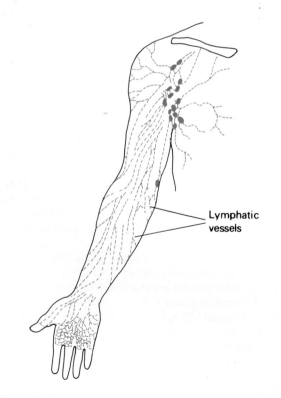

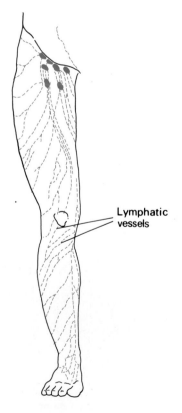

Lymphatic
vessels

Lymphatic
vessels

Fig. 20.5 The lymphatic vessels and nodes of the upper and lower limbs.

The lymphatic ducts

After filtration by the nodes the lymph is emptied by the lymphatic vessels into the two *lymphatic ducts*: the thoracic duct and right lymphatic duct (Fig. 20.6).

The *thoracic duct* is the larger of the two. It begins in a small pouch at the back of the abdomen called the cisterna chyli. Into this empty all the lymphatic vessels from the lower limbs and the abdominal and pelvic organs. Lymph from the intestine is milky in appearance following a meal, because it contains minute fat globules. In this state it is known as *chyle*.

From the cisterna chyli the duct runs up behind the heart to the root of the neck, where it turns to the left and is joined by the lymphatic vessels from the left side of the head and thorax and the left upper limb. It finally empties into the left subclavian vein at its junction with the left internal jugular vein. The thoracic duct is about 45 cm long and is provided with valves to prevent the lymph flowing in the wrong direction.

The *right lymphatic duct* is a comparatively small vessel formed by the joining of the lymphatic vessels from the right side of the head and thorax and the right upper limb at the root of the neck. It is only about 1 cm long and enters the right subclavian vein at its junction with the right internal jugular vein.

The lymphatic ducts thus gather up all the lymph and return it to the bloodstream.

The Functions of the Lymphatic System

The functions of the lymphatic system are as follows:
- The lymphatic vessels gather up the excessive fluid or lymph from the tissues and thus permit a constant stream of fresh fluid to circulate through them.
- It is the channel by which excess proteins in the tissue fluid pass back into the bloodstream.
- The lymphatic tissues, especially the lymph nodes, filter bacteria out of the lymph or tissue fluid.
- The nodes produce fresh lymphocytes for the circulation.
- The lymphatic vessels in the abdominal organs assist in the transport of digested food, especially fat.

The Mechanism of the Lymphatic Circulation

The lymphatic circulation is maintained partly by suction and partly by pressure. Suction is the more important factor. The lymphatics empty into the large veins approaching the heart. Negative pressure is created here due to suction as the heart expands and also during the act of inspiration.

Pressure is exerted on the lymphatics, as on the veins, by contraction of muscles and by the pulsation of the arteries; this outside pressure drives lymph upwards because the valves in the lymph vessels prevent a backward flow. There is also a slight pressure from the fluid in the tissues due to the constant pouring out of fresh fluid from the capillaries. If there is obstruction to the flow of lymph through the lymphatic system, oedema results, i.e. a swelling of the tissues due to excess fluid collecting in them. Oedema can also result from any obstruction of the veins, since these also drain fluid from the tissues.

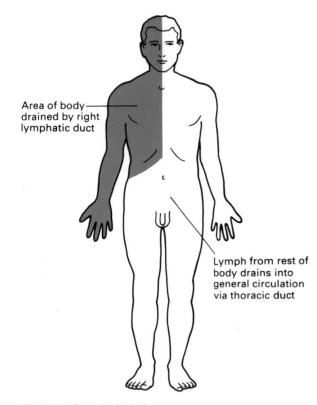

Area of body drained by right lymphatic duct

Lymph from rest of body drains into general circulation via thoracic duct

Fig. 20.6 Lymphatic drainage.

The Spleen

The spleen is a large nodule of lymphoid tissue (Fig. 20.7). It is a deep purplish-red colour, and lies high up at the back of the abdomen on the left side behind the stomach. It is enclosed in a capsule of fibrous tissue, and fibrous strands make a supporting mesh-work throughout the gland. The spaces of this meshwork are filled in with a pulp-like material, called the *splenic pulp*; this contains cells of different types. Many of these are lymphocytes, and these help to produce fresh white cells for the blood-stream. Others are phagocytes or devouring cells which engulf the red blood cells that are beginning to wear out and break them down.

The functions of the spleen are not fully known, but it is thought to be:

● A source of fresh lymphocytes for the bloodstream
● A site for the destruction of red blood cells

The spleen is also thought to assist in fighting infection, as it becomes enlarged in certain diseases in which the blood is infected, e.g. malaria and typhoid fever. It probably also helps in the manufacture of antibodies to fight infection. It is not essential

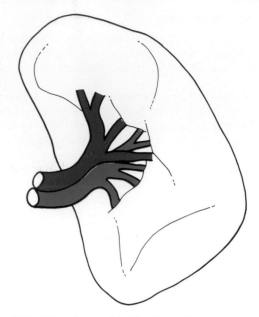

Fig. 20.7   The spleen and its blood vessels.

to life, and can be surgically removed when it is responsible for ill health, e.g. in some types of haemolytic anaemia.

SECTION 8

Colour Plates 7 and 8 relate to this section. The plates are between pages 134 and 135.

—21—

The Respiratory System

Objectives: After studying Chapter 21 you should be able to:

1   Draw and label diagrams showing the main parts of the respiratory tract.
2   Describe the function of the nose and sinuses.
3   Explain the functions of the pharynx, larynx and trachea.
4   Discuss the functions of the lungs and the bronchial tree.
5   Explain the function of the pleura.
6   Describe the work of the muscles used in respiration.
7   State how respiration is controlled.
8   State what is meant by inspiratory reserve volume, tidal volume, expiratory reserve volume, residual volume, inspiratory capacity and vital capacity.
9   Describe the exchange of gases which takes place in internal and external respiration.

All living cells require a constant supply of oxygen in order to carry on their metabolism. Oxygen is in the air, and the respiratory system is constructed in such a way that air can be taken into the lungs, where some of the oxygen is extracted for use by the body and at the same time carbon dioxide and water vapour are given up. The organs of the respiratory system are (Figs. 21.1 and 21.2):

- The nose ⎫
- The pharynx ⎬ leading to the lungs
- The larynx ⎬
- The trachea ⎭
- The bronchi ⎫
- The bronchioles ⎬ within the lungs
- The alveolar ducts and alveoli ⎭

The nose

The *external nose* is the visible part of the nose, formed by the two nasal bones and by cartilage. It is both covered and lined by skin and inside there are hairs which help to prevent foreign material from entering. The *nasal cavity* is a large cavity divided into two by a central septum. The *anterior nares* are the openings which lead in from without and the *posterior nares* are similar openings at the back, leading into the pharynx. The roof is formed by the ethmoid bone at the base of the skull and the floor by the hard and soft palates at the roof of the mouth. The lateral walls of the cavity are formed by the maxilla, the superior and middle nasal conchae of the ethmoid bone, and the inferior nasal concha. The posterior part of the dividing septum is formed by the perpendicular plate of the ethmoid bone and by the vomer, while the anterior part is made of cartilage.

The three nasal conchae project into the nasal cavity on each side and greatly increase the surface area of the inside of the nose. The cavity of the nose is lined throughout with ciliated mucous membrane, which is extremely vascular. This warms the atmospheric air as it passes over the epithelium. The mucus moistens the air and entraps some of the dust; the cilia move the mucus backwards into the pharynx for swallowing or expectoration. The nerve

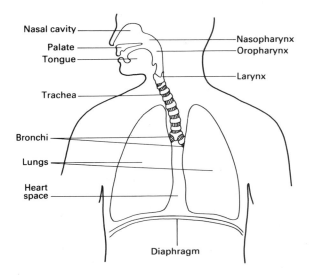

Fig. 21.1   The respiratory tract.

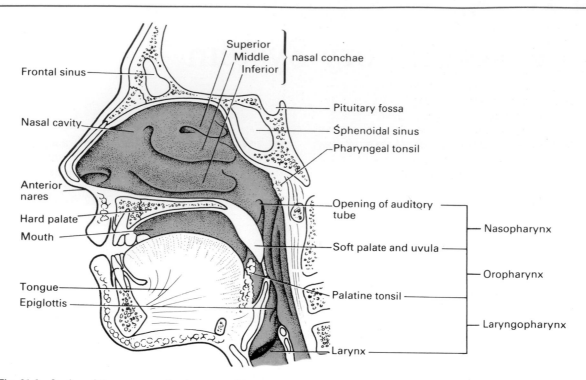

Fig. 21.2   Section of the nose, mouth, pharynx and larynx.

endings for the sense of smell are situated in the highest part of the nasal cavity round the cribriform plate of the ethmoid bone.

The paranasal sinuses

Some of the bones surrounding the nasal cavity are hollow. The hollows in the bones are called the paranasal sinuses, which both lighten the bones and act as sounding chambers for the voice, making it resonant. They consist of:

- The *maxillary sinus*, which lies below the orbit and opens into the lateral wall of the nose
- The *frontal sinus*, which lies above the orbit towards the midline within the frontal bone
- The *ethmoidal sinuses*, which are numerous and are found within the part of the ethmoid bone separating the orbit from the nose
- The *sphenoidal sinus*, which lies in the body of the sphenoid bone

All the paranasal sinuses are lined with mucous membrane and all open into the nasal cavity, from which they may become infected.

The pharynx

The roof of the pharynx is formed by the body of the sphenoid bone and inferiorly it is continuous with the oesophagus. At the back it is separated from the cervical vertebrae by loose connective tissue, while the front wall is incomplete and communicates with the nose, mouth and larynx. The pharynx is divided into three sections, the nasopharynx, which lies behind the nose, the oropharynx, which lies behind the mouth, and the laryngopharynx which lies behind the larynx.

The *nasopharynx* is that part of the pharynx which lies behind the nose above the level of the soft palate. On the posterior wall there are patches of lymphoid tissue called the *pharyngeal tonsils*, which are commonly referred to as the *adenoids*. This tissue sometimes enlarges and blocks the pharynx, causing mouth breathing in children. The auditory tubes open from the lateral walls of the nasopharynx and through them air is carried to the middle ear.

The nasopharynx is lined with ciliated mucous membrane which is continuous with the lining of the nose.

The *oropharynx* lies behind the mouth below the level of the soft palate, with which its lateral walls are continuous. Between the folds of these walls, which are called the *palatoglossal arches*, are collections of lymphoid tissue called the *palatine tonsils*.

The oropharynx is part of both the respiratory tract and the alimentary tract, but it cannot be used for swallowing and breathing simultaneously. During the act of swallowing, breathing stops momentarily and the oropharynx is completely blocked off from the nasopharynx by the raising of the soft palate.

The oropharynx is lined with stratified epithelium.

The larynx

The larynx is continuous with the oropharynx above and with the trachea below. Above it lie the hyoid bone and the root of the tongue. The muscles of the neck lie in front of the larynx, and the laryngopharynx and the cervical vertebrae lie behind. On either side are the lobes of the thyroid gland. The larynx is composed of several irregular cartilages joined together by ligaments and membranes.

The *thyroid cartilage* is formed of two flat pieces of cartilage fused together in the front to form the laryngeal prominence or Adam's apple. Above the prominence is the thyroid notch. The thyroid cartilage is larger in the male than in the female. The upper part is lined with stratified epithelium and the lower part with ciliated epithelium.

The *cricoid cartilage* lies below the thyroid cartilage and is shaped like a signet ring with the broad portion at the back. It forms the lateral and posterior walls of the larynx and is lined with ciliated epithelium.

The *epiglottis* is a leaf-shaped cartilage attached to the inside of the front wall of the thyroid cartilage immediately below the thyroid notch. During swallowing the larynx moves upwards and forwards so that its opening is occluded by the epiglottis.

The *arytenoid cartilages* are a pair of small pyramids made of hyaline cartilage. They are situated on top of the broad part of the cricoid cartilage, and the vocal ligaments are attached to them. They form the posterior wall of the larynx.

The hyoid bone and the laryngeal cartilages (Fig. 21.3) are joined together by ligaments and membranes. One of these, the *cricothyroid membrane*, is attached all round to the upper edge of the cricoid

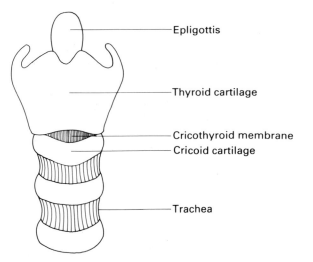

Fig. 21.3 The laryngeal cartilages.

cartilage and has a free upper border, which is not circular like the lower border, but makes two parallel lines running from front to back. The two parallel edges are the *vocal ligaments* or *cords* (Fig. 21.4). They are fixed to the middle of the thyroid cartilage in front and to the arytenoid cartilages behind, and they contain much elastic tissue. When the intrinsic

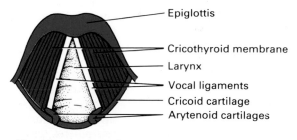

Vocal ligaments resting

Vocal ligaments during speech

Fig. 21.4 The vocal ligaments.

muscles of the larynx alter the position of the arytenoid cartilages the vocal ligaments are pulled together, narrowing the gap between them. If air is forced through the narrow gap, called the chink, during expiration, the vocal ligaments vibrate and sound is produced. The pitch of the sound produced depends on the length and tightness of the ligaments: an increased tension gives a higher note, a slacker tension a lower note. The loudness of the sound depends on the force with which the air is expired. The alteration of the sound into different words depends on the movements of the mouth, tongue, lips and facial muscles.

The trachea

The trachea begins below the larynx and runs down the front of the neck into the chest. It is about 12 cm long and divides into the right and the left main bronchi at the level of the fifth thoracic vertebra. The isthmus of the thyroid gland crosses in front of the upper part of the trachea, and the arch of the aorta lies in front of the lower part, with the manubrium of the sternum in front of that. The oesophagus lies behind the trachea, separating it from the bodies of the thoracic vertebrae. On either side of the trachea lie the lungs, with the lobes of the thyroid gland above them. The wall of the trachea is made of involuntary muscle and fibrous tissue strengthened by incomplete rings of hyaline cartilage. The deficiency in the rings of cartilage lies at the back where the trachea is in contact with the oesophagus. Thus when a bolus of food is swallowed the oesophagus is able to expand without hindrance, but the cartilage maintains the patency of the airway.

The trachea is lined with ciliated epithelium containing goblet cells which secrete mucus. The cilia sweep the mucus and foreign particles up towards the larynx.

The lungs

The lungs are two large spongy organs lying in the thorax on either side of the heart and great vessels. They extend from the root of the neck to the diaphragm and are roughly cone-shaped, with the apex above and the base below. In front of the lungs lie the ribs, costal cartilages and intercostal muscles, and behind them are the ribs, the intercostal muscles and the transverse processes of the thoracic vertebrae. Between the lungs is the *mediastinum*,

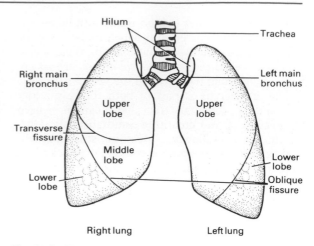

Fig. 21.5   The lobes of the lungs.

which completely separates one side of the thoracic cavity from the other, stretching from the vertebrae behind to the sternum in front. Within the mediastinum lie the heart and great vessels, the trachea and the oesophagus, the thoracic duct and the thymus gland.

The lungs are divided into *lobes* (Fig. 21.5). The left lung has two lobes, separated by the oblique fissure. The upper lobe is above and in front of the lower lobe, which is conical in shape. The right lung has three lobes. The lower lobe is separated by an oblique fissure in a similar manner to the left lobe. The remainder of the lung is separated by the transverse fissure into the upper lobe and the middle lobe. Each lobe is further divided into *bronchopulmonary segments*, separated from each other by a wall of connective tissue and each having an artery and a vein. Each segment is also divided into smaller units called *lobules*.

The bronchi

The two main bronchi commence at the bifurcation of the trachea and one leads into each lung. The left main bronchus is narrower, longer and more horizontal than the right main bronchus because the heart lies a little to the left of the midline. Each main bronchus divides into branches, one for each lobe of the lung. Each of these then divides into named branches, one for each bronchopulmonary segment, which then divide again into progressively smaller bronchi within the lung substance. The bronchi are similar in structure to the trachea but the cartilage is less regular.

The bronchioles

The finest bronchi are called bronchioles. These have no cartilage but are composed of muscular, fibrous and elastic tissue lined with cuboid epithelium. As the bronchioles become smaller, the muscular and fibrous tissue disappears and the smallest tubes, called *terminal bronchioles*, are a single layer of flattened epithelial cells.

The alveolar ducts and alveoli

The terminal bronchioles branch repeatedly to form minute passages called alveolar ducts, from which alveolar sacs and alveoli open (Fig. 21.6). The alveoli are surrounded by a network of capillaries. Deoxygenated blood enters the capillary network from the pulmonary artery and oxygenated blood leaves it to enter the pulmonary veins. It is in the capillary network that the exchange of gases takes place between the air in the alveoli and the blood in the vessels.

The hilum of the lung

The hilum is a triangular-shaped depression on the concave medial surface of the lung. The structures forming the *root of the lung* enter and leave at the hilum, which is at the level of the fifth to the seventh thoracic vertebrae. These structures include:

- The main bronchus
- The pulmonary artery, carrying deoxygenated blood to the alveoli
- The bronchial arteries, carrying oxygenated blood to the bronchi and bronchioles
- Branches of the vagus nerve (the tenth cranial nerve)
- Two pulmonary veins, carrying oxygenated blood to the left side of the heart
- The bronchial veins, carrying deoxygenated away from the bronchi and bronchioles
- Lymphatic vessels

There are also many lymph nodes round the root of the lung.

The pleura

The pleura is a serous membrane which surrounds each lung (Fig. 21.7). It is composed of flattened epithelial cells on a basement membrane and it has two layers. The *visceral layer* is firmly attached to the lungs, covering their surfaces and dipping into the transverse and oblique fissures. At the root of the lungs the visceral layer folds back on itself to become the *parietal layer*, which lines the chest wall and

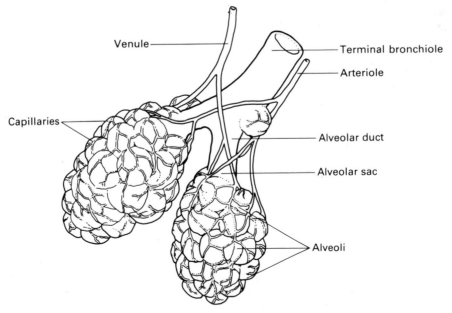

Fig. 21.6 Alveoli.

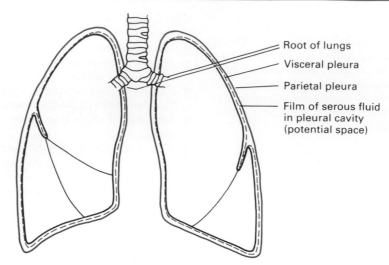

Root of lungs
Visceral pleura
Parietal pleura
Film of serous fluid
in pleural cavity
(potential space)

Fig. 21.7 The pleura.

covers the superior surface of the diaphragm. The two layers of the pleura are normally in close contact with each other, separated only by a film of serous fluid which enables them to glide over one another without friction. This potential space between the layers is called the *pleural cavity*.

Respiration

The muscles of respiration

The chief muscles of respiration are:
- The diaphragm
- The external intercostal muscles
- The internal intercostal muscles

The *diaphragm* is a dome-shaped sheet of muscle dividing the thorax from the abdomen. The border is of muscle, while the centre is a sheet of fibrous tissue (i.e. an aponeurosis). The muscle arises from the tip of the sternum, the lower ribs and their cartilages, and the first three lumbar vertebrae, and is inserted into the central aponeurosis. Three openings in the diaphragm allow the oesophagus, aorta and inferior vena cava to pass through it, together with smaller structures such as the vagus nerve and thoracic duct, which accompany the oesophagus and aorta respectively. When the muscle fibres contract, the dome of the diaphragm is flattened and lowered, which increases the depth of the thorax from top to bottom.

The *external intercostal muscles* lie between the ribs, their fibres running downwards and forwards from one rib to the rib below. Each originates from

the lower border of the rib above and is inserted into the upper border of the rib below. Their action is to draw the ribs upwards and outwards, increasing the size of the thorax from side to side and from back to front.

The *internal intercostal muscles* also lie between the ribs under the external intercostal muscles and are antagonistic to them. Their fibres run downwards and backwards from one rib to the rib below. Each originates from the lower border of the rib above and is inserted into the upper border of the rib below. Their action is to draw the ribs downwards and inwards, decreasing the size of the thorax from side to side and from back to front. They are particularly used in forced expiration.

Respiration consists of two parts, *inspiration* and *expiration*. The chest expands during inspiration owing to contraction of the diaphragm and the external intercostal muscles (Fig. 21.8). When the diaphragm contracts it is flattened and lowered and the thoracic cavity is increased in length. The external intercostal muscles lift the ribs and draw them outwards, increasing the width of the thoracic cavity. These actions together increase the volume of the thoracic cavity. As the chest wall moves up and out, the parietal pleura, which is closely attached to it, moves with it. The visceral pleura follows the parietal pleura, the lung expands to fill the space, and air is sucked into the bronchial tree.

Expiration during quiet breathing is passive. The diaphragm relaxes and assumes its original domed shape, and the intercostal muscles relax and the ribs revert to their previous position. The lungs recoil and air is driven out of the bronchial tree. During

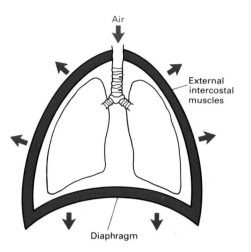

Fig. 21.8 A diagrammatic representation of the action of the external intercostal muscles and the diaphragm during inspiration.

deep or forced breathing, e.g. when the airway is obstructed, the accessory muscles of respiration may be brought into use. During forced inspiration the sternocleidomastoid muscles raise the sternum and increase the diameter of the thorax from front to back. The serratus anterior and pectoralis major muscles pull the ribs outwards when the arm is fixed, e.g. by holding the back of a chair. Latissimus dorsi and the muscles of the anterior abdominal wall help to compress the thorax during forced expiration.

The control of respiration

Respiration is controlled by a part of the brain known as the *respiratory pacemaker*. This is formed by two areas in the medulla oblongata, one responsible for inspiration and the other for expiration, and an area in the pons that is responsible for preventing over-inflation of the lungs. If the inspiratory centre had no counter-control, it would continue to cause inspiration and over-inflate the lungs. The centre in the pons limits the length of inspiration and therefore the depth. Another factor in preventing over-inflation is the existence of stretch receptors in the walls of the bronchioles and bronchii. These send stimuli to the inspiratory centre via the vagus nerve to inhibit inspiration. The expiratory centre is not active in normal quiet breathing as expiration is normally passive. However, when forced expirations are required, e.g. in exercise, the expiratory centre is stimulated.

The respiratory pacemaker is controlled by the pH of the blood and the cerebrospinal fluid. If respiration is too shallow or too slow, carbon dioxide builds up in the blood and the majority of this carbon dioxide reacts with water to form carbonic acid, and thus the pH of the blood and the cerebrospinal fluid falls. This drop in pH is detected by an area of the medulla and stimulates the respiratory pacemaker, which then increases the depth and frequency of respiration, the excess carbon dioxide is lost in the expired air, and the pH of the blood returns to normal.

In addition, the respiratory pacemaker also receives impulses from peripheral chemoreceptors in the great arteries. These are more sensitive to hypoxia (low oxygen) than hypercapnia (high carbon dioxide levels). Impulses from these chemoreceptors are carried by the vagus and glossopharyngeal nerves to the respiratory centre. However, under normal conditions the pH-sensitive area of the medulla is more important in the control of respiration than the peripheral chemoreceptors.

The capacity of the lungs

The *tidal volume* is the amount of air breathed in and out during normal quiet breathing and is usually about 500 ml. After a quiet inspiration it is possible to force about another 2500 ml of air into the lungs; this is known as the *inspiratory reserve volume*. The tidal volume plus the inspiratory reserve volume, i.e. the amount of air that can be taken in during forced inspiration following a normal expiration, is called the *inspiratory capacity*, and is usually about 3000 ml. Likewise, after a quiet expiration it is possible to force about another 1000 ml of air from the lungs, and this is known as the *expiratory reserve volume*. The tidal volume plus the expiratory reserve volume, i.e. the amount of air that can be expelled during forced expiration following a normal inspiration, is known as the *expiratory capacity* and is usually about 1500 ml (Fig. 21.9).

Even after the deepest possible expiration there is still some air left within the lungs. This is known as the *residual volume* and is normally about 1100 ml.

The *vital capacity* is the largest volume of air that can be expired after the deepest possible inspiration and is usually about 4000 ml; it is equal to the expiratory reserve volume plus the tidal volume plus the inspiratory reserve volume.

An important indication of respiratory function is the speed with which the air in the lungs can be

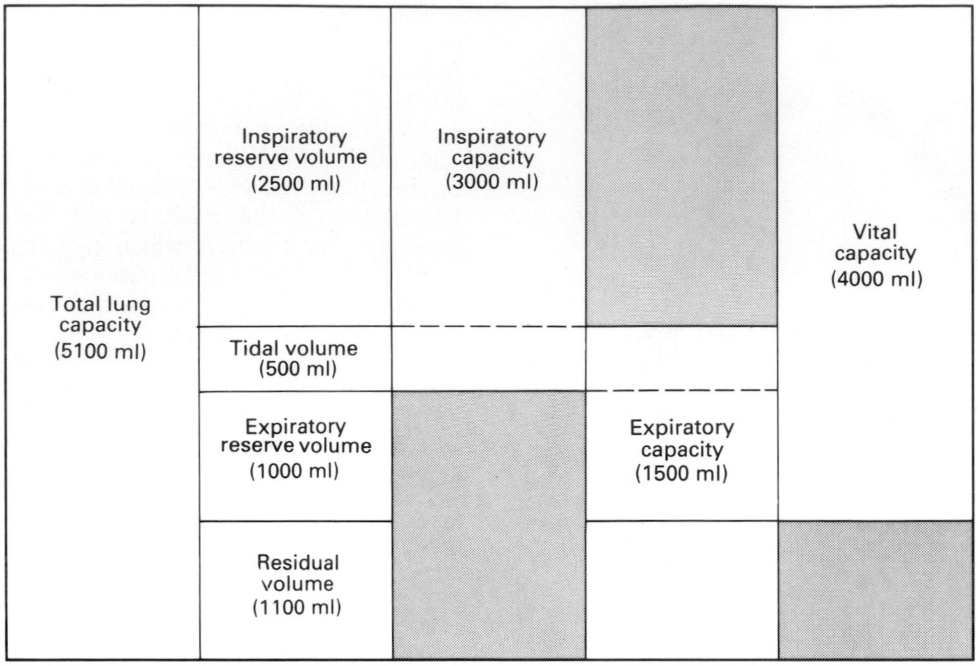

Total lung capacity (5100 ml)	Inspiratory reserve volume (2500 ml)	Inspiratory capacity (3000 ml)		Vital capacity (4000 ml)
	Tidal volume (500 ml)			
	Expiratory reserve volume (1000 ml)		Expiratory capacity (1500 ml)	
	Residual volume (1100 ml)			

Fig. 21.9   The subdivisions of the lung volume.

expelled. This is measured as the *forced expiratory volume in 1 second* (FEV$_1$) and is normally 75–80% of the vital capacity.

Gaseous exchange

Exchange of gases within the body takes place both in the lungs, where it is called *external respiration*, and in the tissues, where it is called *internal respiration* (Figs. 21.10 and 21.11). Gases tend to diffuse from a higher pressure (i.e. a higher concentration) to a lower pressure (i.e. a lower concentration). The air which is breathed in contains several gases.

The composition of inspired air is:
- Nitrogen 79%
- Oxygen 21%

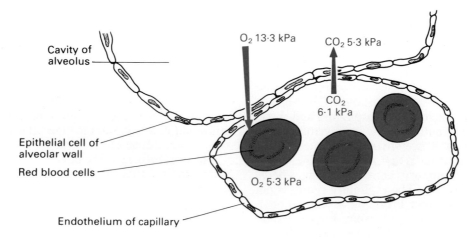

Fig. 21.10   Gaseous exchange in the lungs.

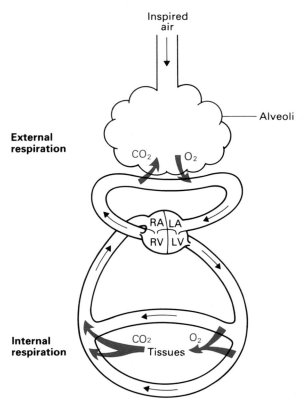

Inspired
air

Alveoli

**External
respiration**

CO_2 O_2

RA LA
RV LV

**Internal
respiration**

CO_2 O_2
Tissues

Fig. 21.11 External and internal respiration. RA = right atrium; RV = right ventricle; LA = left atrium; LV = left ventricle.

- Carbon dioxide 0.04%
- Water vapour
- Traces of other gases

External respiration

When inspired air reaches the alveoli it is in close contact with the blood in the surrounding capillary network. Oxygen in the alveoli at a pressure of 13.3 kPa comes in contact with oxygen in the venous blood at a pressure of 5.3 kPa and therefore oxygen diffuses into the blood until the pressures are equal. At the same time carbon dioxide in the blood at a pressure of 6.1 kPa comes in contact with alveolar carbon dioxide at a pressure of 5.3 kPa and therefore carbon dioxide diffuses out of the blood into the alveoli. Expired air therefore contains less oxygen and more carbon dioxide than inspired air. The nitrogen content remains the same. The composition of expired air is:

- Nitrogen 79%
- Oxygen 16%
- Carbon dioxide 4.5%
- Water vapour
- Traces of other gases

Internal respiration

The oxygen which has diffused into the blood combines with haemoglobin in the red blood cells to form oxyhaemoglobin and is carried to the tissues. Here the pressure of the oxygen is low, so oxygen diffuses out of the blood and into the tissues. At the same time carbon dioxide, produced in the tissues, diffuses into the blood and is carried away.

—SECTION 9————
The Digestive System

Colour Plates 8, 12, 13 and 14 relate to this section. The plates are between pages 134 and 135.

—22—
Nutrition and Metabolism

Objectives: After studying Chapter 22 you should be able to:

1 State the essential foods required by the body.
2 State the major sources of these foods.
3 State the prime use of these foods.
4 Define 'metabolism'.
5 List the main subdivisions of fluid in the body.
6 Describe the ways by which fluid is gained or lost by the body.
7 List the chief anions and cations in the fluid areas.
8 List the main vitamins and state their importance to health.
9 Discuss what is meant by 'a healthy balanced diet'.

Good health is dependent on satisfactory nutrition, i.e. on adequate supplies of the foods which are necessary to healthy life. The term 'malnutrition' is often used to mean a lack of food. However, excess food or an unbalanced diet can also lead to ill-health and are therefore forms of malnutrition.

Substances which can serve as food for the body are those which it can use as *fuel* or *building materials*. Fuel is required to produce the energy for the activities of the body and to maintain the body temperature. Building materials are necessary to repair body tissues as they become worn out; in addition, in pregnant women, infants and children, extra building material is required to build up the new tissues needed for the processes of growth. Fuel supplies and building materials alone are, however, not enough. Certain other substances are necessary to enable the tissues to use the building materials and the fuel supplies, and these are known as vitamins.

There are six essential types of substance with which the body must be constantly supplied through the foods we eat. These are:

- Proteins
- Carbohydrates
- Fats
- Water
- Electrolytes
- Vitamins

Every type of food contains one or more of these substances and is only of value as food because it does contain them. The proteins, water and some electrolytes are the body-building foods; the carbohydrates and fats are the main fuel foods, though the body can also use protein as fuel if more is taken in than is required for body-building or if there is a lack of other fuel, as in starvation. The vitamins and certain electrolytes act as regulators of tissue activity, so that, although vitamins are of no use either as fuel or as body-builders, the nutrition of the tissues suffers if they are not present in sufficient quantities in the food supply.

In order to be of use to the body these foodstuffs must be absorbed into the bloodstream so that it can be carried to the tissues. Proteins, carbohydrates and fats are complicated compounds found in plant and animal matter, and require digestion, i.e. they need to be broken down by digestive juices, before they can be absorbed. Water and electrolytes are simple inorganic substances; they can be absorbed, therefore, without digestion.

Table 22.1 A summary of the uses of the main dietary constituents.

Dietary constituent	Uses
Protein	Growth and repair of tissues Energy production Excess stored as fat
Carbohydrate	Energy production Excess stored as glycogen (short term) or fat (long term)
Fat	Energy production Building of various tissues Excess stored as fat

Metabolism

Metabolism is the term applied to all the changes that occur in the body in connection with the use of energy. It is derived from the Greek word *metaballein*, meaning to change, and covers all the changes concerned with the use of food by the body tissues, the formation of waste products from its use, and the excretion of those waste products.

The changes included in the process of metabolism are of two types:

- Building-up changes, which are called *anabolic changes* or *anabolism*, e.g. the building up of muscle from the amino acids obtained from proteins, or of fat from fatty acid and glycerol.
- Breaking-down changes, which are called *catabolic changes* or *catabolism*, e.g. the breaking down of glucose or fat into carbon dioxide and water to release energy.

These metabolic changes are due to enzyme action and within the body cells they take place continuously and simultaneously; for example, a muscle cell constantly builds up fresh protoplasm from the amino acids provided by the bloodstream; at the same time it breaks down fuel, such as glucose, to provide energy for this activity and for the activity of contraction, and it also breaks up worn out protoplasm into waste products, such as urea, for excretion.

Metabolic changes take place all the time in every living thing, but are increased during activities such as movement or the digestion of food, and are decreased during rest. *Basal metabolism* is the metabolism that is required to keep the body 'ticking over' even when it is at absolute rest. The *basal metabolic rate* (BMR) is sometimes calculated as an indication of the presence of disease; for example, over-activity of the thyroid gland raises the BMR and under-activity lowers it.

Proteins

Proteins are the most complicated of the foodstuffs. They consist of carbon, hydrogen, oxygen, nitrogen and sulphur and usually phosphorus. They are often known as *nitrogenous* substances, as they contain the element nitrogen. They are essential for the building up of living protoplasm. They are found in both animal and plant matter, but animal proteins are the more valuable to the human body as building material, since they are similar to human protein in composition. On the other hand, plant proteins are usually cheaper to produce; they are more useful as body fuel than as body builders, but do provide some of the amino acids (see below) that the body needs for tissue building.

The main sources of protein are:
- Animal
  - (a) Eggs, which contain ovalbumin
  - (b) Lean meat, which contains myosin
  - (c) Milk, which contains caseinogen and lactalbumin
  - (d) Cheese, which contains casein
- Plant
  - (a) Wheat and rye, which contain gluten
  - (b) Pulse foods (e.g. peas and beans), which contain legumin

All proteins are made up of simpler substances known as *amino acids*. There are about 20 of these amino acids, but each protein contains just some of these. The amino acids are like letters from which many words can be made, each word being a different combination of letters. Each protein, whether from an animal or a plant, is a different combination of amino acids.

Most of the amino acids can be synthesized by the body from various food substances. However, there are a number of amino acids which the body cannot build up for itself and which therefore must be present in the proteins eaten. These are known as *essential amino acids*; there are eight in adults and ten in the neonate, as there are two amino acids which the immature liver cannot synthesize. Proteins which contain all eight essential amino acids are called *complete proteins*, e.g. albumin, myosin and casein. Proteins which do not contain all eight are called *incomplete proteins*, e.g. gelatin, which is contained in all fibrous tissue, and is extracted from bone and calves' feet in the making of soups and jelly. Animal proteins, such as those of eggs, milk and meat, not only contain all the eight amino acids the body needs, but contain all of them in good proportion; these are called *first-class proteins* and are the best building material for the body tissues. Plant proteins, such as gluten and legumin, contain only slight quantities of one or more of the eight amino acids essential to the body, and are therefore called *second-class proteins*, as they are not such good building material. Some first-class animal protein is recommended to be included in the diet.

Protein metabolism

Proteins are broken up by the enzymes of the gastric, pancreatic and intestinal juices into polypeptides, which are shorter chains of amino acids and then into individual amino acids. These are absorbed by the villi of the small intestine and carried by the portal vein to the liver (Fig. 22.1).

The chief use of amino acids is to provide material for body building. The new tissue required for the purposes of growth and repair can only be made from this foodstuff, since no other foodstuff contains the nitrogen that is essential for the making of a living cell. Most of the amino acids required for tissue building pass through the liver and are carried by the bloodstream to all parts of the body to be built up into whatever proteins are required. Some remain in the liver and are built up into plasma proteins (see page 147), which are then released into the blood.

Amino acids can also be used as body fuel. Excess amino acids and amino acids unsuitable for body building are split up in the liver to form:
- *Body fuel* in the form of glucose (containing carbon, hydrogen and oxygen)
- Nitrogenous waste matter (containing nitrogen and hydrogen)

This process is termed the *de-amination* of the amino acids. The nitrogenous part of the spare amino acids

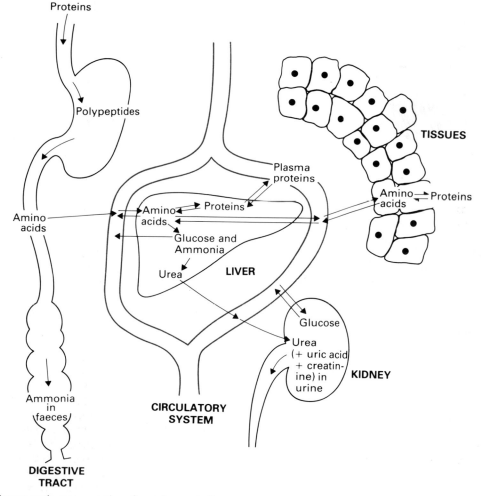

Fig. 22.1 Diagrammatic representation of protein metabolism.

is removed and converted into ammonia, most of which then combines with carbonic acid and splits up into urea and water. The glucose is either utilized or stored as required. The urea is readily soluble, and, being useless for fuel, is carried away by the bloodstream and excreted from the blood by the kidneys.

This mechanism can be used to provide fuel in conditions of starvation. The production of energy must go on continuously to maintain life. If there is lack of other fuel, protein will be sacrificed for use as fuel, even though it is needed for processes of repair and growth. As a result, poor healing and loss of muscle bulk, with resulting weakness, will occur either when the body cannot obtain food, as in famine, or when it cannot digest and absorb it, as in some diseases.

The nitrogenous waste products of protein metabolism are *urea* and to a lesser extent *uric acid* and *creatinine*. Uric acid is less soluble than urea and comes mainly from the breakdown of protein from the nuclei of the cells in our food. Creatinine is a waste product of the breaking-down of muscle tissue within the body. All these waste products are excreted by the kidneys in the urine. About 30 g of urea leave the body each day in this way, as also do traces of uric acid and creatinine.

Carbohydrates

Carbohydrates include *sugar* and *starch*. They consist of carbon, hydrogen and oxygen, and always contain hydrogen and oxygen in the same proportions as in water (H_2O), i.e. twice as much hydrogen as oxygen. They are the chief sources of body fuel, being most easy to digest and absorb and most readily broken down in the tissues into carbon dioxide and water. They are obtained chiefly from plant foods.

The sources of starch are:
- Cereals e.g. wheat, rice and barley
- Tubers and roots e.g. potatoes and parsnips
- Pulse foods e.g. peas, beans and lentils

The sources of sugar are:
- Sugar cane, which contains sucrose
- Beetroot and all sweet vegetables and fruits e.g. grapes, which contain glucose
- Honey
- Milk, which contains milk sugar (lactose)

Carbohydrates are of three types:
- Simple sugars (monosaccharides), such as glucose; formula $C_6H_{12}O_6$
- Complex sugars (disaccharides), such as sucrose and lactose; formula $C_{12}H_{22}O_{11}$
- Polysaccharides, the most complex carbohydrates, including starches such as potatoes, cereals and root vegetables; formula $n(C_6H_{10}O_5)$, where n stands for different numbers in different starches

Starch differs from sugar in that it is insoluble in water. Plants store sugar in the form of starch to prevent it from escaping in solution into the water in the soil in which they live.

All carbohydrates are broken down into monosaccharides before they can be absorbed from the digestive tract.

Carbohydrate metabolism

Carbohydrates in the form of sugar and starch are acted on by the enzymes in the saliva and the pancreatic and intestinal juices, and converted into simple sugars such as glucose ($C_6H_{12}O_6$). These simple sugars are then absorbed by the villi of the small intestine, pass into the blood capillaries, and are carried by the portal vein to the liver (Fig. 22.2).

The main use of glucose is to serve as *body fuel* for the production of energy for work and heat. The glucose required for immediate use is carried straight through the liver into the hepatic veins and inferior vena cava, and so enters the systemic circulation. Any excess not required for the body's immediate needs is converted by the liver cells into *glycogen*, which is insoluble and is stored in the liver and muscles until required for use. Glycogen in the animal world is similar to starch in the plant world—both are insoluble and are formed from sugar by splitting off water from it. When glucose is needed by the body the glycogen is converted back into glucose, which dissolves in the body fluids and so passes into the bloodstream. Both the formation of glycogen from glucose and the forming of glucose from glycogen are the work of enzymes produced by the liver cells.

Glucose can also be converted to fat and stored in fatty tissue for use later as fuel.

Glucose is specially required by the most active tissues of the body—the muscles and glands. The cells of the brain are dependent on glucose as they are not able to use other forms of energy but all

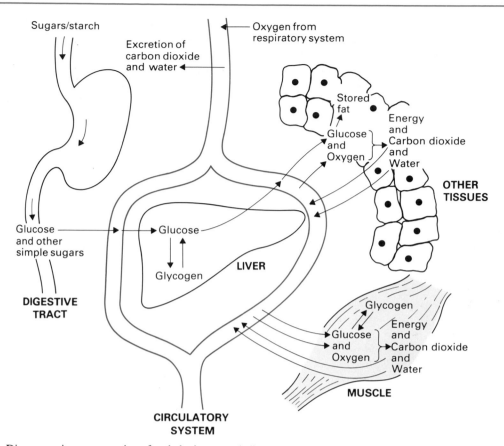

Fig. 22.2 Diagrammatic representation of carbohydrate metabolism.

tissues need it to some extent. The muscles, like the liver, are able to store some glucose in the form of glycogen.

The tissues of the body utilize their fuel very economically. In the muscles, glucose is broken down to produce energy for contraction, but more energy is released than is required for the work of the muscles and the excess energy is used to build up glycogen again from some of the partially broken-down glucose. It is estimated that only about one-fifth of the glucose is completely broken down into the waste products carbon dioxide and water. The remaining four-fifths, after partial breakdown, is built up again into glycogen ready for use when the muscles require it.

The waste products of the breakdown of carbohydrates are *carbon dioxide* and *water*, which are carried away by the bloodstream and excreted from the body. The lungs excrete both carbon dioxide and water, and water is also excreted by the kidneys and skin. The breakdown of glucose may be incomplete if the oxygen supply is insufficient. This gives rise to the production of lactic acid, which causes the pain of acute cramp, as occurs in violent exercise in the muscles. The presence of lactic acid in the blood stimulates the respiration, increasing the oxygen in the blood, and the breakdown of glucose can then be completed (see Chapter 4).

The metabolism of carbohydrate is controlled by *insulin* and *glucagon*, hormones secreted by the pancreas (see Chapter 24). Without insulin the tissues are not able to utilize glucose and the liver is not able to store it as glycogen. If the insulin supply is normal, the amount of glucose in the blood varies only very slightly and is normally about 3.3–5.5 mmol/l of blood. After a meal it will rise slightly. The rise immediately stimulates the pancreas to make and release more insulin, and the extra insulin causes the liver and muscles to store any excess quickly, and the blood glucose falls to normal again.

Glucagon is released as a response to a lowered blood glucose level and stimulates the liver to convert stored glycogen to glucose. If there is a deficiency of insulin, the blood glucose rises too high and neither liver nor muscles can store glucose to this increased extent. This occurs in diabetes mellitus, a condition in which the pancreas fails to produce an adequate quantity of insulin, so that the blood contains excess glucose which cannot be reabsorbed by the renal tubules (see page 237) and is therefore excreted in the urine. Fat is utilized instead of glucose for fuel and this is dangerous (see page 203). A person who has diabetes mellitus may be treated with insulin injections. However, glucose and insulin requirements must be carefully balanced as too much insulin in the blood is very serious and can lead to convulsions, coma and death.

Fats

Fats, like carbohydrates, consist of carbon, hydrogen and oxygen, but do not contain as much oxygen in proportion to the hydrogen present. They also serve as body fuel. They are the best source of fuel from the point of view that 1 g of fat produces twice as much energy as 1 g of sugar. On the other hand, they are not so easy to digest and absorb and not so readily broken down in the tissues. Fats can only be completely broken down to form carbon dioxide and water if glucose is also broken down at the same time. If there is not sufficient glucose, the breakdown of fat is incomplete and acidic *ketone bodies* are formed in the tissues. These cause fatigue in the muscles and if present in large quantities alter the pH of the blood, causing acidosis, which may lead to coma and death. Severe acidosis is only likely to occur in diabetic patients, who are unable to utilize glucose, and in starvation, when the small quantity of glucose which the body can store has been used up and the large quantities of fat which the body can store are forming the main source of body fuel.

Fats are obtained from both animal and plant matter. The chief sources of fat are:
- Animal
  (a) Fat meat and fish oils
  (b) Butter
  (c) Milk and cream
- Plant
  (a) Nut oil, contained in margarine
  (b) Olive oil

Fats are compounds of glycerol and fatty acids. Different fats contain different acids, e.g. fat meat contains stearic acid, butter contains butyric acid and olive oil contains oleic acid.

Animal fats are more expensive to produce than plant fats but are more valuable as food because they contain the fat-soluble vitamins A and D. These vitamins are now added to non-animal fat products, e.g. margarine, in an effort to protect people from deficiency diseases due to lack of these fat-soluble vitamins.

Fat metabolism

Fat is emulsified by bile salts and split up into fatty acids and glycerol by the lipase enzymes in the pancreatic and intestinal juices. The fatty acids and glycerol are absorbed by the lacteals and pass through the lymphatic circulation, up the thoracic duct and into the bloodstream (Fig. 22.3).

Fat serves as fuel for the production of heat and energy in the tissues. Before fats can be used as fuel in the tissues they must be prepared by the liver. This involves a chemical process carried out by the liver cells, and is known as the *desaturation* of fats.

Fat is also required for the building of various tissues, e.g. nerve tissue, fatty tissue and marrow. Fat derivatives are found in the secretions of certain glands and are required for the manufacture of cell membranes.

Fat not required for immediate use as fuel can be stored as fatty tissue. This is found particularly in the subcutaneous tissue and in the body cavities. Whereas glucose can only be stored as glycogen in very limited quantities, the total being about 225 g in liver and muscles, fat can be stored in very large quantities. However, large stores of fat give rise to obesity, which is associated with an increased risk of disease.

The 'putting-on' of fat does not necessarily mean that too much fat is being eaten, as the body can convert excess glucose and excess protein into fat for storage. The metabolism of the three foodstuffs is therefore closely linked and the taking of food of any kind in excess of the needs of the tissues will lead to an increase in weight.

The waste products of complete fat metabolism are *carbon dioxide* and *water*; these are excreted by the lungs, skin and kidneys, as in the case of carbohydrates. If breakdown is incomplete, the ketone bodies formed also leave the body by the same routes. The volatile ketone can be detected in

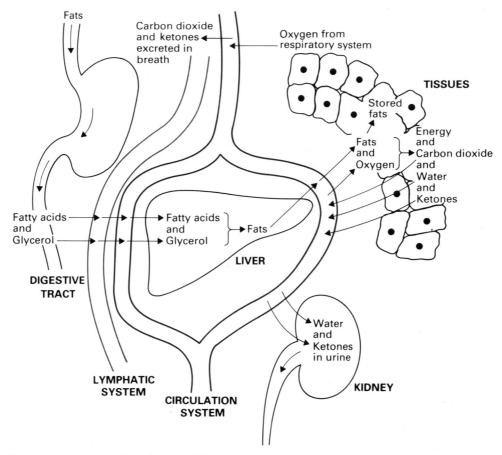

Fig. 22.3 Diagrammatic representation of fat metabolism.

the breath as a 'sweet' smell, and ketones can be found in the urine.

Water

Water is a simple compound of hydrogen and oxygen with the formula H_2O. It forms about 60% of the body weight and is present in most of the foods we eat. Lean meat is three-quarters water, milk contains 87% water, while cabbage contains as much as 92% water. In addition to the water contained in food, the body needs 1.5 to 2 litres of water every day. Water is required for many purposes, the main ones being:
- The building of body tissues and body fluids
- The excretion of waste products
- The making of digestive and lubricating fluids
- The cooling of the body by the evaporation of sweat

Water balance

Water is one of the essential substances, but can be absorbed and used in the body without chemical change. It enters into many of the metabolic reactions which occur in the body, combining with proteins, carbohydrates and fats in digestion and being split off from them when they are used as fuel to produce energy. It is usual to consider the balance rather than the metabolism of water, salts, and the electrolytes which the salts form in the body.

Water forms the greater part of the body cells and the body fluids. This proportion must be maintained since all processes of life require the presence of water. Of the total amount of water in the body,

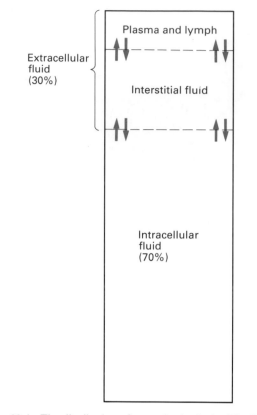

Extracellular fluid (30%)

Plasma and lymph

Interstitial fluid

Intracellular fluid (70%)

Fig. 22.4 The distribution of water in the body. The fluid-containing compartments are separated by semi-permeable membranes, through which water constantly passes.

70% is inside the body cells (*intracellular*) and the remaining 30% is in the body fluids (*extracellular*) (Fig. 22.4); 15 to 20% of the extracellular water is in the interstitial spaces of the tissues, bathing all the body cells, and the remaining 10 to 15% forms the fluid of the blood, i.e. the plasma, and the lymph. These volumes of fluid are separated only by thin semi-permeable membranes—the cell walls and the capillary walls. Water constantly passes through these walls from one of these areas to another, though the volume of each remains remarkably constant in normal health.

The water of which our bodies are largely made is, however, not static. Fresh water is taken in by the body each day and passes out of it by a number of channels. The total quantities taken in and passed out must balance one another. Water is taken in as water and other fluids drunk, and also in the foods eaten, which, like the body, consist largely of water.

On an average the healthy man takes in 1.5–2 litres of fluid as water and other drinks daily and a little over 1 litre in his food, and about 500 ml is formed by the addition of oxygen to hydrogen in the food during its metabolism. A similar quantity of water is passed out of the body via the lungs as water vapour (400–500 ml), via the skin as sweat (800–900 ml), via the kidneys as urine (1000–1500 ml) and via the faeces (150–200 ml) (Fig. 22.5).

The quantities lost in urine, sweat and water vapour from the lungs vary with conditions. In hot weather and heavy work more sweat is produced to cool the body, and less urine is passed; at the same time the loss of fluid causes thirst, so that more fluid is drunk. In fever the same changes take place; there is increased loss of fluid and there must be increased intake to balance it.

Electrolytes

In addition to the balance of the quantity of water in the body, the body fluids must be of the correct composition, i.e. they must contain the correct balance of electrolytes. Electrolytes are ions in solution and are formed when the various salts are dissolved in water (see page 7). They carry electric charges and are of two types—negatively charged particles (anions) and positively charged particles (cations). The total of negatively charged ions must balance the total of positively charged ions. The main negatively charged ions are chloride (Cl^-), bicarbonate (HCO_3^-) and phosphate (HPO_4^{2-}); chloride and bicarbonate are present in quantity in plasma and interstitial fluid, while intracellular fluid contains mainly phosphate. The main positively charged ions are sodium (Na^+) and potassium (K^+), with a little calcium (Ca^{2+}) and magnesium (Mg^{2+}). Sodium is the main positive ion in plasma and interstitial fluid, while intracellular fluid contains chiefly potassium.

Salts and the ions produced from them can pass through the semi-permeable membranes from one fluid area to another, ensuring the quantities of each are maintained correctly for each fluid area. Although the same ions are present in each fluid area, the amount of each varies, as discussed above.

The quantities of the various ions are given in millimoles per litre (mmol/l). In plasma there are normally 155 mmol/l of negatively charged ions, balanced by 155 mmol/l of positively charged ions. The bulk of these are provided by chloride

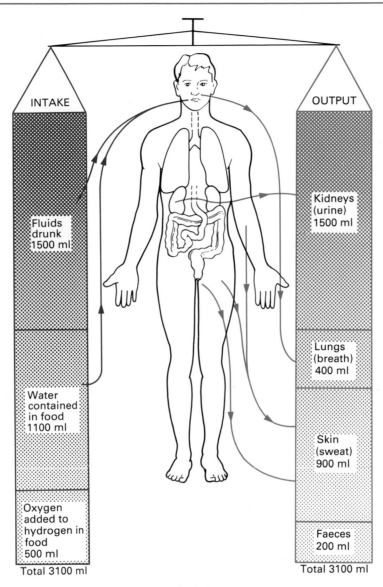

Fig. 22.5 Diagrammatic representation of water balance in the body.

(102 mmol/l) and sodium (143 mmol/l). These figures are given for reference, as the nurse will see them in laboratory results of tests performed to check for deficiencies or excess of various electrolytes in the blood. Such changes may result from altered intake or excretion of the electrolyte concerned.

Salts are contained in all foodstuffs, and in a balanced diet sufficient are ingested to maintain the normal electrolyte balance. Sodium chloride (com-mon salt) is added to food in cooking and when eating for flavour reasons.

Sodium is present in all tissues; the body fluids contain sodium chloride at a concentration of 150 mmol/l. Sodium carbonate and sodium phosphate are also always present in the blood and tissues, where they act as buffers. Sodium salts are mostly obtained from animal foodstuffs.

Potassium is present in all tissue cells. It is obtained particularly from plant foodstuffs.

Calcium is present in all tissues, particularly in bone, in teeth, and in blood, and is necessary for normal functioning of nerves. It is obtained chiefly from milk, cheese, eggs and green vegetables. Adults require 400 to 500 mg daily.

Iron is essential for the formation of the haemoglobin of red blood cells. It is obtained from green vegetables, particularly spinach and cabbage, egg yolk and red meats. Men require 10 mg daily; women 10 to 15 mg.

Phosphorus is needed for the building of the body tissues. It is obtained from the yolk of egg, milk and green vegetables.

Iodine is required for the formation of thyroxine, the hormone secreted by the thyroid gland. It is obtained from seafood and is present in green vegetables.

Vitamins

Vitamins are substances which are also essential to normal health. Without them diseases occur which are known as deficiency diseases. Vitamins are present in small quantities in foodstuffs and only minute traces are required each day. Their discovery dates back to the period following the 1914–18 war, and as their composition was at first unknown they were named after the letters of the alphabet. The chief vitamins are:

- Vitamin A
- The vitamin B complex
- Vitamin C
- Vitamin D
- Vitamin E
- Vitamin K

Vitamins A, D, E, and K are fat-soluble.

Vitamin A

Vitamin A is present in animal fats and is added to margarine during manufacture. In carrots, green vegetables and in all yellow fruits a substance called *carotene* is found. This is formed under the influence of sunlight and may be converted by the body to vitamin A. Lack of vitamin A causes stunted growth and lowered resistance to infection; the mucous membranes are particularly affected and allow easy access to bacteria. The conjunctiva of the eye is also affected; a form of conjunctivitis known as xerophthalmia occurs, in which the conjunctiva loses its transparency and becomes thickened or cornified. Vitamin A deficiency also has an effect on the retina, causing night blindness i.e. an inability to see at night.

The vitamin B complex

The vitamin B complex consists of a number of vitamins, although it was originally thought to be a single substance. These factors are found particularly in the husks and germs of cereals and pulses, and in yeast and yeast extracts. They are also present to a lesser extent in vegetables, fruit, milk, eggs and meat. White flour and the bread, cakes and pastries made from it do not contain the B vitamins, nor do polished rice and barley. Hence brown bread and wholemeal flour have a food value that white bread and flour lack and where the latter form a large part of the diet a subnormal state of health or even deficiency disease may be present.

The chief factors in the vitamin B complex are:

Vitamin B_1 (aneurine or thiamine)

This is essential for carbohydrate metabolism and the nutrition of nerve cells; a marked deficiency of it leads to beri-beri, in which there is inflammation of the nerves, causing weakness and numbness of the legs.

Vitamin B_2 (riboflavin)

This is essential for proper functioning of cell enzymes.

Vitamin B_3 (nicotinic acid)

This is essential for carbohydrate metabolism. A lack of this factor causes pellagra, in which there are skin eruptions, gastrointestinal changes and mental changes.

Vitamin B_6 (pyroxidine)

This is believed to be necessary for protein metabolism.

Vitamin B_{12} (cyanocobalamin)

This is an anti-anaemic substance which is absorbed by the villi of the small intestine and stored in the liver. It is satisfactorily absorbed only in the presence of hydrochloric acid and an intrinsic factor produced by the lining of the stomach. Vitamin B_{12} is essential for the proper development of red cells in the red bone marrow. Lack of it in the diet, or inability to absorb it, causes pernicious anaemia.

Folic acid

This is also necessary for the maturation of red blood cells.

Vitamin C

Vitamin C (ascorbic acid) is water-soluble and is found in fresh fruit, particularly citrus fruits (oranges, grapefruit and lemons), in green vegetables and in potatoes. It is important in tissue respiration, wound repair and resistance to infection, and affects the condition of capillary walls, which become abnormally fragile if it is not present in plentiful supply in the diet. Lack of vitamin C causes the condition known as scurvy.

Table 22.2 The chief vitamins.

Vitamin	Found in	Problems caused by deficiency	Special properties
A	Animal fats Carrots Green vegetables	Stunted growth Lowered resistance to infection Disorders of the conjunctiva and retina (night blindness)	Fat-soluble Can be manufactured by the body from carotene
B complex B_1 (aneurine, thiamine)	Unrefined cereals and pulses Yeast/yeast extracts Vegetables, fruit, milk, eggs, meat	Affects carbohydrate metabolism and nutrition of nerve cells Beri-beri	
B_2 (riboflavine)	As for B_1	Inadequate functioning of cell enzymes	
B_3 (nicotinic acid)	As for B_1	Affects carbohydrate metabolism Pellagra	
B_6 (pyridoxine)	As for B_1	Affects protein metabolism	
B_{12} (cyanocobalamin)	As for B_1	Pernicious anaemia	Absorbed by villi of small intestine and stored in liver
Folic acid	As for B_1	Anaemia	
C (ascorbic acid)	Fresh fruit (especially citrus) Green vegetables Potatoes	Fragility of capillary wall Lowered resistance to infection Retards tissue repair and wound healing Scurvy	Water-soluble Readily destroyed by heat
D	Animal fats Cod liver oil Halibut liver oil	Inadequate development of bones and teeth Rickets	Can be made in the skin by action of sunlight (UV rays) on ergosterols present Fat-soluble
E	Vegetable oils Cereals	Rarely deficient in man	Fat-soluble
K	Green vegetables Liver	Tendency to haemorrhage	Fat-soluble

Vitamin C is particularly readily destroyed by heat, hence some fresh fruit or salad should be included in the daily diet. Cabbage and other greens provide a very rich source of vitamin C and are comparatively cheap. However, cooking for a long period of time lessens the content of vitamin C; for this reason, they should be eaten raw or finely shredded and cooked only until tender.

Under normal circumstances the eating of a balanced diet containing plenty of fresh fruit and vegetables makes the taking of vitamin C in tablet form unnecessary and inadvisable.

Vitamin D

Vitamin D is found in animal fats; cod-liver and halibut-liver oil are very rich sources. It is also added to margarine during manufacture. Vitamin D can also be made in the body by the action of ultraviolet rays on substances in the skin known as ergosterols.

Vitamin D is essential for the development of bone and teeth, as it affects the use of calcium and phosphorus in the body. Lack of vitamin D causes rickets in children, so that it is also known as the antirachitic vitamin.

Vitamin E

Vitamin E is present in vegetable oils and cereals. It has been shown to be essential for reproduction in rats, but little is known of its importance in human beings.

Vitamin K

Vitamin K can be obtained from green vegetables and liver. Deficiency leads to impaired blood clotting, since vitamin K is involved in the formation of prothrombin and other clotting factors in the blood. Vitamin K is also synthesized in the intestine by bacteria.

Roughage (dietary fibre)

As well as the foodstuffs discussed above, the diet should also contain fibre. This is formed from the cellulose found in plant foods. Man does not have the appropriate enzyme to break down cellulose, so it remains in the gastrointestinal tract and is eliminated in the faeces. Research strongly suggests that a diet low in fibre predisposes to diseases of the bowel.

Some researchers think that cancer of the bowel is caused because a low-fibre diet results in less frequent eliminations, so that the cells of the bowel are in contact longer with possible carcinogenic substances in the food. Other researchers have found that a diet high in fibre decreases the pressure inside the large bowel, reducing the pressure on the bowel wall; this is thought to prevent the development of diverticular disease. A slow-moving bowel, because of a lack of fibre, also enables more water to be reabsorbed from the faeces and this contributes towards constipation.

It must be remembered that faeces consists mainly of water (about 75% of its weight) and that the solid portion is formed not only of dietary substances but also consists of bacteria, dead cells, bile pigments and salts. This means that faeces can be formed and excreted even if a person is fasting.

Diet

The diet is the daily ration of foods required by the individual. Humans require a mixed diet, i.e. a diet consisting of different animal and plant foods, as no single article of food contains all the essential foodstuffs in the proportions required for health. Milk and oysters contain all the nutrients or foodstuffs required, but not in the proportions the body requires. Cow's milk contains on average:

Protein (caseinogen, lactalbumin)	4%
Lactose	4–5%
Fats	3.5%
Mineral salts	0.7%
Water	87–88%

A well-balanced diet should contain foodstuffs roughly in the following proportions by weight: 1 part protein, 1 part fat, 4 parts carbohydrate. In addition it must contain traces of the various vitamins. The standard daily requirements are estimated by many authorities to be:

Protein	46–56 g
Fats	66–80 g or 25% of the total calorie intake
Carbohydrate	300–400 g or 50–60% of the total calorie intake

Health may be maintained with a well-balanced diet containing the above foodstuffs in the proportions consistent with the needs of the individual. Larger amounts of protein are required by persons carrying out heavy work, either manual labour or a hard athletic programme, and also by pregnant women and growing children, especially in late adolescence. In the first group more tissue needs repairing, and in the second there is the demand for building material to make new tissue for growth, in addition to the constant repair of cells that are worn out. More fat is especially desirable for persons living in a cold environment and when prolonged staying power is required, since it is more slowly digested and absorbed. In many of the under-developed and densely populated countries, lack of animal protein and fat is responsible for a low standard of health and a high death rate, especially in the younger age groups.

The amount of carbohydrate required depends on the energy output. A man doing heavy work requires more than a sedentary worker.

The energy value of foods

The energy value of foods depends on the amount of energy which they release when broken down. The energy value of each type of foodstuff is as follows:
- 1 g of protein has an energy value of 17 kJ
- 1 g of carbohydrate has an energy value of 17 kJ
- 1 g of fat has an energy value of 38 kJ

The total energy value of an average diet should be 10 464 to 12 556 kJ per day. A man doing active work will require 12 682 kJ per day, whereas one doing sedentary work will require about 11 928 kJ. A woman will require about 9209.1 kJ per day.

The energy required by the individual is affected by:
- *Age*. Children require more energy in proportion to their weight, because they need energy for growth as well as other activities; a baby requires approximately 42 kJ/kg. They need more protein in proportion to fuel foods, because they are growing rapidly. In those aged 16 to 18 years, males require on an average one-fifth more than male adults, and females require the same quantity as male adults; this is because of the rapid growth and development that takes place at this period, in addition to the energy expended in physical activity.
- *Exercise and occupation* (see above)
- *Sex*. Males require more energy than females, females needing four-fifths of the quantity males require.
- *Weight and build*. The heavier the individual, the more food is required, except where the excess weight is due to fat.

—23

The Digestive Tract

Objectives: After studying Chapter 23 you should be able to:

1 List the parts of the digestive tract and the accessory organs.
2 Draw and label a diagram of the digestive tract indicating the relative positions of those parts.
3 State the sites of release of the digestive juices.
4 List the functions of the digestive juices.
5 Describe the process of the digestion of food-stuffs, including the absorption of their end-products.

6 State the function of the large bowel.
7 State the method of defecation.

The digestive system (Fig. 23.1) is concerned with the chewing, swallowing, digestion and absorption of food and with the elimination from the body of indigestible and undigested food. It consists of the digestive tract or alimentary canal and the accessory organs of digestion.

The *digestive tract* is about 9 m long and consists of the following parts:
● The mouth
● The pharynx
● The oesophagus
● The stomach
● The small intestine
● The large intestine, which reaches the surface of the body at the anus

The *accessory organs* are:
● The teeth
● Three pairs of salivary glands
● The liver and bile ducts (see Chapter 24)
● The pancreas (see Chapter 24).

The Mouth

The mouth is a cavity bounded externally by the lips and cheeks and leading into the pharynx (Fig. 23.2). The roof is formed by the hard and soft palates. The anterior two-thirds of the tongue fills the floor of the mouth. The walls are formed by the muscles of the cheeks. The mucous membrane which lines the mouth is continuous with the skin of the lips and with the mucous lining of the pharynx. The orbicularis oris muscle surrounds the opening of the mouth; when contracted it presses the lips together.

The *hard palate* is formed by part of the palatine bones and the palatine processes of the maxillae; its upper surface forms the floor of the nasal cavity. The *soft palate* is suspended from the posterior border of

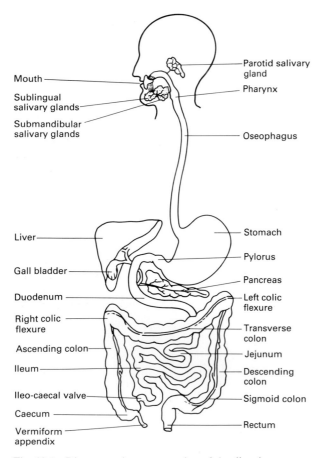

Mouth

Sublingual salivary glands

Submandibular salivary glands

Parotid salivary gland

Pharynx

Oseophagus

Liver

Gall bladder

Duodenum

Right colic flexure

Ascending colon

Ileum

Ileo-caecal valve

Caecum

Vermiform appendix

Stomach

Pylorus

Pancreas

Left colic flexure

Transverse colon

Jejunum

Descending colon

Sigmoid colon

Rectum

Fig. 23.1 Diagrammatic representation of the digestive system.

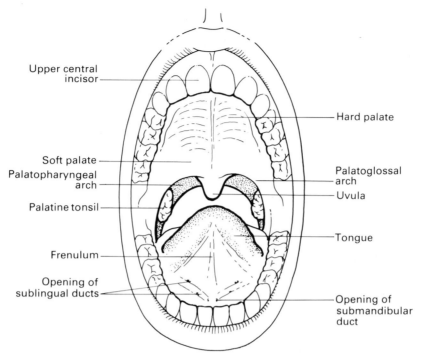

Fig. 23.2   The mouth.

the hard palate, dividing the oral and the nasal parts of the pharynx. Its lower border forms a curtain between the mouth and the pharynx and a small conical process, called the *uvula*, hangs down from it. Two curved folds of mucous membrane extend sideways and downwards from each side of the base of the uvula; these are called the *palatoglossal* and *palatopharyngeal arches*, between which lie the masses of lymphoid tissue known as the *palatine tonsils*.

The tongue

The tongue is a muscular organ which is attached to the hyoid bone and the mandible. In certain areas there are projections of the mucous membrane called *papillae*, which increase the surface area. In addition, specialized structures called *taste buds* (see page 129) are widespread over almost the entire area of the tongue. The undersurface of the anterior part of the tongue is connected to the floor of the mouth by a fold of mucous membrane called the *frenulum*.

The functions of the tongue are as follows:
- It is the organ of *taste*.
- It assists in the *mastication* of food.
- It assists in *swallowing*.
- It assists with *speech*.

The teeth

Humans are provided with two sets of teeth which appear at different ages. The first set are *deciduous* or *primary* teeth and erupt through the gums during the first and second years of life. The second set begin to replace the first about the sixth year and the process is usually complete by the 25th year. Since these cannot be replaced, and may be retained until old age, they are known as the *permanent* teeth.

Each tooth consists of three parts:
- The *crown*, which projects beyond the gum
- The *root*, which is embedded in the alveolar part of the maxilla or mandible—a tooth may have one, two or three roots
- The *neck*, which is the constricted part between the crown and the root

Each tooth contains a centre of *pulp* surrounded by a yellowish-white layer called *dentine*, which forms the main part of the tooth. The outer layer of the tooth is in two parts: that covering the crown is called *enamel* and is a hard, white layer, while that covering the root is called *cement* and is a thin layer resembling bone in structure. The pulp is richly supplied with blood vessels and nerves which enter

Table 23.1 The different types of teeth.

	Molars	Premolars	Canines	Incisors		Canines	Premolars	Molars
Deciduous teeth								
Upper jaw	2	—	1	2	2	1	—	2
Lower jaw	2	—	1	2	2	1	—	2
Permanent teeth								
Upper jaw	3	2	1	2	2	1	2	3
Lower jaw	3	2	1	2	2	1	2	3

the tooth through the foramen at the apex of each root (Fig. 23.3).

There are four types of teeth:

- The *incisors* have chisel-shaped crowns, giving a sharp cutting edge for biting food.
- The *canines* have large conical crowns.
- The *premolars* (or *bicuspids*) have almost circular crowns with two cusps for grinding food.
- The *molars* are the largest teeth, and have broad crowns with four or five cusps.

There are 20 deciduous teeth and 32 permanent teeth.

The lower central incisors are the first of the deciduous teeth to appear at the age of about 6–8 months, though occasionally they are present at birth. The upper and lateral incisors follow by the age of about 1 year and all the teeth have generally erupted by the age of 2–2½ years, though, again, there may be a wide variation.

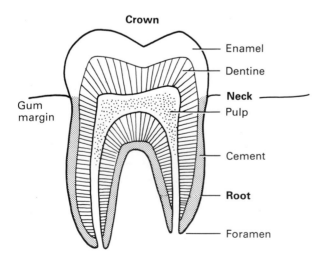

Fig. 23.3 Section of a tooth.

By the sixth year the first permanent molars have usually erupted and there are 24 teeth altogether. Next, the deciduous teeth, beginning with the incisors, drop out and the permanent teeth, which have been developing in the jaw throughout childhood, gradually replace them. All the permanent teeth have usually erupted by the age of 14 years, with the exception of the third molar, or wisdom tooth, which does not erupt until between 18 and 25 years of age. Normally the grinding teeth in the upper and lower jaws do not lie exactly opposite each other because the upper incisors are wider than the lower. This enables the cusps of the upper teeth to grind effectively with the cusps of the lower teeth. The lower teeth are usually half a tooth's width in front of the upper.

For the development of good teeth it is important that both the mother during pregnancy and the child throughout the growing period receive adequate foods rich in calcium, such as milk and eggs, and in vitamin D, which controls bone formation. It is also important that the jaws are well exercised by feeding, followed by the giving of hard foods, so that the jaws and teeth receive a good blood supply. Poor enamel, due to lack of vitamin D or calcium, will result in the early development of tooth decay. Starchy and sugary foods left in contact with the teeth, especially during the night, decompose in the mouth, producing acids which act on the calcium of the teeth and make it soluble. This causes the teeth to become softer and thus allows bacteria to enter. Poor jaw development from lack of exercise will cause the teeth to be crowded and out of position, often overlapping.

The salivary glands

There are three main pairs of salivary glands. The *parotid gland* is the largest and lies just below the ear;

its duct is about 5 cm long and opens into the mouth opposite the second upper molar tooth. It is this gland which is affected by the disease commonly known as mumps. The *submandibular gland* and the *sublingual gland* both lie under the floor of the mouth and open into it. Secretion of *saliva* is stimulated reflexly by the presence of food in the mouth or as a conditioned (or learned) reflex triggered by the sight, smell or thought of food.

Saliva

Saliva contains:

- A large amount of water which moistens and softens the food
- Mucus, which holds the food together and lubricates it for its passage down the oesophagus
- The enzyme *salivary amylase* (ptyalin) which acts on cooked starch (carbohydrate) and splits it into the disaccharide maltose and dextrin

Lubrication of food by saliva enables the taste buds to be stimulated. Saliva also cleanses the mouth and teeth and keeps the soft parts supple.

The Pharynx and Swallowing

When the food is well chewed and moistened the tongue rolls it into a *bolus* and propels it towards the oropharynx. The soft palate rises up to occlude the nasopharynx and the epiglottis moves upwards and forwards so that the bolus passes over the closed inlet of the larynx and on into the laryngopharynx and thence to the oesophagus (Fig. 23.4). The act of swallowing is an example of a situation where good muscular co-ordination is vital; if this is not achieved correctly 'choking' will result.

The Oesophagus

The oesophagus is a muscular canal about 25 cm long extending from the pharynx to the stomach. It begins at the level of the sixth cervical vertebra and descends through the mediastinum in front of the vertebral column and behind the trachea. It passes through the diaphragm at the level of the tenth thoracic vertebra and ends at the cardiac orifice of the stomach at the level of the eleventh thoracic vertebra. On each side of the upper part of the oesophagus are the corresponding common carotid arteries and parts of the thyroid gland.

The wall of the oesophagus has four coats and is similar in structure to the remainder of the alimentary canal:

- The *fibrous outer coat* consists of areolar tissue containing many elastic fibres.
- The *muscular coat* has two layers, the outer fibres running longitudinally and the inner layer running in a circular manner.
- The *submucous coat* (or areolar) connects the mucous and muscular coats and contains the larger blood vessels and nerves, as well as the mucous glands.
- The *mucous membrane* inner lining which secretes mucus.

The muscular coat of the upper two-thirds of the oesophagus is of striped voluntary muscle; the lower one-third contains unstriped involuntary muscle. The oesophagus is innervated by the vagus nerve (the tenth cranial nerve).

Movement of food through the oesophagus is by peristaltic action. *Peristalsis* means a wave of dilatation followed by a wave of contraction as succeeding muscle fibres relax and contract (see page 221). It takes about 9 seconds for a wave of peristalsis to pass the bolus of food from the pharynx to the stomach.

The Peritoneum

The peritoneum is a serous membrane which lines the abdominal cavity and covers the abdominal organs. In the male it is a closed sac, but in the female it is continuous with outside of the body as the free ends of the uterine tubes open into the peritoneal cavity (Fig. 23.6). The part which lines the abdominal wall is named the *parietal portion* (or layer) of the peritoneum; that part which covers the organs is called the *visceral portion* (or layer). The two layers are in contact with each other but have a potential space between them named the *peritoneal cavity*. Serous peritoneal fluid lubricates both the surfaces. The cavity can be divided into the greater peritoneal sac and the lesser peritoneal sac.

Other specially named areas are:

- The *greater omentum*, a double fold of peritoneum which descends from the lower border of the stomach and loops up again to the transverse colon, and helps to prevent the spread of infection from the organs into the peritoneum
- The *lesser omentum*, a fold which extends to the

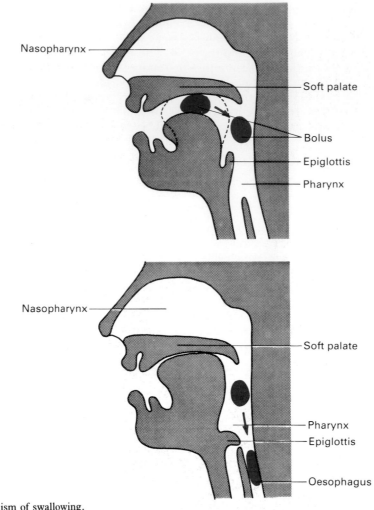

Fig. 23.4 The mechanism of swallowing.

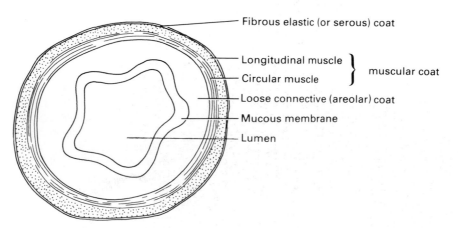

Fig. 23.5 Cross-section of the alimentary canal.

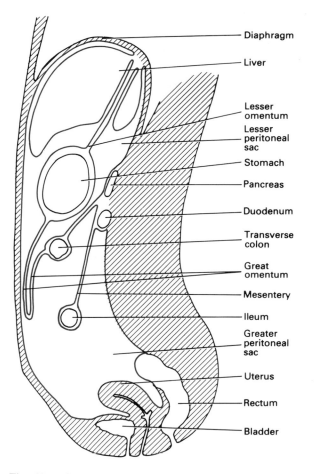

Fig. 23.6 Sagittal section through the body to show the peritoneum in a female.

liver from the lesser curvature of the stomach and the duodenum
- The *mesentery*, a broad, fan-shaped fold of peritoneum connecting the coils of the small intestine to the posterior abdominal wall

Functions of the peritoneum

The peritoneum has four main functions:
- To prevent friction as the abdominal organs move on one another and against the abdominal wall, as its free surfaces are always moist with serous fluid, which makes them smooth and glistening
- To attach the abdominal organs to the abdominal wall, except in the case of the kidneys, duodenum and pancreas, which lie behind it. The ascending and descending colon are also covered only on their anterior surface by peritoneum; this means that only the transverse or sigmoid colon can be brought on to the anterior abdominal wall for a colostomy operation
- To carry blood vessels, lymphatics and nerves to some of the abdominal organs; these run between the two folds of the mesentery
- To fight infection, as the peritoneum contains many lymphatic nodes

The Stomach

The stomach is the most dilated part of the digestive tract and is situated between the end of the oesophagus and the beginning of the small intestine. It lies below the diaphragm, slightly to the left of the

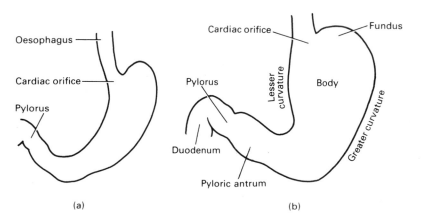

Fig. 23.7 The stomach. (a) Empty. (b) Containing food.

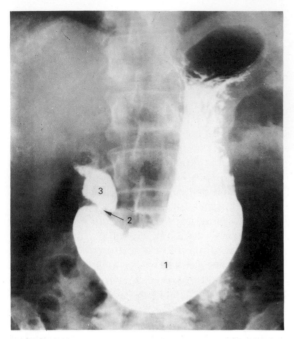

Fig. 23.8 An x-ray of the stomach after a barium meal, showing the body of the stomach (1), the constriction of the pylorus (2), and the beginning of the duodenum (3) filled with barium.

midline, but its shape and position are altered by changes within the abdominal cavity and by the stomach contents.

The stomach is approximately J-shaped and has two curved borders or curvatures. The *lesser curvature* forms the right (or posterior) border of the stomach. The *greater curvature* is much longer than the lesser curvature. It first forms an arch upwards and to the left over the *fundus* of the stomach; it then passes downwards and finally turns right to the point where it joins the duodenum. The capacity of the stomach is about 1500 ml in the adult.

The upper opening where the oesophagus joins is called the *cardiac orifice*. The circular muscle fibres of the oesophagus are slightly thicker at this point and constitute a weak *cardiac sphincter* muscle. The lower opening, into the duodenum, is called the *pyloric orifice* or *pylorus* and it is guarded by the strong *pyloric sphincter*. The function of these sphincter muscles is to prevent food regurgitating backwards.

The wall of the stomach consists of four coats:
- The outer *serous coat*, which is also the visceral layer of the peritoneum
- The *muscular coat*, which consists of three layers

of unstriped muscle fibres, the outer being longitudinal, the middle being circular and the inner being oblique
- The *submucous coat* of loose areolar tissue
- The *lining of mucous membrane*, which is honeycombed in appearance because of the presence of the gastric glands and their openings. The mucous membrane is inelastic and arranged in numerous folds, called *rugae*, which run longitudinally and which flatten out when the stomach is full. The mucus secreted by this membrane helps to lubricate the food and helps protect the stomach from destruction by its own digestive juices

Functions of the stomach

The stomach has three main functions:
- To churn up the food, breaking it up still further and mixing it with the secretions from the gastric

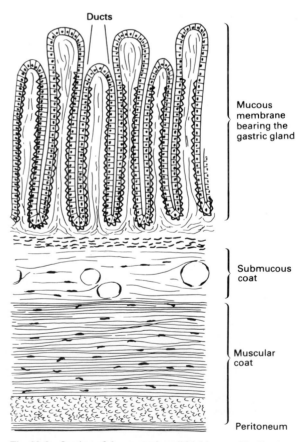

Fig. 23.9 Section of the stomach wall highly magnified to show the gastric glands.

glands. The part of the stomach just before the pyloric sphincter—the *pyloric antrum*—plays a large part in this movement; muscular contraction and relaxation sends some of the food, when liquid, through the sphincter into the small intestine and returns some to the body of the stomach for further mixing

- To continue the digestion of food by means of the gastric juice
- To secrete intrinsic factor

Very little absorption occurs in the stomach.

Three types of cell in the mucosa of the stomach produce substances which together make up the gastric juice:

- *Mucous cells* (*goblet cells*) secrete mucus, which protects the mucous membrane from the action of the other gastric juices and helps to lubricate the food
- *Chief cells* secrete an enzyme known as *pepsinogen*, and in infants another called *rennin*
- *Oxyntic cells* secrete hydrochloric acid

The secretion of the gastric juice occurs reflexly in the same way as the saliva (see page 213), causing a copious flow of fluid before and during the taking of food; this ensures gastric juices are present when food enters the stomach, so the process of digestion is not halted. The gastric glands are also stimulated by an internal secretion or hormone called *gastrin*. Gastrin is released from *G-cells* in the stomach mucosa and passes directly into the circulation; when it reaches the gastric glands it stimulates them to increase the production of gastric juice.

Gastric juice

Gastric juice consists of:

- Water, mineral salts and mucus
- Hydrochloric acid (HCl)
- Pepsinogen, which is inactive until converted by hydrochloric acid into the active enzyme pepsin; pepsin converts proteins into polypeptides
- Rennin, which is found only in infants prior to pepsin production; it converts milk protein, caseinogen, into casein and then into polypeptides

The hydrochloric acid in the gastric juice serves several purposes:

- It gives the acid pH required by the gastric enzymes.
- It kills bacteria.

- It controls the action of the pyloric sphincter.
- It stops the action of salivary amylase.
- It converts pepsinogen to pepsin (see above).

Food enters the cardiac end of the stomach, which acts as a reservoir. It may remain here for 15 to 30 minutes. The gastric juice and the churning action of the stomach muscles eventually make the food more liquid and lower in pH (more acid). Until it becomes acid, the salivary amylase in the saliva continues to act on any cooked starch in the food. When the food becomes acid, pepsin (and rennin in infants) acts on the proteins. When the food reaches the pyloric end of the stomach it is quickly acidified. The action of the muscle here is very marked, so that it acts like a mill, churning the food up and mixing it with the gastric juice.

The food remains in the stomach for a total of half to three hours or more, according to the nature of the food and the muscularity of the individual stomach. A meal rich in carbohydrate but containing little protein, such as tea, toast and cake, will leave the stomach in half-an-hour. A good mixed meal of, for example, meat, potatoes, carrots and greens, will remain for two-and-a-half to three hours or more, though it may leave earlier or stay longer according to the tone and activity of the muscular coat of the stomach.

The churning of the stomach serves to emulsify coarsely any fat which may be present and which the body heat will have softened. This converts the food into a greyish-white fluid called *chyme*.

The pyloric sphincter is normally contracted. When there is food in the stomach the gastric juice makes the contents gradually more and more acid at the pyloric end. When it reaches a certain degree of acidity the pyloric sphincter relaxes and a little food passes into the duodenum. The presence of acid food in the duodenum causes the pyloric sphincter to close and the tone of the stomach wall drives food from the cardiac reservoir down to mix with the food in the pyloric end, making it less acid. Gradually the food in the duodenum is made alkaline and that in the pyloric end of the stomach again becomes more acid; this causes the pylorus to open again, and a little more food passes into the duodenum.

The Small Intestine

The small intestine is a convoluted tube extending from the pyloric sphincter to its junction with the

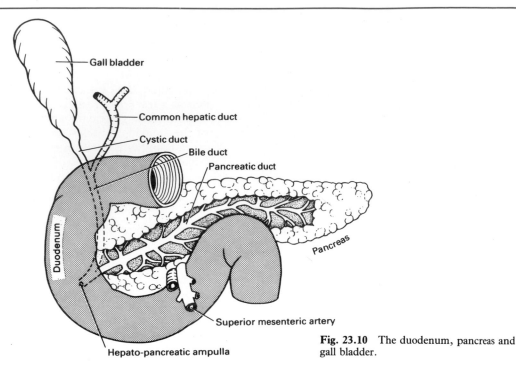

Fig. 23.10   The duodenum, pancreas and gall bladder.

large intestine at the ileo-caecal valve. It is about six metres in length and lies in the central and lower parts of the abdominal cavity, usually within the curves of the large intestine (see Fig. 23.1, page 210). The small intestine consists of the duodenum, the jejunum and the ileum.

The *duodenum* is the first part of the small intestine. It is a short curved portion of about 25 cm long and is the widest and most fixed part. It is roughly C-shaped and curves round the head of the pancreas. Ducts from the gall bladder, liver and pancreas enter the medial aspect of the duodenum through the *hepato-pancreatic ampulla*, which is guarded by a sphincter-like muscle.

The *jejunum* is the upper two-fifths of the small intestine between the duodenum and ileum. The lower three-fifths is called the *ileum*. Both are attached to the posterior abdominal wall by a fold of peritoneum called the *mesentery* (see Fig. 23.6).

The wall of the small intestine has the same four coats as the remainder of the alimentary tract:
- A serous coat, formed of peritoneum
- A muscular coat, with a thin external layer of longitudinal fibres and a thick internal layer of circular fibres

- A submucous coat, containing blood vessels, lymph vessels and nerves
- A mucous membrane lining.

The mucous membrane lining has three special features:
- It is thrown into circular folds which, unlike the rugae of the stomach, are permanent and are not obliterated when the intestine is distended. They increase the area available for absorption.
- It has a velvety appearance due to the presence of fine hair-like projections called *villi*, each containing a lymph vessel called a *lacteal* and blood vessels.
- It is supplied with *glands* of the simple, tubular type which secrete *intestinal juice*.

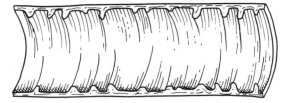

Fig. 23.11   Section of the small intestine, showing the circular folds.

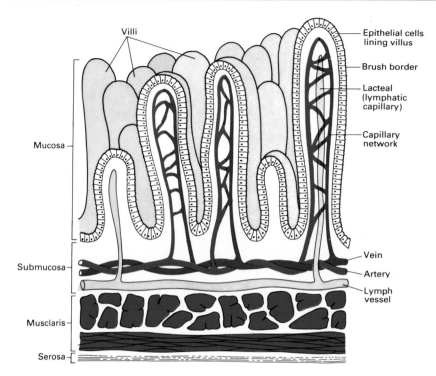

Fig. 23.12 Section of the wall of the small intestine, showing the villi.

The small intestine contains considerable amounts of lymphoid tissue (see page 179). *Solitary lymphatic follicles* are found throughout the mucous membrane but are most numerous in the lower part of the ileum. *Aggregated lymphatic follicles* form circular or oval patches large enough to be seen with the naked eye. These nodules deal with bacteria which may be absorbed from the intestine.

Functions of the small intestine

The functions of the small intestine are the digestion and absorption of food.

Digestion

Digestion is carried out by the pancreatic juice, bile and intestinal juice. The pancreatic and intestinal juices are secreted reflexly due to the presence of food in the small intestine and also in response to a hormone called *secretin* produced by the lining of the intestine (in a similar way to gastrin being secreted by the stomach wall). When food, especially that containing fat, enters the duodenum, the hormone *cholecystokinin* (CCK), which is also known as *pan-creozymin* (PZ), is released. This hormone enters the bloodstream and when it reaches the gall bladder stimulates it to contract, ejecting bile into the small intestine.

The juices are alkaline and make the food alkaline in reaction. The alkalinity finely emulsifies the fat.

The *pancreatic juice* consists of water, alkaline salts and four enzymes acting on three different foodstuffs:

- *Trypsinogen*, which is inactive until converted into active *trypsin* by enterokinase (from the intestinal juice). Trypsin converts polypeptides into small peptides consisting of only two or three amino acids. It becomes active only when it mixes with the food and the intestinal juice within the bowel. Active trypsin is not secreted by the pancreas as it would be able to digest the protein of the cells which form the gland and its ducts.
- *Carboxypeptidase*, which converts small peptides into single amino acids
- *Amylase*, which breaks up starch, cooked and uncooked, into the disaccharide maltose and dextrin
- *Lipase*, which splits fat into fatty acids and glycerol. This is helped by the action of bile, which

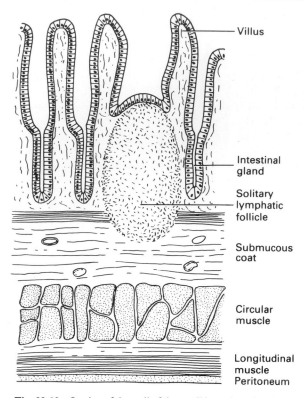

Villus

Intestinal gland

Solitary lymphatic follicle

Submucous coat

Circular muscle

Longitudinal muscle
Peritoneum

Fig. 23.13 Section of the wall of the small intestine, showing the lymphoid tissue.

emulsifies the fat, increasing its surface area and thereby increasing the area on which the lipase can act.

The *bile* contains no enzymes, but is rich in alkaline salts, which emulsify and saponify (i.e. make soaps from) the fats.

The *intestinal juice* contains water, salts and enzymes. The enzymes are:

- *Enterokinase*, which converts trypsinogen secreted by the pancreas to active trypsin
- *Peptidases*, which act on small peptides, breaking them up into single amino acids
- *Maltase*, which breaks up maltose to form glucose
- *Sucrase*, which breaks up the disaccharide cane sugar (sucrose) to form glucose and another simple sugar
- *Lactase*, which breaks up the disaccharide lactose to form glucose and another simple sugar
- *Lipase*, which completes the conversion of fats to fatty acids and glycerol

These juices are mixed with the food by the muscular action of the wall of the small intestine known as *peristalsis* (Fig. 23.14). The contractions occur first at one place and then at another and are followed by relaxation. They have a kneading or

Table 23.2 Enzymes involved in the digestion of foodstuffs.

Enzyme	Acts on:	To produce:
Mouth		
Salivary amylase	Cooked starch (carbohydrate)	Maltose (a disaccharide) + dextrin
Stomach		
Pepsin	Proteins	Polypeptides
Rennin (in infants)	Milk protein	Polypeptides
Pancreatic juice		
Trypsin	Polypeptides	Small peptides
Carboxypeptidase	Small peptides	Amino acids
Amylase	Starch (carbohydrate)	Maltose (a disaccharide) + dextrin
Lipase	Fats	Fatty acids + glycerol
Intestinal juice		
Peptidases	Small peptides	Amino acids
Maltase	Maltose	Glucose
Sucrase	Sucrose (a disaccharide)	Glucose + another simple sugar
Lactase	Lactose (a disaccharide)	Glucose + another simple sugar
Lipase	Fats	Fatty acids + glycerol

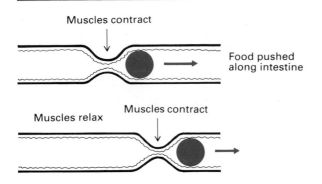

Fig. 23.14   Diagrammatic representation of peristalsis.

churning effect and bring the mucous lining into close contact with the contents of the bowel.

Absorption

The absorption of the products of digested proteins, carbohydrates and fats takes place almost entirely through the villi in the small intestine. Very little food is absorbed from the stomach, as it is not yet sufficiently digested. Even food which is absorbable (e.g. glucose and water) does not usually stay in the stomach, but merely passes through it. *Proteins* in the form of amino acids and *carbohydrates* in the form of simple sugars are absorbed by the cells covering the villi and pass into the *blood capillaries*, and are carried by the portal vein to the liver. *Fats* in the form of fatty acids and glycerol are absorbed by the cells covering the villi and built up again by them into droplets of fat. These pass into the lymph within the villi and are drained away by the lymphatic capillaries or *lacteals*, which are so named because the lymph they contain looks milk-like due to the droplets of fat in suspension. The fat passes via the lymphatic vessels to the cisterna chyli and is carried up the thoracic duct into the bloodstream (see page 181).

The Large Intestine

The large intestine (Fig. 23.15) extends from the end of the ileum to the anus and is about 1.5 metres long. It forms an arch which encloses most of the small intestine, and is divided into seven sections:
- The caecum
- The ascending colon
- The transverse colon
- The descending colon
- The sigmoid colon
- The rectum
- The anal canal

The *caecum* lies in the right iliac fossa. It is a dilated sac which is continuous above with the ascending colon. The ileum opens into the caecum through the *ileo-caecal valve*. This valve is a sphincter which is normally closed and prevents the caecal contents passing back into the ileum. Taking food into the stomach initiates peristalsis of the duodenum and the rest of the small intestine. The ileo-caecal valve opens in response and allows the passage of the contents of the ileum into the caecum. This is called the *gastro-colic reflex*.

The *vermiform appendix* is a narrow blind-ended tube which opens out of the caecum about 2 cm below the ileo-caecal valve. It is usually about 9 cm long, though it can vary from 2–20 cm in length and can occupy a variety of positions within the abdomen. The submucous coat of the appendix contains considerable amounts of lymphoid tissue. It has no apparent function in man.

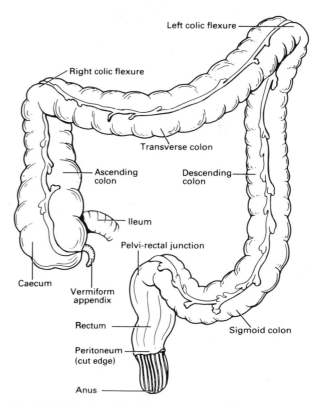

Fig. 23.15   The large intestine.

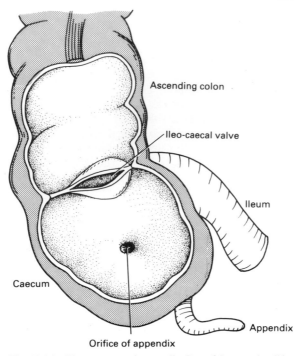

Fig. 23.16   The caecum and appendix. Part of the caecal wall has been cut away.

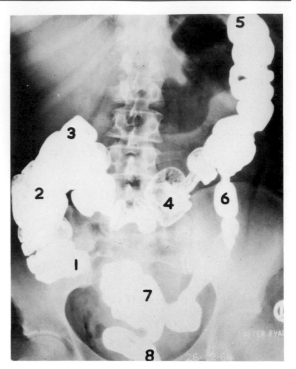

Fig. 23.17   An x-ray of the colon. 1 = caecum and appendix; 2 = ascending colon; 3 = right colic flexure; 4 = transverse colon; 5 = left colic flexure; 6 = descending colon; 7 = sigmoid colon; 8 = beginning of rectum.

The *ascending colon* is about 15 cm in length and is narrower than the caecum. It ascends the right side of the abdomen to the undersurface of the liver, where it bends forwards and to the left at the *right colic* or *hepatic flexure*.

The *transverse colon* is about 50 cm in length and passes across the abdomen to the undersurface of the spleen in an inverted arch. Here it curves sharply downwards at the *left colic* or *splenic flexure*.

The *descending colon* is about 25 cm in length and passes down the left side of the abdomen to the inlet of the lesser pelvis, where it becomes the sigmoid colon.

The *sigmoid colon* forms a loop which is about 40 cm in length and lies within the lesser pelvis.

The *rectum* is continuous above with the sigmoid colon. It is about 12 cm long and passes through the pelvic floor to become the anal canal.

The *anal canal* passes downwards and backwards to end at the anus. At the junction of the rectum and the anus the unstriped circular muscle becomes thickened to form the *internal anal sphincter* which surrounds the upper three-quarters of the anal canal. The *external anal sphincter* surrounds the whole length of the anal canal. It is the tone of these

sphincters which keeps the anal canal and the anus closed. The external sphincter can be contracted voluntarily to close the anus more firmly.

The wall of the large intestine has the same four coats as the remainder of the alimentary tract:

- The outer serous coat of peritoneum
- The muscular coat of external longitudinal and internal circular fibres. The longitudinal fibres form a continuous layer, but in some places the layer is thickened to form three bands called the

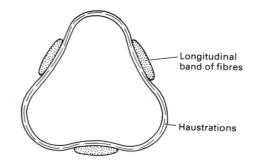

Fig. 23.18   Cross-section of the large intestine.

taeniae coli. These bands are shorter than the other coats of the large intestine and produce a puckered or sacculated appearance. The sacculations are called the *haustrations* or *haustra.*
- The submucous coat
- The lining of mucous membrane

Functions of the large intestine

The large intestine has two main functions:
- To absorb water and salts (although absorption also occurs in the small intestine)
- To eliminate faeces

The material which enters the large intestine is in a very fluid state and consists of:
- Water
- Salts
- Cellulose, which is indigestible
- Dead cells from the lining of the intestine
- Minimal food, as this has been digested and absorbed
- Bacteria, which are very numerous

Although many are killed in the stomach by the acid there, the alkaline medium, food, warmth and moisture in the small intestine encourage the growth of bacteria. In the colon, water and salts are quickly absorbed, so that the fluid is rapidly turned into a paste containing the cellulose, dead cells and bacteria. This paste forms the faeces.

Movements of the colon are similar to those seen in the small intestine, but waves of peristalsis occur less frequently. A very strong wave of peristalsis occurs three to four times a day and moves material on into the sigmoid colon. At intervals movements propel the faeces into the rectum, from which they are eliminated.

Defecation, or the passing of faeces out of the body, occurs because of the movement of food residue from the sigmoid colon into the rectum, which becomes distended. This distension causes a reflex contraction of the rectal muscles which tends to expel the contents through the anus, though this depends on the relaxation of the external anal sphincter. Defecation is therefore a reflex action which can be inhibited voluntarily. The gastro-colic reflex also causes emptying of the rectum (see page

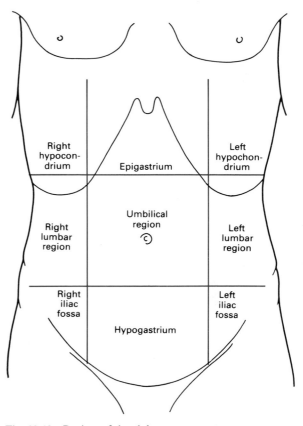

Fig. 23.19 Regions of the abdomen.

221). If defecation is delayed the sensation of fullness in the rectum passes off, more water is absorbed from the faeces through the rectal wall and constipation may occur.

Regions of the Abdomen

For the purposes of description the abdomen is divided into nine regions by two transverse and two vertical lines. The regions in which they lie may be used to describe the position of organs; for example, the stomach lies in the left hypochondriac, epigastric and umbilical regions. The kidneys are in the right and left lumbar regions respectively. The caecum is in the right iliac fossa. The bladder, when full, rises into the hypogastric region.

24

The Liver, Biliary System and Pancreas

Objectives: After studying Chapter 24 you should be able to:

1 Describe the structure of the liver.
2 List the functions of the liver.
3 Discuss these functions in detail.
4 Describe the structure of the biliary system.
5 State the functions of the gall bladder.
6 Describe the functions of bile.
7 Describe the structure of the pancreas.
8 List the enzymes produced by the pancreas.
9 List the hormones produced by the pancreas and state their functions.

The Liver

The liver (Fig. 24.1) is situated in the upper right part of the abdominal cavity, occupying almost all of the right hypochondrium and fitting under the diaphragm. It is divided into two main *lobes* by the *falciform ligament*, the right lobe being much larger than the left. The right lobe lies over the right colic flexure and the right kidney, and the left lobe lies over the stomach.

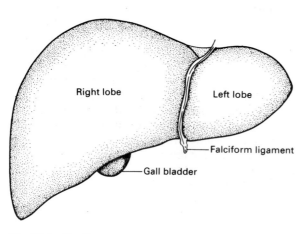

Fig. 24.1 The liver.

Structure of the liver

The two lobes of the liver consist of a large number of *hepatic lobules* (Fig. 24.2) which appear polygonal in shape when cut through. Each is about 1 mm in diameter and has a small central intralobular vein (a tributary of the hepatic veins). Around the edges of the lobules are the *portal canals*, each containing a branch of the *portal vein* (interlobular vein), a branch of the *hepatic artery* and a small *bile duct*. These three structures together are known as the *portal triad*.

The lobules are composed of *liver cells*. These are large cells with one or two nuclei and fine granular cytoplasm. The liver cells are arranged in sheets, one cell in thickness, called *hepatic laminae*. These laminae are arranged irregularly to form walls with bridges of liver cells connecting adjacent laminae. Between the laminae are spaces which contain small veins with many connections between them and small bile ducts known as *bile canaliculi*.

The portal vein brings blood rich in foodstuffs from the alimentary tract to the liver. The hepatic artery brings blood rich in oxygen from the arterial system. These blood vessels divide up into smaller vessels and form large blood channels known as *sinusoids* among the liver cells forming the hepatic laminae. The blood in the sinusoids then drains into the small veins in the centre of each lobule, which eventually drain into the hepatic vein. In this way the hepatic vein carries away the blood which was brought to the liver by both the portal vein and the hepatic artery.

Functions of the liver

The functions of the liver can be divided into three: metabolic, storage and secretory.

Metabolic functions

● Stored fat is broken down to provide energy.

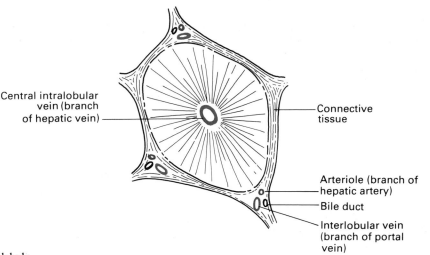

Fig. 24.2   A liver lobule.

Labels on figure:
- Central intralobular vein (branch of hepatic vein)
- Connective tissue
- Arteriole (branch of hepatic artery)
- Bile duct
- Interlobular vein (branch of portal vein)

- Excess amino acids are broken down and the nitrogen converted to urea (see page 200).
- Drugs and poisons are detoxicated.
- Vitamin A is synthesized from carotene.
- Some plasma proteins are synthesized.
- Worn-out tissue cells are broken down to form uric acid and urea.
- Excess carbohydrate is converted to fat for storage in the fat depots.
- The proteins prothrombin and fibrinogen, which are involved in blood clotting, are synthesized from amino acids.
- Antibodies and antitoxins are manufactured.
- Heparin is manufactured.
- The liver is the main heat-producing organ of the body.

Storage functions

The liver stores:
- Vitamins A, B_{12} and D
- Iron from the diet and from worn-out blood cells
- Glucose, which is stored as glycogen and converted back to glucose in the presence of the hormone glucagon as required

Secretory functions

The formation of urea. The amino acids derived from the diet are absorbed by the villi of the small intestine and brought by the portal vein to the liver.

Other amino acids are derived from normal cell breakdown. The amino acids required to make good the wear and tear of tissue and produce its growth and other proteins in the body are allowed to pass straight through the liver into the bloodstream. Others are used in the liver to form the blood proteins. Any excess protein or protein which is unsuitable for tissue building undergoes *de-amination* in the liver to form body fuel and urea (see page 199). Urea is a soluble substance which the bloodstream carries from the liver to the kidneys for excretion from the body.

The secretion of bile. Bile is formed from constituents brought by the blood. It is a thick, alkaline, greenish-yellow fluid secreted by the liver cells. The liver secretes on average about one litre of bile each day. The bile consists of water, bile salts, bile pigments and cholesterol. The bile salts are sodium salts of organic acids. The bile pigments are derived from the haem part of the haemoglobin of worn-out red blood cells. The pigments, *bilirubin* and to a lesser extent *biliverdin* are changed by bacterial action as they pass through the bowel to *stercobilinogen* and *stercobilin*, which give the normal colour to the faeces. Some of the pigments are reabsorbed into the bloodstream as they pass through the bowel and are found in the blood. They are then excreted via the kidney as *urobilinogen*.

The functions of bile are given below:
- It helps to *emulsify* and *saponify* fats in the small intestine. This is a function of the bile salts. In

this way the surface area is increased, providing a greater area for the action of enzymes.

- It stimulates *peristalsis* in the intestine.
- It is a channel for *excretion* of pigments and toxic substances from the bloodstream, such as the breakdown products of some drugs.
- It acts as a *deodorant* to the faeces, lessening their offensive odour.

From the list of its functions it will be seen that the liver is essential to life. It is, however, able to undertake more work than is usually demanded of it and a considerable part may be destroyed by disease before liver failure occurs.

The Biliary System

The biliary system consists of:
- The *right* and *left hepatic ducts*, which leave the liver and unite to form the *common hepatic duct*
- The *gall bladder*, which acts as a reservoir for bile
- The *cystic duct*, which leads from the gall bladder to the bile duct
- The *common bile duct*, which is formed by the joining of the common hepatic and cystic ducts.

The *gall bladder* is a pear-shaped organ situated on the undersurface of the right lobe of the liver. The *cystic duct*, which is about 3–4 cm long, passes from the gall bladder in a backwards and downwards

direction to join the *common hepatic duct*; together they form the *common bile duct* (Fig. 24.3). If the bile secreted by the liver is not required immediately for purposes of digestion it passes up the cystic duct into

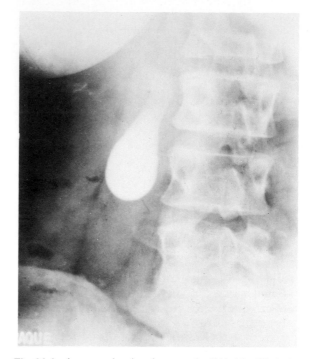

Fig. 24.4 An x-ray showing the normal gall bladder filled with contrast medium.

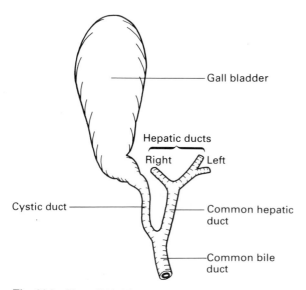

Fig. 24.3 The gall bladder and its ducts.

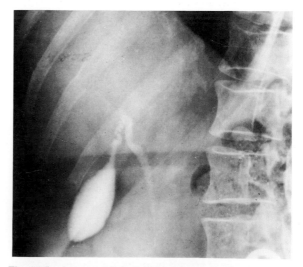

Fig. 24.5 An x-ray of the gall bladder emptying after a fatty meal, the contrast medium filling the cystic and common bile ducts.

the gall bladder, where it is both concentrated and stored. The capacity of the gall bladder is between 30 and 60 ml, but because of the ability of the gall bladder to absorb water the bile it contains becomes increasingly concentrated. When fatty food enters the duodenum the sphincter at the entrance to the bile duct relaxes and bile stored in the gall bladder is driven into the intestine by contraction of the walls of the gall bladder (Figs. 24.4 and 24.5).

The gall bladder and cystic ducts are composed of three layers: a serous layer, a muscular layer and a mucosal lining. The mucosal lining is arranged in ridges or *rugae*. It is the spasm of the muscular layer which causes pain when a gall stone obstructs the biliary system.

The Pancreas

The pancreas is a soft, greyish-pink gland, 12–15 cm in length, which lies transversely across the posterior abdominal wall (see Fig. 23.10, page 218) behind the stomach. The *head* of the gland lies within the curve of the duodenum and the *tail* extends as far as the spleen. The *body* and *neck* lie between these two. The *pancreatic duct* lies within the gland. It begins with the junction of the small ducts from the pancreatic lobules in the tail of the pancreas and runs from left to right through the gland, receiving small ducts all the way. At the head of the pancreas the pancreatic duct is joined by the bile duct and they usually open together into the

duodenum at the *hepato-pancreatic ampulla*, though occasionally there are two separate openings.

The pancreas is composed of lobules (Fig. 24.6), each of which consists of one of the tiny vessels which lead to the main duct and ends in a number of *alveoli*. The alveoli are lined with cells which secrete enzymes called *trypsinogen*, *amylase* and *lipase*. (For the action of these enzymes, see pages 219 and 220.)

Between the alveoli, collections of cells are found forming a network in which there are many capillaries. These groups of cells are called *interalveolar cell islets* or *islets of Langerhans* and they secrete a hormone which passes directly into the bloodstream. The pancreas therefore has both a digestive and an endocrine function. Each islet consists of two types of cell, which are known as alpha and beta. *Alpha cells* form about 25% of the total number of islet cells and produce a hormone called *glucagon*, which is secreted in response to a fall in blood glucose. Glucagon stimulates the conversion of stored glycogen to glucose, thus raising the blood glucose level. *Beta cells* form the remaining 75% of the islets. They secrete the hormone *insulin* in response to a rise in blood glucose level, e.g. after a meal. Insulin lowers the blood glucose level by stimulating the conversion of glucose to glycogen for storage and by increasing the uptake of glucose by cells. It will be apparent therefore that the blood glucose level is maintained by a balance between the two hormones insulin and glucagon.

As the metabolism of proteins and fats are closely related to carbohydrate metabolism, a disturbance in one type of metabolism will affect the others. A

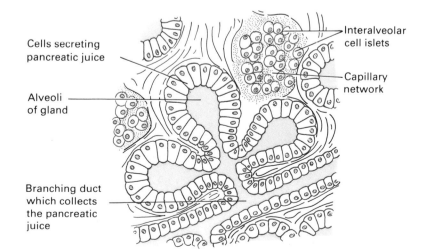

Cells secreting pancreatic juice

Alveoli of gland

Branching duct which collects the pancreatic juice

Interalveolar cell islets

Capillary network

Fig. 24.6 The minute structure of the pancreas, showing the saccules secreting the pancreatic juice and the islet cells, which secrete insulin.

deficiency of insulin results in the condition called diabetes mellitus. The blood glucose level is higher than normal and glucose is excreted in the urine. Because the cells cannot utilize glucose, they begin to use fatty acids for energy instead. This results in an accumulation of ketone bodies (see page 202) which causes acidosis and may lead to coma and death if untreated.

SECTION 10
The Urinary System

Colour Plates 15 and 16 relate to this section. The plates are between pages 134 and 135.

—25—
The Structure of the Urinary System

Objectives: After studying Chapter 25 you should be able to:

1 List the structures of the urinary system.
2 Describe the position and gross structure of the kidney.
3 Describe the structure and function of the ureters.
4 Describe the structure and function of the bladder.
5 Describe the mechanism of micturition.
6 Describe the structure of the urethra, differentiating between the male and female.

The urinary system consists of (Fig. 25.1):
- The kidneys
- The ureters
- The bladder
- The urethra

The Kidneys

The kidneys (Fig. 25.2) are two bean-shaped organs situated on the posterior wall of the abdomen, one on each side of the vertebral column, behind the peritoneum. They lie at the level of the twelfth thoracic to the third lumbar vertebrae, though the right kidney is usually slightly lower than the left, lying just beneath the liver. Each kidney is about 11 cm long, 6 cm wide and 3 cm thick and is embedded in a bed of fat called the *perirenal fat.*

The medial border of each kidney is concave in the centre. This area is called the *hilus* and it is the point at which the blood vessels, nerves and ureters enter or leave the kidney.

The kidney is enclosed in a *capsule* of fibrous tissue which can be easily stripped off. If cut through vertically the kidney can be seen to have

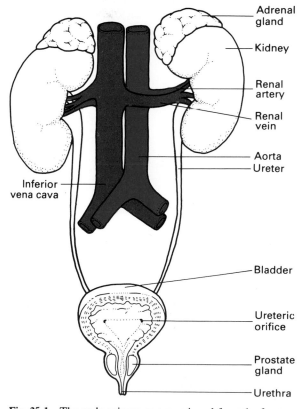

Fig. 25.1 The male urinary system, viewed from the front.

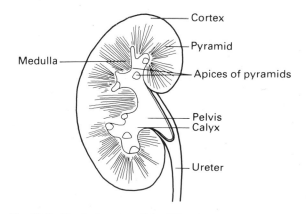

Fig. 25.2 Vertical section of the kidney.

two distinct parts. The dark outer part is called the *cortex* and the paler inner portion is called the *medulla*. Tubules from the medulla lead into the collecting space which is called the renal *pelvis*.

The kidney substance consists of countless minute wavy tubules called *nephrons* (Fig. 25.3). There are over one million nephrons in each kidney. Each of the nephrons begins in a cup-shaped expansion found in the cortex called the *Bowman's capsule*, from which the tubule leads. In the cup of each capsule a fine branch of the renal artery is found forming a tuft of capillaries in close contact with the inner wall of the capsule; the capillary tuft is called the *glomerulus* (Fig. 25.4). The arteriole bringing blood to the glomerulus is called the *afferent arteriole*, and the arteriole which carries the blood away is known as the *efferent arteriole* and is slightly smaller than the afferent vessel. The blood in the glomerulus is under high pressure.

The tubule makes a number of turns or convolutions on leaving the capsule. This section of the tubule is known as the *proximal convoluted tubule*. The tubule then forms a long loop, the loop of Henle, which dips down into the medulla and passes back to the cortex. The tubule next makes a distal or second series of convolutions, where it is known as the *distal convoluted tubule*, and ultimately forms a straight collecting tubule in the medulla. The medulla or inner portion of the kidney therefore consists of loops of Henle and straight collecting tubules.

The efferent arteriole which comes from the capillary tuft or glomerulus in the capsule divides to form a second set of capillaries around the walls of the convoluted tubules in the cortex. Thus the blood passes through two sets of capillaries within one organ, which does not happen in any other part of the body. The blood is collected from the second set of capillaries by small veins, which unite with other small veins to empty blood into the renal vein.

The medulla forms a number of cone-shaped masses which project into the pelvis of the kidney. These are called the *pyramids* of the medulla and are from eight to twelve in number. The apices of the pyramids project into the renal pelvis. They are covered with the mouths of the fine collecting tubules from which urine enters the renal pelvis.

The pelvis is an irregular, branched cavity, which lies at the root or hilum of the kidney and leads like a funnel to the ureter (Fig. 25.5). Its branches, known

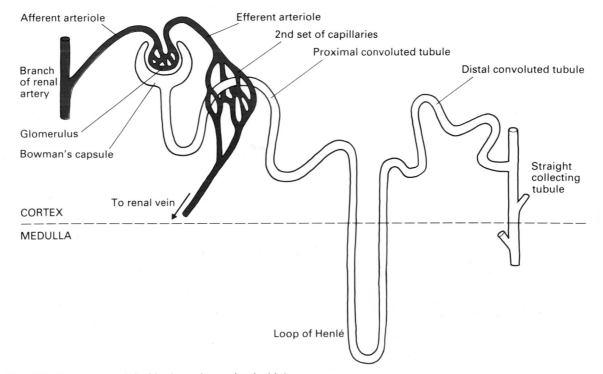

Fig. 25.3 A nephron and the blood vessels associated with it.

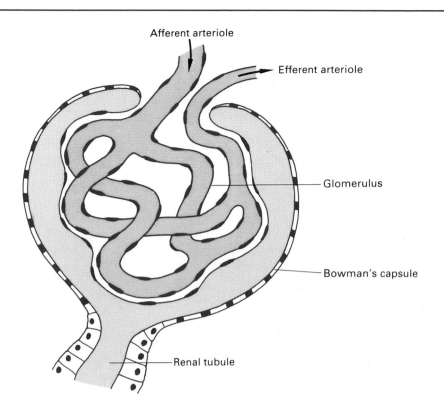

Fig. 25.4   The glomerulus and its capsule.

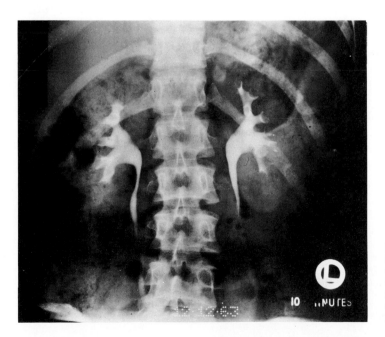
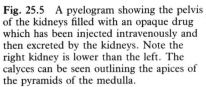

Fig. 25.5   A pyelogram showing the pelvis of the kidneys filled with an opaque drug which has been injected intravenously and then excreted by the kidneys. Note the right kidney is lower than the left. The calyces can be seen outlining the apices of the pyramids of the medulla.

as the *calyces* of the pelvis, penetrate into the kidney substance between the pyramids of the medulla. The pelvis conveys urine emerging from the pyramids to the ureter.

The Ureters

The ureters are the two tubes which carry the urine from the kidneys to the bladder. Each is a thick-walled, narrow tube which is continuous with the renal pelvis and which opens into the base of the bladder and is about 25–30 cm in length. They are about 3 mm in diameter but are slightly constricted in three places:

- At the junction with the renal pelvis
- Where it crosses the brim of the lesser pelvis
- As it passes through the wall of the bladder

These narrowed portions may be the site of impaction of a ureteric calculus (stone). The ureters, the renal pelvis and the calyces can be seen by radiography following the intravenous injection of a radio-paque substance.

The wall of the ureter has three layers:

- An outer fibrous coat continuous with the fibrous capsule of the kidney
- A muscular coat which has an outer circular and an inner longitudinal layer
- A lining of mucous membrane which is continuous with the lining of the renal pelvis and the bladder

The muscular layer of the ureter undergoes peristaltic contractions (see page 221), usually about four or five times a minute, which move the urine down from the kidney towards the bladder.

The Bladder

The bladder is a reservoir for urine (Fig. 25.6). Its size, shape and position vary with the amount of fluid it contains. When empty, it lies within the lesser pelvis, but as it becomes distended with urine it expands upwards and forwards into the abdominal cavity.

Both ureters enter and the urethra leaves the bladder at its *base*. An imaginary line drawn to connect these three openings outlines the area known as the *trigone*. The *neck* of the bladder is the lowest and most fixed part of the organ; it lies 3–4 cm

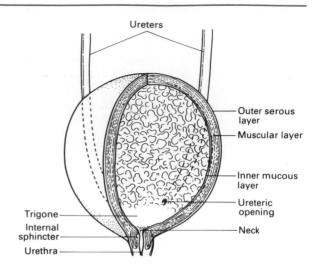

Fig. 25.6   The urinary bladder.

behind the symphysis pubis. The bladder can hold over 500 ml of urine, though this would cause pain; the desire to empty the bladder is normally felt when the organ contains 200–300 ml of urine.

The bladder has three coats:

- The outer serous layer is of peritoneum, but this is found only on the superior surface.
- The muscular layer contains both circular and longitudinal muscle fibres; there are also two bands of oblique fibres which are situated close to the ureteric openings and which prevent urine flowing back into the ureters.
- The inner mucous coat is loose and is thrown into folds or rugae when the bladder is empty. This allows for expansion when the organ is filling with urine. The bladder is lined with transitional epithelial tissue (see page 40) which is continuous with the lining of the urethra.

The Urethra

The urethra extends from the internal urethral orifice in the bladder to the external urethral orifice.

In the *male* the urethra is 18–20 cm in length and serves as a common canal for both the reproductive and the urinary system (Fig. 25.7). It is divided into three portions:

- The *prostatic portion* is about 3 cm in length and is surrounded by the prostate gland. It is lined with transitional epithelium and the orifices of the

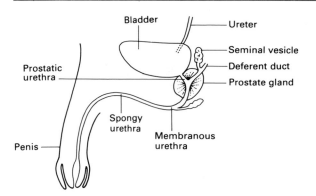

Fig. 25.7 The portions of the male urethra.

prostatic ducts and the *ejaculatory ducts* open into it.

- The *membranous portion* is 1–2 cm in length and is the narrowest part of the urethra. It passes through the pelvic floor.
- The *spongy portion* is about 15 cm in length and lies within the penis.

In the *female* the urethra is about 4 cm long and serves as a canal for the urinary system only. It begins at the internal urethral orifice of the bladder and passes downwards behind the symphysis pubis embedded in the anterior wall of the vagina.

The urethra has two sphincters which control the flow of urine. These are found near to where it leaves the bladder. The *internal sphincter* is involuntary, whereas the *external sphincter* is under voluntary control except in early infancy and in nerve injury or disease. The perineal muscles, which are under voluntary control, are also used to control micturition.

It should be noted that the lining of the renal system is continuous throughout. This is of great significance in the aetiology of urinary tract infections and should be remembered when performing nursing procedures involving the urinary tract.

Micturition

Micturition is the passing (or voiding) of urine. Urine is constantly passing into the bladder from the ureters. When there is 200–300 ml of urine in the mature bladder the desire to pass urine occurs due to stimulation of the sensory nerves because of increased tension in the bladder wall (Fig. 25.8). As the sensory impulses increase in number and

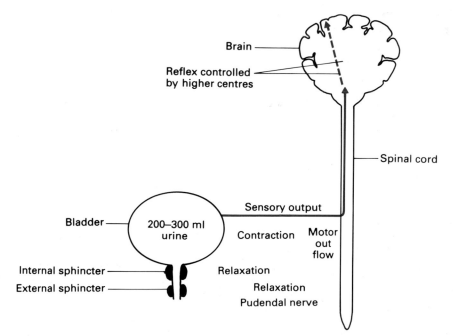

Fig. 25.8 The nervous control of micturition.

frequency, the motor impulses from the brain cause a reflex contraction of the bladder and relaxation of the internal sphincter. The external sphincter is controlled by the pudendal nerve. During normal development, the individual learns to inhibit the spinal reflexes which cause the bladder to contract, and micturition can be delayed for a considerable time or can be induced voluntarily.

26

The Functions of the Kidney

Objectives: After studying Chapter 26 you should be able to:

1   State the functions of the kidney.
2   Describe the formation of urine.
3   Describe the role of the kidney in maintaining homeostasis.

The kidneys are important organs for maintaining homeostasis. They achieve this by four main functions:

- The formation of urine
- The production of the erythropoietin factor
- The production of renin
- The conversion of vitamin D to a more active form

The formation of urine

The composition of the blood must not vary beyond certain limits if the tissues are to remain healthy. To ensure the correct composition a regulating system is essential. This regulation is carried out mainly by the kidneys and involves the removal of harmful waste products from the body and the conservation of the correct amount of water and electrolytes in the body by the process of urine formation.

Urine is produced by three processes:

- Filtration
- Selective reabsorption
- Selective secretion

Filtration

Filtration of the blood occurs due to the high blood pressure in the glomeruli. The anatomical structure already described (see page 232) and nervous control of the blood flow, together with the hormones adrenaline and noradrenaline, maintain the blood pressure with the glomeruli at the high level required for filtration from the capillary tufts to occur. The thin walls of the capillaries and the Bowman's capsules are the only structures which separate the blood from the renal tubules (see Fig.

25.4). The walls of the glomeruli are permeable to water and to other small molecules but they are not permeable to large molecules, such as blood cells and proteins; blood cells and protein molecules are only filtered if the kidney is diseased. Because the blood in the glomerulus is under pressure, some of the constituents pass through the walls of the capillaries and the Bowman's capsule and enter the cavity of the capsule. This fluid is known as the *glomerular filtrate* and contains glucose, amino acids, fatty acids, salts, urea and uric acid in the same proportions as in plasma. About 600 ml of blood per minute pass through the glomeruli and of this about 125 ml becomes the glomerular filtrate. If this were all excreted 150 to 180 litres of urine would be passed each day! The average amount of urine passed each day is 1.5 litres, so it is obvious that reabsorption must occur.

Selective reabsorption

Selective reabsorption occurs because the cells lining the convoluted tubules are able to absorb certain substances. The amount of each substance absorbed is closely related to the body's needs for a particular substance.

Most of the reabsorption occurs in the proximal tubules. The sodium in the filtrate is actively reabsorbed by the tubular cells, and to maintain an ionic balance the chloride follows passively. Water is also reabsorbed passively, probably following concentration gradients. Other constituents required by the body are reabsorbed; in particular, all the glucose in the glomerular filtrate is reabsorbed and none is excreted in the urine in normal health.

Reabsorption of water and electrolytes also occurs in the distal convoluted and collecting tubules, but here it is variable and is controlled by the secretion of two hormones:

- The *antidiuretic hormone* (ADH) from the posterior pituitary gland
- *Aldosterone* from the adrenal cortex

When the body requires to rid itself of fluid there is a

decrease in the secretion of ADH, causing less water to be reabsorbed in the collecting tubules and therefore more water is excreted as urine. Conversely, an increase in ADH production causes a greater reabsorption of water and less water is excreted as urine. The amount of ADH produced is mainly regulated by sensory cells in the hypothalamus which monitor the blood concentration.

The reabsorption of electrolytes, specifically sodium, is controlled by aldosterone. The mechanism which stimulates aldosterone production is comparatively complex. A low blood sodium concentration will cause a low blood pressure. This is detected by receptors in the kidney and results in the production of *renin* by the kidney cells. The renin converts the inactive plasma substance *angiotensinogen* to *angiotensin I*, which in turn is converted by another enzyme to *angiotensin II*. This latter substance stimulates the adrenal cortex to release aldosterone. The aldosterone acts on the distal tubules, causing them to reabsorb more sodium ions, which are then followed passively by chloride ions and water. There is also an increase in the excretion of potassium. Angiotensin II also has a powerful vasoconstricting effect, and so raises the blood pressure, thereby increasing the rate at which the glomerular filtrate is produced.

Active secretion

Active secretion occurs because the cells lining the tubules have the ability to secrete some substances such as hydrogen ions, bicarbonate and ammonia from the blood in the second capillary network (see Fig. 25.3) into the lumen of the tubule. This is of utmost importance in maintaining the blood pH at about 7.4 and accounts for the varying acidity of the urine.

The composition of the urine

Normal urine, therefore, is formed partly by filtration under pressure into the Bowman's capsules and partly by reabsorption and secretion in the tubules. It is an amber-coloured fluid varying in colour according to its quantity. It is usually acid, but may vary between pH 4.5 and 8.5 depending on the blood pH and whether this needs to be raised or lowered. It has a specific gravity of 1015 to 1025. (The specific gravity is the weight compared with the weight of an equal quantity of water, water being 1000.)

Table 26.1 The composition and characteristics of urine.

Composition	
Water	96%
Urea	2%
Uric acid/salts	2%
pH (depends on blood pH)	4.5–8.5
Specific gravity	1015–1025

Urine consists of water, salts and protein waste products, namely, urea, uric acid and creatinine. The average composition is:
- Water   96%
- Urea   2%
- Uric acid and salts   2%

The concentration of urea in blood plasma is 0.04% compared with 2% in the urine, hence the concentration has been increased 50 times by the work of the kidney. The salts consist chiefly of sodium chloride and also of phosphates and sulphates, produced partly from the phosphorus and sulphur present in protein foods. These salts must be reabsorbed or got rid of in the quantities necessary to keep the blood at its normal pH (7.4) and maintain the water and electrolyte balance. Since the pH and salt concentration are both essential to the life of the blood corpuscles and the tissue cells, this function of the kidney is very important. The normal quantity of urine secreted is 1.5 litres in 24 hours, but it is increased by drinking and in cold weather, and is decreased by reducing fluid intake and in hot weather, exercise and fever, since these increase sweating. Potassium salts are normally filtered out and then reabsorbed or excreted as required to keep the correct level in body fluids. In renal failure, their excretion may be reduced so that the amount of potassium in the body fluids and tissues rises.

The production of erythropoietin factor

This is discussed on page 150.

The production of renin

This has been discussed under 'Selective reabsorption'.

The conversion of vitamin D

Fat-soluble vitamin D is converted by the kidney to a more active water-soluble form.

—SECTION 11————————————

Colour Plates 15 and 16 relate to this section. The plates are between pages 134 and 135.

—27—
The Reproductive Systems

Objectives: After studying Chapter 27 you should be able to:

1 List the male genital organs.
2 Describe the production, route and transport method of the spermatozoa.
3 List the external female genital organs.
4 List the internal female reproductive organs.
5 Describe the mechanism of ovulation.
6 Describe the mechanism of menstruation.
7 Describe the structure of the breast.
8 Describe the mechanism of lactation.

The Male Genital Organs (Fig. 27.1)

The male genital organs consist of:
- The testes and epididymides
- The deferent ducts
- The seminal vesicles
- The ejaculatory ducts and the penis
- The prostate
- The bulbourethral glands

The testes

The testes are the main reproductive glands in the male (Fig. 27.2). They are suspended in the *scrotum* by the spermatic cords but they develop high up in the abdomen close to the kidneys and gradually descend through the inguinal canal into the scrotum shortly before birth. Occasionally one or both glands fail to descend and remain in the abdomen or in the inguinal canal; surgery may then be required to relocate them.

As each testis descends it brings down with it a pouch of peritoneum called the *tunica vaginalis*. This forms a serous covering for the testis, but the rest of the pouch is normally obliterated. Each testis

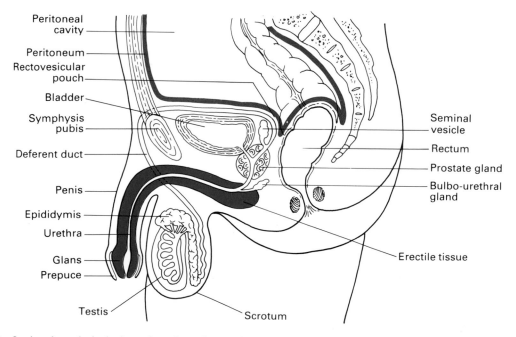

Fig. 27.1 Section through the body to show the male reproductive organs.

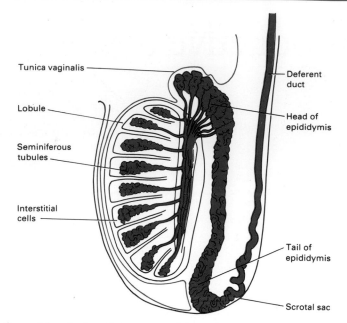

Tunica vaginalis

Lobule

Seminiferous
tubules

Interstitial
cells

Deferent
duct

Head of
epididymis

Tail of
epididymis

Scrotal sac

Fig. 27.2   Section through the scrotal sac to show the structure of the testis.

consists of 200–300 lobules, each containing up to three tiny wavy or convoluted tubules called the *convoluted seminiferous tubules*. The epithelial lining of the walls of these tubules contains cells which develop into spermatozoa by a process of meiotic cell division (see page 28). The tubules are supported by loose connective tissue which contains groups of *interstitial cells* which secrete the male hormone *testosterone*.

The epididymides

Each epididymis is a fine, tightly coiled tube which is packed together to form a long narrow body attached to the back of the testis. The seminiferous tubules of the testis open into it and it leads into the deferent duct.

The deferent ducts

Each deferent duct or *ductus deferens* is a continuation of the duct of the epididymis. It passes through the inguinal canal and runs between the base of the bladder and the rectum to the base of the prostate gland, where it is joined by the duct of the seminal vesicle.

The seminal vesicles

The seminal vesicles are two pouches lying between the base of the bladder and the rectum. They secrete an alkaline fluid containing nourishment which forms a large part of the seminal fluid (Fig. 27.3).

The ejaculatory ducts

The ejaculatory ducts are formed by the union of the ducts of the seminal vesicles and the deferent ducts. They pass through the prostate to open into the prostatic part of the urethra.

The penis

The penis is a tubular organ plentifully supplied with large venous sinuses which can fill with blood, causing erection of the organ. It contains the urethra, which serves both the urinary and the reproductive systems in the male. At the tip of the penis is an enlargement called the *glans penis*, in the centre of which the urethra ends at the *urinary meatus* or opening. The glans is normally covered by a loose double fold of skin called the *prepuce* or foreskin. It should be possible to draw the foreskin back over the glans penis but sometimes the opening in it is too small. This is known as phimosis and is

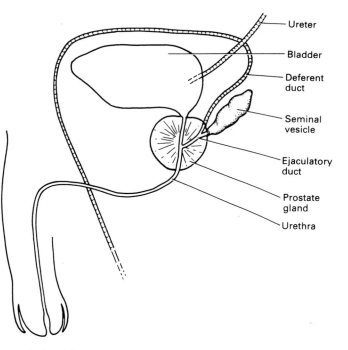

Fig. 27.3 The position of the seminal vesicles.

treated either by stretching the foreskin or by circumcision, i.e. a cutting away of the foreskin.

The prostate

The prostate surrounds the commencement of the urethra in the male. It is about the size of a chestnut and contains the urethra and the ejaculatory ducts. It consists partly of glandular tissue and partly of involuntary muscle and produces a secretion which is alkaline and provides nourishment for the sperm. This secretion forms part of the seminal fluid.

The bulbourethral glands

The bulbourethral glands are situated on either side of the membranous portion of the urethra. The ducts open into the spongy portion of the urethra and the glands secrete a substance which forms part of the seminal fluid.

The seminal fluid

The seminal fluid or semen is composed of substances secreted by the testes, the seminal vesicles, the prostate and the bulbourethral glands; it con-

tains spermatozoa (Fig. 27.4). The alkalinity of this fluid helps protect the spermatozoa from the acidity of the female vagina.

The *spermatozoa* are minute cells each with a tail-

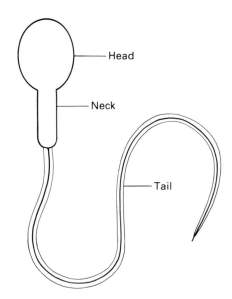

Fig. 27.4 A spermatozoon.

like projection joined to the head portion by a constricted part called the neck. The tail has a lashing movement which enables the cell to move after the seminal fluid leaves the male reproductive tract. As a result, when the spermatozoa are deposited in the female vagina they can make their way up the uterus and uterine tubes in search of the ova. They are produced in enormous numbers and it is estimated that on average 300 000 000 are deposited in the vagina at one time, though only one is necessary to fertilize the ovum.

The role of testosterone

The hormone testosterone is produced by the undescended testes in the male fetus and is responsible for the descent of the testes into the scrotum (where they are at birth). During childhood the testosterone produced by the interstitial cells inhibits the hypothalamus. However, at the age of about ten the presence of testosterone no longer inhibits the hypothalamus but stimulates it to cause the anterior pituitary gland to produce the male *gonadotrophic hormones*, i.e. follicle stimulating hormone (FSH) and luteinizing hormone (LH). The FSH aids the convoluted seminiferous tubules to develop and is thought also to have some role in sperm production. The LH activates the interstitial cells to secrete testosterone.

Testosterone is needed for growth in the male and is essential for the male primary and secondary sex characteristics. It is present in the male in large quantities by about the age of 13, when growth is rapid and the development of the primary sex organs occurs. Secondary sex characteristics also develop at this time (which is known as *puberty*), also under the influence of testosterone, e.g. hair develops on the face, axillae and pubic area, the vocal chords develop and thicken, therefore deepening the voice (the voice 'breaks') and the sebaceous glands increase in their secretions.

The Female Genital Organs

The female genital organs can be divided into an external and an internal group.

External organs

The external genital organs in the female are collectively called the *vulva* (Fig. 27.5). They consist of:

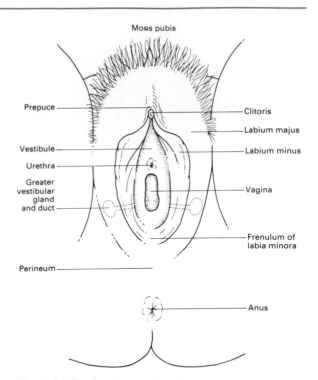

Fig. 27.5   The female external genital organs.

- The mons pubis
- The labia majora and minora
- The clitoris
- The vestibule of the vagina
- The greater vestibular glands

The *mons pubis* is a pad of fat covered with skin lying over the symphysis pubis. It bears hairs after puberty.

The *labia majora* are two folds of fatty tissue covered with skin extending backwards from the mons on either side of the vulva and disappearing into the perineum behind. They develop at puberty and are covered with hair on the outer surface after that stage. They atrophy after the menopause.

The *labia minora* are two smaller fleshy folds within the labia majora. They meet in front to form a hood-like structure called the *prepuce* which surrounds and protects the clitoris. The labia minora unite behind to form the *frenulum of the labia minora* or *fourchette*. This is merely a fold of skin which is often torn in the first labour. The labia minora are covered with modified skin rich in sweat and sebaceous glands to lubricate their surfaces.

The *clitoris* is a small sensitive organ containing

erectile tissue corresponding to the male penis. It lies towards the front of the vulva immediately below the mons pubis and is protected by the prepuce.

The *vestibule* is the area between the labia minora. The orifice of the vagina and the orifice of the urethra open into it. The *orifice of the urethra* lies towards the front of the vestibule and projects slightly from the normal surface level. At the entrance there are two fine tubular glands, called urethral glands, which secrete lubricating fluid. Apart from the lubricating function these are important because they tend to harbour infection in cases of gonorrhoea. The *orifice of the vagina* occupies the space between the labia minora behind the urethral opening. It is normally a slit from front to back, the side walls of the vagina being in contact. The orifice is largely blocked in the virgin by the *hymen*. This is a thin double fold of mucous membrane, usually crescent-shaped, and leaving a gap at the centre for the escape of the menstrual flow. Sometimes it has a number of small perforations; this is called a fenestrated hymen. The hymen is placed a little inside the orifice of the vagina.

The *greater vestibular glands* are two small glands lying one under each labium majus on either side of the vaginal orifice. Their ducts open laterally to the vagina. They secrete a lubricating fluid to moisten the surface of the vulva and so facilitate sexual intercourse.

The whole surface of the vulva is covered with modified skin, i.e. stratified epithelium. It carries hair on the outer surfaces only but the inner surfaces are exceptionally rich in sebaceous and sweat glands so that the surfaces are moist.

The *perineum* is the expanse of skin from the vaginal orifice back to the anus. It is about 5 cm in length and bears hair. It lies over the *perineal body*, a mass of muscle and fibrous tissue separating the vagina from the rectum. The muscle of the perineal body is largely formed from part of the levator ani, the chief muscle of the pelvic floor.

Internal organs

The internal organs, which are situated within the lesser pelvis, are (Fig. 27.6):
- The ovaries
- The uterine tubes
- The uterus
- The vagina

The ovaries (Fig. 27.7)

The ovaries are two small glands about the size and shape of almonds which are situated in the lesser pelvis, one on either side of the uterus, behind and below the uterine tubes. Each is attached to the broad ligament by a fold of peritoneum called the *mesovarium*. The fimbriated ends of the uterine tube and a suspensory ligament (the *ovarian ligament*) are also attached to the ovary.

The ovaries have an outer cortex which contains numerous *primary ovarian follicles*. The inner medulla (ovarian stroma) is highly vascular. At puberty the cortex becomes much thicker and some

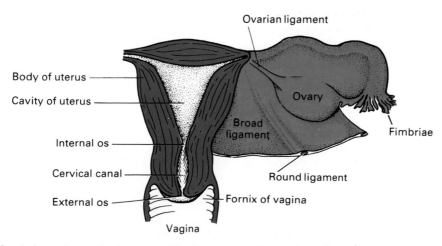

Fig. 27.6 The female internal reproductive organs. The uterus and vagina are shown in section.

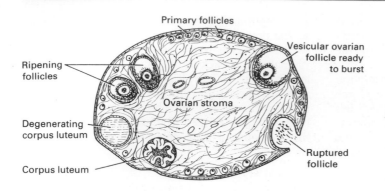

Fig. 27.7 The ovary, showing primary follicles, ripening follicles and a corpus luteum.

of the primary ovarian follicles develop each month to form *vesicular ovarian follicles* (graafian follicles), one of which usually matures and ruptures, releasing an ovum. This process is called *ovulation*. The ovum passes into the uterine tube via its fimbriated end and may be fertilized by a male spermatozoa. If fertilization occurs it usually takes place in the lateral third of the uterine tube.

After ovulation the vesicular ovarian follicle is converted to a mass of specialized tissue called the *corpus luteum*. If fertilization occurs the corpus luteum remains active until late in the pregnancy; if fertilization does not occur the corpus luteum begins to degenerate after about 14 days. The corpus luteum produces the hormones *progesterone* and *oestrogen*; these hormones cause the lining of the uterus, the endometrium, to become thickened, ready to receive the fertilized ovum. However, if fertilization does not occur the hormones are withdrawn as the corpus luteum degenerates and the endometrium is shed in the process called menstruation (see page 248).

The ovaries begin to function at puberty and continue to discharge ova at monthly intervals from about the age of 13 to about the age of 45 years, the usual time of the menopause. The ovaries are smooth in childhood but the scars which follow the rupture of the follicles pucker up the surface, so that they finally become very irregular and rather like almonds in appearance as well as shape.

Hormones from the ovaries are also responsible for the development of the reproductive system and the general development which marks puberty in the female and occurs at about 13 years of age. There is marked development of the external genitals, of the uterus and the breasts. Hair grows on the genitals and in the axillae, there is a general rounding of the figure and a gradual development of the traits of the female personality.

The uterine tubes (Fig. 27.8)

The uterine tubes are situated in the upper part of the broad ligaments of the uterus. They are about 10 cm long and transmit the ova from the ovaries to the cavity of the uterus. Each tube has four parts:

- The *infundibulum* is a trumpet-shaped expansion which opens into the abdominal cavity close to the ovary and has a number of processes called *fimbriae*.
- The *ampulla* is a thin-walled, tortuous part which forms rather more than half the tube.
- The *isthmus* is round and forms about one-third of the tube.
- The *uterine part* passes through the wall of the uterus and is about 1 cm in length.

The uterine tubes have three coats:
- An outer serous covering of peritoneum
- A muscular coat
- A lining of ciliated epithelium

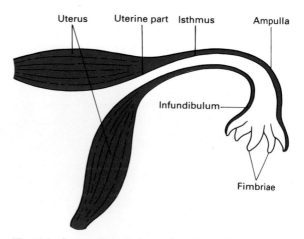

Fig. 27.8 Section through the uterine tube, to show the parts of the tube.

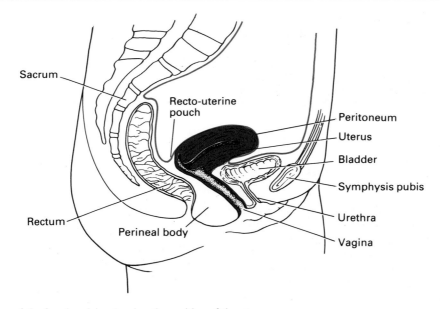

Fig. 27.9 Section of the female pelvis, showing the position of the uterus.

The ova are conveyed along the tube by the peristaltic action of the muscular coat and by the action of the cilia.

The uterus

The uterus is a hollow, thick-walled, muscular organ situated in the lesser pelvis between the rectum and the bladder (Fig. 27.9). It is about 7.5 cm long, 5 cm across and 2.5 cm thick, and it weighs about 30 g. It communicates with the uterine tubes, which open into the upper part of the uterus, and the vagina, which leads from the lower part. The uterus forms almost a right angle with the vagina, into which the cervix of the uterus protrudes.

The upper part of the uterus is broad and is called the *body* of the uterus; the part of the body above the entrance of the uterine tubes is called the *fundus*. The *cervix* is narrower and more cylindrical than the body and projects through the anterior vaginal wall. The narrow opening at the upper end of the cervix is

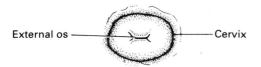

Fig. 27.10 The external os as seen through a vaginal speculum.

called the *internal os*, while the lower opening is called the *external os* (Fig. 27.10).

The uterus has three coats:
- An outer serous coat derived from the peritoneum
- A muscular coat consisting of involuntary muscle, the fibres of which are arranged in longitudinal, oblique, transverse and circular layers
- A lining of mucous membrane and columnar epithelium known as the *endometrium*

The *broad ligaments*, which are formed from a double fold of peritoneum, pass from the uterus to the lateral walls of the pelvis. The *round ligaments* are situated in the lower edges of the broad ligament below the uterine tubes. The uterus normally lies in an *anteverted* position, i.e. with the fundus facing the abdominal wall and the cervix pointing towards the sacrum. There is also some *anteflexion*, the body of the uterus being bent forwards on the cervix. The uterus is maintained in this position by the *transverse ligaments*, which run from the cervix to the lateral walls of the pelvis, and by the *uterosacral* ligaments, which run from the cervix to the sacrum. The uterus is also supported indirectly by the pelvic floor.

If the ovum is fertilized in the uterine tube, it passes into the uterine cavity and embeds in the thickened, vascular endometrium which has been prepared to receive it by the action of the hormones. The developing fetus remains there, increasing in size until it fills the uterus, after which the uterus grows with it until the end of the period of pregnancy. At the site of implantation the placenta develops; this is the organ through which the fetus receives nourishment and oxygen from the maternal blood during intrauterine life (Fig. 27.11).

Menstruation is the shedding of the thickened endometrium with some blood which occurs, if fertilization has not taken place, each month after puberty until the menopause (Fig. 27.12).

Menstruation is controlled by hormones secreted from the hypothalamus and affecting the anterior pituitary gland. The anterior lobe of the pituitary gland secretes *follicle-stimulating hormone* (*FSH*) which initiates the development of a follicle in the ovary. As the ovum matures the follicle secretes *oestrogen*, which is necessary for the growth of the endometrium and its preparation to receive the fertilized ovum. Oestrogen is also responsible for the gradual development of secondary sex characteristics at puberty. When the amount of oestrogen in the blood reaches a high level, further secretion of FSH is prevented and the anterior lobe of the pituitary begins to release *luteinizing hormone* (*LH*). Following ovulation (the release of the ovum from the follicle) LH converts the ruptured follicle into the corpus luteum, which then secretes the hormone *progesterone*. This hormone completes the develop-

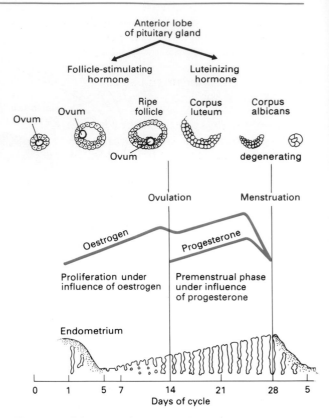

Fig. 27.12 Diagrammatic representation of the changes in the endometrium in the menstrual cycle.

ment of the endometrium. If the ovum is not fertilized the corpus luteum begins to degenerate (to become the corpus albicans), the level of progesterone decreases and the endometrium is shed. The low progesterone level also stimulates the anterior pituitary to secrete more FSH and the cycle begins again. For convenience of description the first day of the menstrual flow is designated day 1 of the menstrual cycle; ovulation usually occurs about the 14th day.

The vagina

The vagina extends from the uterus to the labia. It lies behind the bladder and urethra and in front of the rectum and anal canal. The cervix enters the anterior wall of the vagina at right angles so the posterior wall of the vagina is longer than the anterior wall (see Fig. 27.10). The recesses formed by the projection of the cervix into the vagina are called *fornices*.

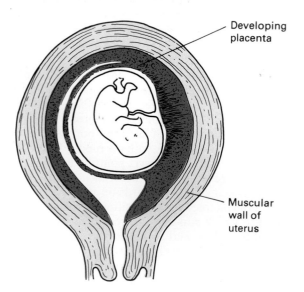

Fig. 27.11 The uterus at about the tenth week of pregnancy, showing the developing placenta and fetus.

The walls of the vagina are normally in contact with each other. The vagina has two coats:

- A muscular coat which has longitudinal and circular fibres
- An inner lining of mucous membrane which is in folds or rugae

After puberty the lining becomes thick and is rich in glycogen; the action of certain bacteria (Döderlein's bacilli) on the glycogen renders the vaginal secretion acid.

The peritoneum passes over the body of the uterus on to the back of the cervix and close to the posterior fornix of the vagina before being folded back to cover the front of the rectum (see Fig. 27.10). This fold is called the *recto-uterine pouch*.

The Breasts

The breasts are accessory organs to the female reproductive system (Fig. 27.13). They are present in rudimentary form in the male. They lie on the anterior aspect of the thorax and vary considerably in size. They are circular in outline and convex anteriorly. In the centre of the surface is the *nipple*, which normally projects from the skin level and is pink in the female prior to pregnancy but pigmented after the first pregnancy.

The breast is a compound saccular gland (see page 40) with its ducts converging to the nipple and opening on its surface in large numbers. The gland tissue is similar to the tissue of the sebaceous gland but is more highly developed and produces nutritional fluids in place of sebum. The gland is divided into lobes by partitions of fibrous tissue—a fact which makes the draining of an abscess in the breast difficult. The lobes are subdivided into lobules.

The breasts develop at puberty under the influence of hormones and further development occurs during pregnancy as a result of hormones from the pituitary gland and ovaries. Fluid known

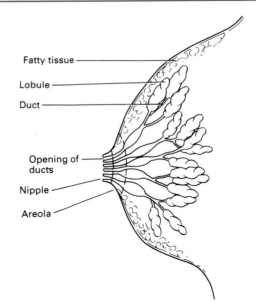

Fig. 27.13   Section through the breast.

as colostrum is secreted in small amounts by the gland during pregnancy and at the time of childbirth, but true milk is not secreted till about the third day after giving birth.

Milk production (*lactogenesis*) is under the control of an anterior pituitary hormone called *prolactin*. The formulation of prolactin is inhibited during pregnancy by the high levels of progesterone. After birth the oestrogen levels stimulate its production. It is also produced in surges following the suckling of the infant in preparation for the next feed.

Lactation (the letting down of the milk) is stimulated by the baby suckling the nipple. The nerve impulse is transmitted to the hypothalamus, which responds by stimulating the posterior pituitary gland to produce *oxytocin*. This hormone acts on the breast to permit the release of the milk; it also aids in causing contraction of the uterus back to normal size.

Further reading

Anthony, C.P. & Thibodeau, G.A. (1983) *Textbook of Anatomy and Physiology*. 11th edn. St Louis: C. V. Mosby.

Clarke, C.A. (1977) *Human Genetics and Medicine*, 2nd edn. London: Edward Arnold.

Eyton, A. (1982) *F-Plan Diet*. Harmondsworth: Penguin.

Glenn, J.A. & McCaugherty, D. (1981) *SI Units for Nurses*. London: Harper & Row.

Green, J.H. (1976) *An Introduction to Human Physiology*. 4th edn. Oxford: Oxford University Press.

Green, J.H. (1979) *Basic Clinical Physiology*. 3rd edn. Oxford: Oxford University Press.

Guyton, A.C. (1983) *Physiology of the Human Body*. 6th edn. Philadelphia: W.B. Saunders.

Hare, R. & Cooke, E.M. (1984) *Bacteriology and Immunity for Nurses*. Edinburgh: Churchill Livingstone.

Kilgour, O.F.G. (1978) *Introduction to the Physical Aspects of Nursing Science*. London: William Heinemann Medical Books.

McNaught, A.B. & Callander, R. (1983) *Illustrated Physiology*. 4th edn. Edinburgh: Churchill Livingstone.

Ministry of Agriculture and Fisheries and Food (1976) *Manual of Nutrition*. 8th edn. London: HMSO.

Nathan, S.S. & Murphy, S.K. (1968) *Organic Chemistry Made Simple*. London: W.H. Allen.

Parker, M.J. & Stucke, V.A. (1982) *Microbiology for Nurses*. 6th edn. London: Baillière Tindall.

Roberts, M.B.V. (1982) *Biology: A Functional Approach*. 3rd edn. Walton-on-Thames: Nelson.

Ross, J.R.W. & Marks, K. (1986) *Baillière's Anatomy Illustrated*. London: Baillière Tindall.

Ross, J.S. & Wilson, K.J.W. (1981) *Foundations of Anatomy and Physiology*. 5th edn. Edinburgh: Churchill Livingstone.

Sears, W.G. & Winwood, R.S. (1974) *Anatomy and Physiology for Nurses and Students of Human Biology*. 5th edn. London: Edward Arnold.

Solomon, E.P. & Davis, P.W. (1983) *Human Anatomy and Physiology*. New York: Holt, Rinehart & Winston.

Index